NASA SP-426

Sun, Weather, and Climate

John R. Herman
and
Richard A. Goldberg

Scientific and Technical Information Branch   1978
NATIONAL AERONAUTICS AND SPACE ADMINISTRATION
Washington, D.C.

Library of Congress Cataloging in Publication Data

Herman, John R
   Sun, weather, and climate.

   (NASA SP ; 426)
   Includes indexes.
   Supt. of Docs. no. : NAS 1.21:426
   1. Solar activity. 2. Weather. 3. Climatology.
I. Goldberg, Richard A., joint author. II. Title.
III. Series: United States. National Aeronautics and
Space Administration. NASA SP ; 426.
QC883.2.S6H47   551.5   78-606053

For sale by the Superintendent of Documents, U.S. Government Printing Office
Washington, D.C. 20402 (Paper cover)

Stock Number 033-000-00747-7

Foreword

"A growing mass of evidence suggests that transient events on the Sun affect our weather and long-term variations of the Sun's energy output affect our climate. Solar terrestrial exploration can help establish the physical cause and effect relationships between solar stimuli and terrestrial responses. When these relationships are understood, science will have an essential tool for weather and climate prediction." This paragraph, written by Robert D. Chapman as part of a proposal for a five-year plan for Solar Terrestrial Programs in the National Aeronautics and Space Administration, is an indication of the present status of Sun–weather/climate investigations.

The literature on this subject covers a period of more than 100 years, and many distinguished scientists have contributed. Nevertheless, until very recently, Sun–weather/climate investigations have not been taken very seriously by many scientists. In the last few years, compelling (but not absolutely conclusive) evidence for correlations between solar variations and the area of tropospheric cyclones has helped to make this subject suitable for serious studies. Almost every large solar-terrestrial symposium now includes at least one session on Sun–weather/climate investigations.

This book is particularly welcome at a time at which many astronomers, space scientists, geophysicists, and meteorologists are entering the field of Sun–weather/climate investigation. The subject is an example par excellence of an interdisciplinary endeavor in which any single scientist is not likely to have professional competence throughout the entire range of relevant subject matter. The literature on the subject is often confusing and contradictory and of highly variable quality.

This book provides an excellent opportunity for a scientist considering this new field to get an overall view of the present status of the subject in its many disciplinary aspects. The existing correlations provide a strong suggestion that some physical mechanism exists linking the variable Sun and the weather and climate, but the details of such a mechanism or mechanisms are quite unknown at present. Several attractive possibilities are described in the book.

It seems likely that Sun-weather/climate investigations will occupy an increasingly prominent role in the coming decade, and the publication of this book should give a significant impetus to these efforts.

John M. Wilcox
Stanford University

Preface

This book introduces the general field of Sun–weather/climate relationships, that is, apparent weather and climate responses to solar activity, and provides theoretical and experimental suggestions for further research to identify and investigate the unknown causal mechanisms. It is directed to researchers active in the atmospheric and space sciences who wish to expand their background for meeting the challenge of this newly emerging field and to students who desire a general background in the several disciplinary areas of the field.

In the 200-year history of Sun-weather studies, a large body of information has accumulated. Even though the reported results have sometimes been confused, disjointed, and contradictory, there has emerged a growing belief that there are connections between changes on the Sun and changes in the lower atmosphere. There is, however, a deplorable lack of acceptable physical mechanisms to explain those probable connections, and this has prevented widespread acceptance of the reality of solar activity effects on the weather and climate. The discovery of viable mechanisms will strengthen the scientific basis of Sun-weather relationships and may lead to improved predictions of weather and climate. It is obvious that improved predictions would have a profound impact on several crucial societal problems, especially in the areas of global food production and utilization of solar energy for man's needs.

This book reviews the correlations between solar activity and weather and climate reported in historical and contemporary literature, addresses the physical linking mechanisms, and suggests experimental concepts for future investigations of such mechanisms. It is our intention to fill a gap in the literature by combining a review of the nature and quality of existing correlations with the basic physics underlying the various scientific disciplines required to pursue studies of physical linking mechanisms. We emphasize the multidisciplinary nature of the subject while providing a basic background in each of the various areas thought to play a role in coupling processes. In following this approach, we hope to acquaint meteorologists with solar and geophysical phenomena, solar physicists with terrestrial atmospheric processes, and so on, thereby stimulating the cross fertilization we believe is necessary for further progress in Sun-weather studies.

In providing a reasonably comprehensive review of reported correlations, we have applied appropriate critiques when possible; however, in several cases the statistical significance is difficult to assess. Other correlations have been omitted because we believe they are faulty. The correlations are divided into two basic categories, long and short term, to correspond to climate and weather relationships, respectively. Sufficient quantities of the various types have been retained to reflect the true flavor of the Sun-weather field at this time. Correlations with other phenomena, such as apparent lunar and tropospheric influences on geomagnetic activity, are included to demonstrate how relationships with solar activity might be masked by competing effects.

The book covers some of the more recent suggestions concerning causal processes and provides examples of explanations for short-, intermediate-, and long-term relationships between solar activity and weather and climate. The coverage is not meant to be comprehensive, but rather a sampling of the ideas now emerging in this field. The last part of the book briefly discusses a general outline for experimental procedures to investigate possible mechanisms. More detailed plans have been proposed, but at the present stage of evolution, we feel that this book should guide rather than specify. This is especially true in view of the rapid progress now being made in the field — progress that is certain to make obsolete many of the current suggestions.

Intertwined throughout the book are numerous discussions of basic physical processes, definitions, and geophysical phenomena, introduced when they are appropriate and relevant to the relationships and/or mechanisms under discussion. In addition, an introduction to the many geophysical and solar-related phenomena and indices used for discussion of the correlations is given early in the book.

Although it may appear that the treatment is favorably oriented to the Sun-weather field, we have attempted to be objective while maintaining an agnostic attitude. In our opinion, there is no conclusive evidence for or *against* the relationships at this time. We do feel, however, that the hard statistical evidence that has emerged recently is more than fortuitous and justifies a strong research effort to search for, identify, and study the unidentified physical coupling processes that may be responsible for the observed correlations.

In a multidisciplinary effort of this kind, we cannot be experts in all fields, and we have therefore drawn freely on the advice, comments, and suggestions of numerous colleagues who gave willingly of their time to help us clarify our thinking. Any errors and misinterpretations in the book are our responsibility.

We are especially indebted to Dr. Ray Wexler, Dr. John M. Wilcox, Dr. S. J. Bauer, and Dr. Leif Svalgaard for reading several complete drafts and revisions and offering constructive criticism. Others who read complete drafts and contributed helpful comments include Dr. George C. Reid, Dr. James Barcus, Dr. Rudolf Penndorf, Dr. Kaichi Maeda, Dr. Eldon Ferguson, and Dr. A. Ebel.

We greatly appreciate the help on various portions of the manuscript given by Mr. Ernest Hilsenrath, Dr. Kenneth Schatten, Dr. Leslie C. Hale, Dr. Masahisa Sugiura, and Dr. Roger E. Olson. Helpful advice and comments were also received from Dr. Bruce Guenther, Dr. Walter Orr Roberts, and Dr. T. Matsuno. With particular pleasure we thank Dr. Donald F. Heath, Mr. William E. Bandeen, and Dr. David Atlas for their support of work leading to this book and their encouragement to publish it.

John R. Herman
Radio Sciences Co.

and

Richard A. Goldberg
NASA Goddard Space Flight Center

November 1977

Table of Contents

1 Introduction

It has long been suspected that fluctuations in the energy output of the Sun may affect Earth's weather and climate. If we can understand the linking mechanisms of the phenomena, we may be able to solve several of man's most perplexing problems. For example, the critical role played by adverse weather and climatic changes on world food supply has come into sharp focus in recent years (Laur, 1976). The ability to predict such changes with greater certitude than is now possible, especially the time and place of drought occurrence, could greatly improve global crop production schedules and thus alleviate incidences of famine. Less attention has been paid to the impact of weather and climate on the effective utilization of solar energy. In its quest to make the United States self-sufficient for its energy needs within the next decade, several agencies of the Federal Government are examining closely the possibility of harnessing solar radiation. Billions of dollars are to be expended on this research and a special Federal laboratory for solar energy research has been approved.

One of the most important variables that affects the utilization of solar energy is related to the weather and climate. For example, temperature extremes, both hot and cold, demand additional energy for cooling and heating, respectively. Strong cold winds introduce an additional chill factor for which the increased use of heat energy must compensate. The degree of cloud cover directly affects the amount of solar energy reaching solar collectors on the Earth's surface. Alternative energy sources must be tapped when there are many consecutive cloudy days.

Since the meteorological and climatological parameters that affect solar energy use vary with time on both long- and short-term bases, it is evident that the demands on solar energy and the efficiency of its utilization will also vary with time. To ensure maximum benefit from this energy source and to allow for efficient scheduling of alternate energy sources, variations in meteorological and climatological parameters must be predictable to a high degree of accuracy.

The social implications of Sun-weather relationships are beyond the scope of this book; rather, we address the scientific questions that

1

may lead to an understanding of the linking mechanisms between solar activity and climatological and meteorological responses. With such understanding, it may be possible to improve predictions of weather and climate, which could contribute to the solution of the related social problems.

Within the present state of meteorological art, short-term weather forecasts for a given region are rarely accurate beyond a lead time of about 2 days. Longer-term forecasts (up to about 30 days) based on computer modeling of atmosphere systems are marginally effective, and long-term changes in climate are anybody's guess.

The only way in which this state of affairs can be improved is to improve the predictability of weather and climate. Standard meteorological techniques, even with more sophisticated and complicated computer modeling techniques, can be improved only by introducing new concepts of the workings of the whole atmospheric system. One key element that has been largely ignored and that we believe could be crucial to a better understanding and predictability of weather and climate is the possible influence of solar activity on meteorological and climatological parameters. We use the term solar activity to distinguish the transient and energetic outbursts of solar energy from the more regular radiation often termed the solar constant.

The basic measure of solar activity is the number of sunspots visible on the solar disk at any given time; the more spots, the more active is the Sun. An active Sun produces transient events such as solar flares, which are bursts of electromagnetic energy in the visible, ultraviolet, and X-ray portions of the spectrum. A solar flare eruption may last from a few minutes to a few hours and is sometimes accompanied by electromagnetic emissions in the microwave radio frequency range. With large flares, the Sun often emits relativistic charged particles, protons, alphas, and electrons, sometimes referred to as solar cosmic rays. The most abundant charged particle is the solar proton. We use the term solar proton in preference to the term solar cosmic ray to avoid confusion with galactic cosmic rays, which refers to the high-energy charged particles continuously arriving at the Earth from all directions, excluding those of solar origin.

Indirect indicators of solar activity include auroral displays, geomagnetic storms, and variations in the intensity of galactic cosmic rays. The recent recognition that the Sun's magnetic field exhibits a well-ordered structure wherein the field lines stream away from or toward the Sun within well-defined sectors separated by a sharp boundary (Wilcox and Ness, 1965) has led to a new indicator, namely, solar magnetic sector boundary crossings, which appear to be associated with several of the other indicators of solar activity (e.g., geomagnetic activity and galactic cosmic ray variations).

Almost all these indicators, both direct and indirect, have been utilized for correlations with weather and climate parameters at one time or another, with varying degrees of success.

Forcing functions other than solar activity have, up to now, been more seriously considered for changing climate. For example, some investigators believe that the oceans are more important than the atmosphere for transporting heat from the equator toward the poles. Changes in ocean temperatures and circulation would foster changes in atmospheric heat distribution and therefore in weather and climate. Others have suggested that volcanic eruptions introduce widespread dust in the atmosphere that would block the Sun's rays, leading to a cooling trend, cloud formation, and greater rainfall. Changes in the area and extent of the polar ice caps may also force the world's climate to change, and recently Talbot et al. (1976) postulated that the passage of the solar system through interstellar clouds might affect the Earth's climate. A discussion of these interesting lines of inquiry cannot be included here; to do them justice we would have to give them as much attention as we give to solar activity as a forcing function. However, the recently revived theory of Milankovitch (1930), which suggested that the ice ages could have been caused by variations in the Earth's orbit over thousands of years, is of interest because it depends on a variable amount of solar energy incident at the top of the atmosphere brought about by the orbital changes.

Although the subject of Sun-weather relationships has been studied for more than a century, there has been no widespread acceptance of the results and no attempt to incorporate the results into weather forecasting or climate prediction methods in the United States. The main objection to serious consideration of the subject has been threefold: (1) Observed correlations between solar activity parameters and meteorological and climatological responses sometimes break down after several solar cycles, and contradictory results abound in the literature. (2) No acceptable physical explanations of why there should be a causal relationship between activity on the Sun and terrestrial weather have been forthcoming, and no linking mechanisms

3

to relate the two have been identified. (3) The amount of energy from the Sun due to solar activity is miniscule compared to the continuous radiant energy believed to be the driving force for our weather machine; thus solar activity should at best only trigger changes in the Earth's weather and climate. To date, it appears that a healthy skepticism has prevented any Sun-weather research results from being incorporated into weather and climate predictions.

Part of the difficulty lies in the fact that solar energy comes to the Earth in a variety of forms, some of which can be shunted around by the geomagnetic field, and there are numerous possible arrangements of the altitudes, latitudes, and longitudes at which the energy is ultimately transformed into heat and thereby becomes available to drive the circulation of the atmosphere or some component of it (Mitchell, 1965). Further, several of the solar energy forms are statistically correlated, but the morphology, or time and space history, of solar events and their accompanying or following terrestrial responses may exhibit different lag times in different altitude regimes and geographic regions.

Compounding the difficulty is a complex meteorological mechanism with many feedbacks and second-order effects apparently not related to solar activity, but that may well obscure its influence. An increase in temperature, for example, can cause an increase in evaporation, a rise in absolute humidity, and atmospheric instability. A consequence would be the formation of clouds, which, since clouds are better reflectors than the Earth's surface, would cause a decrease in the amount of solar radiation reaching the lower atmosphere and an accompanying decrease in temperature by day. Associated meteorological effects would be an increased cyclogenesis, leading to the development of low pressure centers, and an increase in winds and rainfall (Battan, 1974). The complexity of the atmospheric system and climatic feedback linkages is graphically illustrated in figure 1.1. Interactions within this intricately coupled network have been summarized by Kellogg and Schneider (1974). In this book we concentrate primarily on variations of the energy input parameter depicted in the upper left-hand corner of figure 1.1. As used here, variations in this parameter, "solar radiation," include solar activity in all its manifestations.

Thus the study of the effects of solar activity on specific meteorological parameters tells only part of the story, and actual effects on

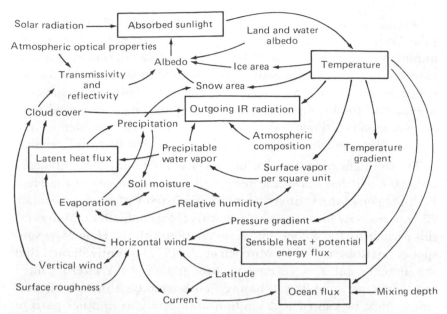

Figure 1.1. A model of the weather and climate machine illustrating its complex and intricate feedback mechanisms. The influence of several of the feedback processes are comparable in magnitude but opposite in direction. It is clear that variations in the energy input parameter at the top left may affect several of the meteorological parameters within the machine. From Kellogg and Schneider (1974).

weather and climate may be masked by the various feedback mechanisms. In spite of these problems, many investigators have found evidence of meteorological and climatological responses to solar activity. Three recent lines of inquiry are especially encouraging in this respect. First, Roberts and Olson (1973a,b) discovered that atmospheric vorticity (a meteorological measure of cyclogenesis) dramatically increases 3–4 days after the commencement of a geomagnetic storm, but Hines (1973) suggested that the geomagnetic activity could have been produced by upward propagating energy from the tropospheric phenomenon. Wilcox et al. (1973a,b) then showed that the atmospheric vorticity index utilized by Roberts and Olson responds in a similar way to a purely solar parameter (i.e., solar magnetic sector boundary crossings). The earlier criticisms were thus negated (Hines and Halevy, 1975; 1977); it is now generally accepted that increases in atmospheric vorticity and accompanying stormy weather conditions are actually associated with certain solar variables. However, the physical reason for this association is as yet unclear.

Second, a strong case has been made by the scholarly studies of John Eddy (1976) that the coldest part of the climatic temperature minimum known as the "Little Ice Age" coincided in time with a prolonged minimum in solar activity as measured by sunspots. In this so-called Maunder minimum spanning the years 1645–1715, sunspots were almost totally absent; fewer appeared in the entire period than are now seen in a single active year. Eddy's work does not identify any physical links, but his results strongly suggest that such links exist.

The third line of inquiry has not yet established any physical mechanisms, but it has led to the recognition that droughts in the High Plains region of the United States have occurred with an approximate 22-yr periodicity for more than a century (Marshall, 1972). Moreover, this periodicity has a constant phase relation with the Hale 22-yr sunspot cycle (Roberts, 1975). Mitchell et al. (1977) recently showed that the annual total area covered by droughts in the Western United States has the same 22-yr phasing. These results, although encouraging, must be viewed with caution until droughts in other parts of the world are similarly analyzed (Gerety et al., 1977).

The various results have been published in a literature notable for its disparity. That is, papers are to be found not only in meteorological and atmospheric science journals, but also in serials dealing with water and conservation, geography, astronomy, solar physics, the ionosphere, and general science, among others. Therefore bibliographic compilations are of great value in approaching the study of Sun-weather relationships. The most recent compilation (Shapley and Kroehl, 1977) concentrates on work reported from 1958 to early 1977 and is an update of the compilation by Shapley et al. (1975). Prior to 1958 compilations were made by Helland-Hansen and Nansen (1920), Brooks (1926, 1936, 1939), Clayton (1923), and Nuppen and Kageorge (1958).

Recent reviews of interest include those by Meadows (1975), who addressed the Sun-weather controversies of the past century, King (1975), who emphasized long-term or climatic aspects, and Wilcox (1975), who concentrated on short-term (weather) variations. In addition, two recent books on weather and climate written for the nonspecialist consider the possible meteorological effects of solar activity (Calder, 1975; Gribben, 1976). An excellent book on classical climatology is that of Lamb (1972).

Special conferences held within the past few years include a symposium on "Possible Relationships Between Solar Activity and Meteorological Phenomena" convened at NASA Goddard Space Flight Center in November 1973; a session on "Solar Variability and Meteorological Response" at the 55th Annual Meeting of the American Meteorological Society in Denver, January 1975; sessions organized by W. O. Roberts at the 16th General Assembly of the International Union of Geodesy and Geophysics at Grenoble, France, August 1975; sessions at the International Symposium of Solar-Terrestrial Physics at Boulder, June 1976; special symposia at the IAGA/IAMAP Conference in Seattle, Washington, August 1977. (The papers presented at the 1973 NASA conference have been collected and edited by Bandeen and Maran (1975).)

This work reviews both long and short-term meteorological variations related to solar activity and the few physical linking mechanisms that have been suggested to explain the relationships. Several new mechanisms are postulated with varying degrees of completeness to supplement those already reported in the literature. Physical background material is provided where appropriate to assist the reader in grasping the concepts presented.

The book also examines some experimental concepts useful for investigating physical links between solar variability and meteorological responses. The rationale for this objective is that, despite the vast literature supporting a probable connection between the two phenomena, there is considerable disbelief for such a connection. This disbelief seems to be based principally on the fact that no plausible physical mechanisms have been identified to explain how the relatively minor fluctuations in solar energy output can influence or drive the vastly more energetic meteorological processes. If linking mechanisms can be identified, the subject of Sun-weather relationships will be on much firmer ground, and improved predictions of climatic trends and weather changes may in fact become possible.

From these few introductory remarks it can be appreciated that the subject we address is truly multidisciplinary. It will be seen in subsequent pages that even the present modest effort touches on solar physics, magnetospheric physics, atmospheric physics and chemistry, atmospheric electricity, cosmic rays, geomagnetism, and meteorology. To gain new insights into Sun-weather relationships we believe it is necessary to combine the extant knowledge of all these disciplines and interpret that knowledge in new ways. We do not claim to do that here, but we do attempt to bring together, and in some cases simply point out, the essential ingredients required.

In that spirit, the characteristics of solar variables and solar energy sources suggested to be related to weather and climate fluctuations are discussed in chapter 2. Included are galactic cosmic rays and geomagnetic activity, since variations in the intensity of these phenomena are related to solar activity, and both have been observed to be correlated with weather changes.

Long-term climatic trends and their association with solar activity are examined in chapter 3. In some cases it has been noted that correlations between meteorological phenomena and the sunspot cycle may persist for several cycles and then break down or even reverse sign. These peculiarities may be indicative of a fortuitous correlation between unrelated variables, or they may point toward an as yet undiscovered key to an undefined link between two seemingly independent variables that are in fact related. Because of these two important possibilities, a separate section (3.3) is devoted to such breakdowns and reversals.

Short-term correlations between meteorological parameters and transient solar phenomena, such as solar flares and solar magnetic sector boundaries, are treated in chapter 4. Correlations between weather changes and magnetic activity as an indicator of solar variability are included in this chapter.

In chapter 5, the possibility that observed correlations between magnetic activity and weather phenomena are unrelated to solar activity is examined briefly.

The heart of the problem, that is, the physical processes and mechanisms that produce the observed correlations, is addressed in chapter 6. Here the discussion must be speculatory and in some cases naive, because no hypotheses have been proven that explain the physical links to couple solar variations to the troposphere.

A summary of the highlights of Sun-weather relationships and an extensive table of reported correlations are given in chapter 7. This narrative summary can be read first to gain an overview of the subject.

The principal weather and climate factors that affect man and his activities are summarized in chapter 8, along with an argument for a continuation and intensification of Sun-weather research. Meteorological and solar-related measurement parameters required in such future research are also summarized in this chapter, and some experimental guidelines for searching out physical linking mechanisms are suggested. Following this final chapter, a comprehensive list of references is collected.

Basic physical properties of the atmosphere (temperature, pressure, density) up to 50 km, along with conversion factors for pressure units are given in appendix A. Acronyms, abbreviations, units, and symbols used in the text are collected in appendix B.

2 Solar-Related Correlation Factors and Energy Sources

In the general picture of Sun-weather relationships there are four major facets. First, there are the manifestations of solar activity, some of which exhibit fairly well-defined periodicities; others occur as unpredictable transient events. Second, meteorological and climatological observations and studies have revealed both periodic and aperiodic features that can be explained only partially on the basis of short- and long-term meteorological processes. The third facet is an outgrowth of the first two; that is, the similarity of periodicities observed in both solar activity and weather phenomena has led to the long-held suspicion that there must be some connection between the two, and a great deal of correlative analysis has been devoted to a search for such connections. Finally, the sometimes contradictory, confusing, and controversial results that have emerged from many studies have forced recognition of the fourth, and perhaps most important, facet, namely, what are the atmospheric physical and chemical processes that allow the relatively minor, solar activity-induced fluctuations in the Sun's energy reaching the Earth to influence the vastly more energetic dynamics of the troposphere? This facet is the most recent in the Sun-weather problem, and it is the least polished.

To understand and ultimately solve the general problem, it is necessary to address all its major aspects. The first two facets represent fairly complex geophysical disciplines, and the third tries to bring them together (with an attendant increase in complexity). The fourth facet must not only correctly utilize the knowledge already extant and continuously evolving in the fields of solar activity, weather, and climate, but must also delineate the physical and chemical processes involved in interactions between them. For guidance in the fourth aspect, existing correlative evidence and new results from additional ongoing studies can and should be utilized.

To fully appreciate this fascinating and often frustrating puzzle, it is helpful to examine the pieces separately but with an eye to how they might fit together. We begin in this chapter with an examination of those features of solar activity which have been demonstrated to have a bearing on the overall problem.

Sunspots and their variations with time are addressed first, because they are not only a basic indicator of solar activity but also have been the most commonly used parameter in past correlation studies. Further, a number of other solar activity parameters are associated with sunspots on a correlative or a one-to-one basis. These are discussed later in this chapter and include solar flares, solar energetic particles, cosmic rays, solar and interplanetary magnetic sector structure, and geomagnetic activity. The Sun's radiant energy, although not necessarily variable with sunspot activity, is also discussed in relation to its role in meteorology.

Subsequent chapters are devoted to the remaining facets of the Sun-weather problem. However, the discussion of appropriate meteorological concepts is interwoven with the treatments of long- and short-term correlations in chapters 3 and 4.

2.1 Sunspots

A sunspot is a relatively dark, sharply defined region on the solar disk, marked by an umbra some 2000 K cooler than the effective photospheric temperature, surrounded by a less dark but also sharply bounded penumbra. The average spot diameter is about 37 000 km, and exceptionally large spots can be up to 245 000 km across. Although a single small spot sometimes appears alone, most sunspots are found in groups of two or more. The magnetic field of sunspots is much higher than that of the disk as a whole, and the polarity of the leading spot in a bipolar group is opposite to that for the following spot.

Galileo is credited with discovering sunspots telescopically around 1610, although it is now recognized that naked-eye sightings of large sunspots had already been recorded in China for at least 15 centuries.

2.1.1 Sunspot Number Variability

Surprisingly, the fact that sunspots come and go in cycles was not appreciated until 1843, when the amateur astronomer Heinrich Schwabe (1844) published a short paper on his sunspot observations for the years 1826–1843. Schwabe found the cycle length to be about 10 yr. Prompted by this startling report, Rudolf Wolf, director of the astronomical observatory in Zurich, Switzerland, devised a quantitative definition for sunspot number and applied it to the existing historical data to see if Schwabe's cyclical variation could be found in longer spans of time. For the years 1700–1848, Wolf did find such cycles, and the average cycle length was 11.1 yr (cf. Waldmeier, 1961). In deference to its original discoverer, we often refer to the 11-yr cycle as the "Schwabe cycle" in this book.

In its present form, the Wolf sunspot number R is defined as

$$R = k(10g + f) \tag{2.1}$$

where f is the total number of spots regardless of size, g is the number of spot groups, and k normalizes the counts from different observatories. It is evident that much greater weight is given to the groups than to individual spots. The Wolf sunspot number is also referred to as the "Wolfer sunspot number" (after the man who succeeded Wolf as director of the Zurich Observatory), the "Zurich relative sunspot number" denoted by R_z (after the observatory itself), or simply as the "relative sunspot number."

Daily counts are made routinely at many astronomical observatories (continuously since 1848, when they were instituted by Wolf), and the data combined according to equation (2.1) are available from the Zurich Observatory or the World Data Center in Boulder, Colorado, as daily numbers, monthly means, and yearly means. The sunspot data from 1848 to the present are the most reliable. Because of the way they were derived, Wolf numbers from 1700 to 1748 are poor; those from 1749 to 1817 are questionable, and those from 1818 to 1847 are good (Eddy, 1976).

A typical plot of yearly mean Wolf numbers is given in figure 2.1. The most prominent feature is the Schwabe (11-yr) cycle, but longer period variations are also evident. Because of the influence of the longer period variations, the annual mean Wolf number varies from 0 to 10 in years of minimum and from 50 to 190 for maximum years. (Daily numbers can range from 0 to 355 or more.) The Schwabe cycle length varies from about 8.5 to 14 yr between successive minima and from 7.3 to about 17 yr between maxima. In the two epochs 1784–1797 and 1843–1856, the cycle length was 13 yr.

The beginning of each new 11-yr cycle is marked by the appearance of new sunspots and groups of sunspots at high solar latitudes.

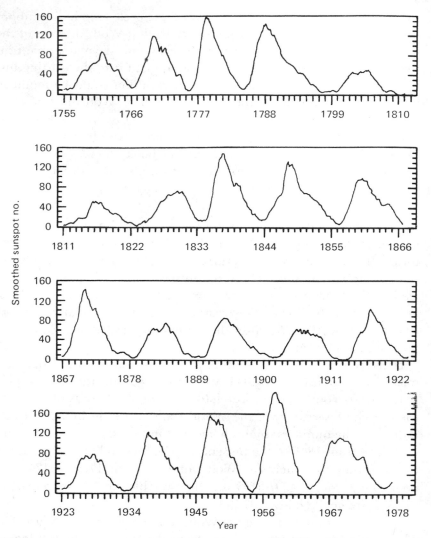

Figure 2.1. Variations in annual mean Zurich sunspot number (World Data Center for Solar-Terrestrial Physics). The value for 1977 is the provisional average through September.

As the cycle progresses, sunspots appear at successively lower latitudes, until most appear within 5° of the solar equator near the end of an 11-yr period. The magnetic polarity of a new high-latitude group is opposite to that of low-latitude groups belonging to the old cycle. The beginning of a new cycle usually overlaps the end of the old cycle, sometimes by a year or more. An old spot or two near the equator can exist simultaneously with a new high-latitude spot or group of spots of opposite magnetic polarity, or spots belonging to the ending cycle may reappear near the equator several months after the apparent start of the new cycle and may persist for one or two solar rotations. The precise time of sunspot minimum is established only in retrospect and only approximately by the minimum number of spots observed in a specified period, usually a month. It has become common practice to refer to each 11-yr cycle (measured from minimum to minimum) by number; somewhat arbitrarily the period 1755–1766 has been assigned cycle 1. Cycle 20 is thus the period 1964–1976, and we are now in cycle 21.

Observations of the latitudinal progression of sunspots led to the discovery of the differential rotation of the Sun. That is, at the solar equator the rotation period is 25 days, at 30° latitude it is 27.5 days, and at the solar poles it is 35 days. The average rotation period is 27 days, and it is this period that is most often referred to in Sun-weather literature.

With respect to long-term variations, one can see in figure 2.1 some similarity in the structure of the two time spans 1755–1799 and 1934–1974. That is, cycles 1, 2, 3, and 4 are similar to cycles 17, 18, 19, and 20, and this implies a 180-yr periodicity. Also, one can almost see a similarity between the cycle sets 5, 6, 7 and 12, 13, 14, suggesting another superimposed long cycle of about 80 yr. Other cycle lengths have been identified by spectral analysis (section 2.1.2).

When the magnetic characteristics of sunspots are taken into account, one complete fundamental cycle requires two Schwabe cycles, or about 22 yr. The principal characteristic of this so-called double sunspot cycle, first delineated by Hale (1908) and Hale and Nicholson (1925), is that it is the period in which the magnetic polarity of bipolar sunspots completes a cycle of change. The polarity reversal takes place at a minimum in the 11-yr cycle; the 22-yr cycle encompasses two successive 11-yr cycles. In the "positive" 11-yr cycle, the magnetic polarity of the leading spot of a bipolar spot group in the northern solar hemisphere is outward (positive), and that in the southern hemisphere is inward (negative). At the close of the positive cycle, these spot polarities reverse and persist throughout the next 11-yr period, the "negative" cycle. The Hale sunspot (22-yr) cycle is plotted in figure 2.2, where alternate 11-yr maxima are plotted as positive or negative peaks. The length of the Hale cycle (only nominally 22 yr) varies in accordance with the lengths of its positive and

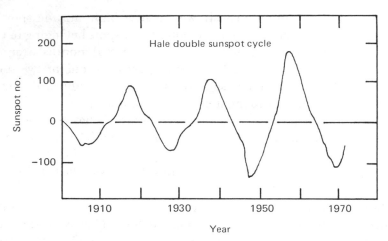

Figure 2.2. Hale double sunspot cycle, with alternate maxima in the 11-yr cycle plotted with opposite sign. From Roberts (1975).

negative halves. A 22-yr variation in geomagnetic activity associated with the reversal of the polar fields of the Sun has been pointed out by Chernosky (1966). Also, a component of the diurnal variation of cosmic rays exhibits an amplitude variation apparently related to the Hale cycle (Forbush, 1973; Pomerantz and Duggal, 1974). Meteorological phenomena with 22-yr periodicities are discussed in section 3.2.

Apart from direct observations of sunspots, several indirect parameters have been utilized in attempts to extend the sunspot cycle curve backward in time. Tree-ring growth, which relies on an assumed correlation between sunspots and floral growth factors (such as temperature and rainfall) was a popular parameter for a time (e.g., Schove, 1955). This extrapolation procedure has been improved by radiocarbon dating of tree rings (e.g., Stuiver, 1961; Mitchell et al., 1977). The frequency of auroral occurrences (Harang, 1951) and the size of the solar corona observable during total solar eclipses are correlated with sunspot number, and Eddy (1976) relied partly on this type of data in extending sunspot cycle history back to 1100 AD.

Recent evidence suggests that the Sun has not always been so well behaved with respect to 11-, 22-, or even 180-yr cycles; within the past 1000 yr there have been three times at which the cyclic variation evidently ceased altogether. In a herculean effort based on ancient manuscripts, old literature, modern data and interpretations, and indirect inferences, Eddy (1976) extended sunspot records back to

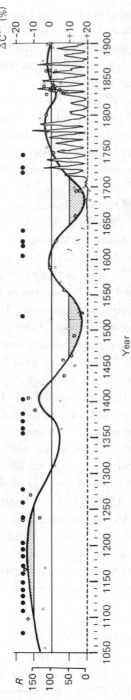

Figure 2.3. Historical sunspot variability as deduced by Eddy (1976). The heavy solid line is variation in C^{14} concentration in tree rings and the thin curve is Wolf sunspot numbers (R). Solid circles are from historical Oriental sunspot records; open circles are from tree ring analysis. Shaded portions of the C^{14} curve are the Spörer and Maunder sunspot minimums.

about 1100 AD. From direct reports of solar observations, old auroral records, and, notably, carbon 14 (C^{14}) analyses of tree rings, he showed that two prolonged deep minima and one major prolonged maximum in sunspot activity must have occurred. In these three apparently aperiodic events, no 11-yr variation in sunspot activity was discernible. The "12th Century Grand Maximum" in sunspot activity spanned the years 1100-1250 AD. A gradual decline then ensued until 1520, interrupted only by a relatively brief minor maximum centered at about 1400 (see fig. 2.3). The first deep prolonged minimum centered at 1520, labeled by Eddy the "Spörer Minimum" after the German scientist who first noted it in 1887, covered the years 1460-1550. Finally, the "Maunder minimum," named after the British astronomer who first called attention to it in 1890, occurred during the years 1645-1715. Climatic variations associated with these anomalies are discussed in section 3.1.3.

A word about the use of C^{14} analysis to derive sunspot activity is in order. This isotope is formed in the atmosphere by the action of cosmic-ray neutron secondaries on nitrogen. When the isotope is assimilated by trees in the form of CO_2, it decays with a half-life of approximately 5700 yr. Each ring of the tree represents one growing season; thus analysis of the C^{14} abundance year by year can yield the relative annual incidence of cosmic rays after appropriate corrections are made (DeVries, 1958; Lingenfelter, 1963). From the known inverse relationship between cosmic-ray intensity and sunspot number (sec. 2.4.1), long-term changes in C^{14} abundance can thus be interpreted as corresponding inverse changes in sunspot activity (Stuiver, 1961; Suess, 1965). A different interpretation of changes in C^{14} abundance is that they reflect alternating periods of slow and fast mixing of the oceans (Damon et al., 1966), which presumably yield lesser or greater amounts of CO_2 to the atmosphere. Eddy's (1976) work, based not only on C^{14} analysis but on other direct and indirect data pertaining to sunspots, strongly suggests that the cosmic-ray effect is the correct interpretation. In either case, there is an approximately 40-yr lag from the time C^{14} is produced in the atmosphere to the time of its assimilation into trees.

2.1.2 Spectral Analysis of Sunspot Cycles

From figure 2.1 it is evident that the variability of sunspot numbers plotted over long time scales exhibits several different apparent periodicities. The curve can be regarded as a periodic function so that spectral analysis techniques can be used to identify the different cycle lengths. However, care must be exercised in applying these techniques. For example, since the sunspot curve is only approximately periodic, different sample lengths give somewhat different spectra. The problem of irregularities, particularly in the early data, can lead to invalid results (Mayaud, 1977). Also, if the limitations of the analytical technique are exceeded, aliasing and spectrum foldover may produce misleading or erroneous results. Spectral analysis, being a strictly mathematical artifact, gives no clue to the physical processes involved in sunspot cycle variations. Of course, the 22-yr Hale cycle does not show up in spectral analysis of Wolf number amplitudes, which are independent of magnetic sign. In spite of these shortcomings, spectral analyses have revealed a number of specific period lengths, some of which are also discernible in such climatic data as temperature and rainfall.

A power spectrum analysis of annual mean R_z for 1700-1960 by Mitchell (1965) clearly shows the dominance of the Schwabe cycle (fig. 2.4) and reveals additional peaks corresponding to cycle lengths of 5.7, 8.4, and 90 yr. This 90-yr period is within the 80-100-yr cycle length first identified by Gleissberg (1944). With twentieth century data, the average Schwabe cycle length was found to be 10.6 ± 0.3 yr (Chernosky, 1966; Currie, 1974). A recent analysis of annual mean R_z from 1884 to 1972 by Radoski et al. (1975), using the maximum entropy method to obtain improved spectral resolution, found the 11-yr cycle peak to be a triplet of 12.9, 10.9, and 9.5 yr. The Radoski spectrum also exhibited peaks at frequencies corresponding to cycle lengths of 5.3 and 129 yr. Courtillot et al. (1977) have shown that the triplet and the long-period cycle length may both be due to limitations in the maximum entropy analysis method and therefore may not be real.

Changes in sunspot spectrum due to sample selection are illustrated by the maximum entropy results of Cohen and Lintz (1974). First omitting the less reliable early Wolf numbers, they used 12-month running means from 1844 to 1971 and found spectral peaks corresponding to periods of 110, 10.9, 9.7, and 8.0 yr. The years 1750-1963 yielded periods of 95.8, 11.0, 9.8, and 8.3 yr. Finally, the total data span from 1750 to 1971 produced a spectrum with peaks at 89.6, 11.2, 9.9, and 8.1 yr. Thus, by using different portions of the same data base, the positions of the spectral peaks are shifted. Nevertheless, the gross characteristics of the various spectra are similar in

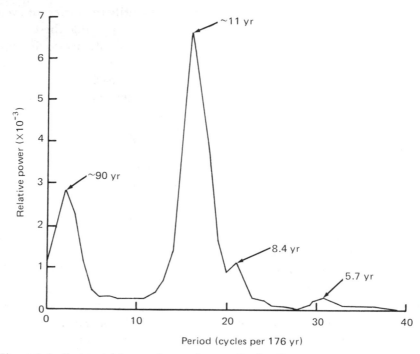

Figure 2.4. Power spectrum of annual mean R_z for 1700–1960. Maximum lag of 88 yr used in analysis, with only low-frequency half of spectrum shown. From Mitchell (1965).

three major respects. That is, there seems to be a short cycle of about 5½ yr; the 11-yr cycle peak could be a triplet with periods as short as 8 yr and as long as 13 yr; there is a long cycle that is found most often with a period of about 90 yr but ranges from 89.6 to 129 yr. From other analyses not reviewed here, there is evidence of a 180-yr cycle in sunspot numbers (see Sleeper, 1972).

In summary, if we assume the difference in these various results to be due to sample selection effects and errors introduced by the spectral analysis techniques utilized, the major periodicities in sunspot number identified to date have approximate, average cycle lengths of (yr)

5.5

8.1, 9.7, 11.2

100

180

The short cycle of 5.5 yr has received scant attention in the literature and may indeed be merely a harmonic, mathematically correct but physically unreal. However, it may become more important in the future, as additional studies of meteorological responses to solar activity are made, since Bigelow (1915) pointed out years ago some periodicities in weather phenomena with lengths of "about half of a solar cycle" (that is, half the 11-yr cycle).

The 11-yr cycle has received by far the most attention; as Shaw (1928, p. 6) pointed out, any weather phenomenon with an 11.1-yr period may be associated with sunspots. Mitchell (1965) reminds us that a number of investigations give evidence of an 11-yr variation in meteorological processes, but in some, the correlation holds up well for a few cycles and then seems to break down. It is these failures which suggest the importance of the longer-term cycles and the possibility of long-term, nonperiodic trends. Correlation breakdowns are discussed in section 3.3.

2.1.3 Prediction of Future Sunspot Variability

If sunspots are a key factor, that is, a good usable indicator of solar activity for Sun-weather relationships, an obvious condition must be met before sunspot numbers can be used to predict changes in weather and climate: The sunspots themselves must be predictable. As succeeding chapters reveal, it is premature to demand a full understanding of sunspot predictability for Sun-weather purposes at this time. In this section the question of sunspot predictability is therefore only briefly addressed.

As with many other geophysical time variants, sunspot predictions can be made either on the purely statistical basis of past variability or on a model of the physical processes that cause the number of sunspots to change with time. The accuracy of the prediction is a function of the reliability of the statistics or the viability of the physical model. Most probably, a combination of statistics and physical models would improve the accuracy.

It has already been demonstrated that sunspot history is marked with a multiplicity of cycles and sometimes an absence of cycles. Thus extrapolation to the future by statistics alone is unreliable because it is difficult to determine which sequence in the past most nearly reflects present trends. For example, Bray (1966), noting that the period 1914–1964 was similar to the periods 1100–1203 and 1724–1798, has suggested that sunspot activity may remain high for "several more cycles," possibly extending almost to the close of the twentieth century. On the other hand, Cohen and Lintz (1974), relying on the similarity of cycles 1, 2, 3, 4 and 17, 18, 19, 20 and the attendant implication of a 180-yr cycle, predicted in 1974 that ". . . the next 40 years may be characterized by relatively low sunspot activity as compared with the activity of the last 40 years."

Jose (1965) suggested that the 180-yr (actually 179-yr) cycle is associated with planetary resonances; the beginning of the next such cycle would be expected in about 1980, near the time of the next concurrent conjunction of all the planets. Presumably, planetary tides induced on the Sun by the gravitational pull of the planets would affect the formation of sunspots (Wood and Wood, 1965).

Cohen and Lintz (1974) argued that the 180-yr cycle is simply a beat frequency phenomenon. To see this, let us recall that if two sinusoidal signals of frequency f_1 and f_2 are mixed together, there result two additional modulating (beat) frequencies f_3 and f_4 whose values are equal to the sum and difference of f_1 and f_2, respectively. In terms of period,

$$1/T_3 = 1/T_1 + 1/T_2 \qquad (2.2)$$

$$1/T_4 = 1/T_1 - 1/T_2 \qquad (2.3)$$

where T_1 is the cycle length (years per cycle) corresponding to the frequency f_1 (cycles per year). Under the proper circumstances f_3 and f_4 may beat together to form still more frequencies, and harmonics (integral multiples) of the original frequencies may be generated. Thus Cohen and Lintz suggested that the 180-yr cycle is merely the period of twice the beat frequency generated by the 9.9 and 11.2-yr cycles. Okal and Anderson (1975) said that this result ". . . removes the basis for [Jose's] planetary theory of sunspots."

Let us take a different view of the problem. Planetary tidal theory has evolved essentially because a number of planetary resonances have periods that are close to the cycle lengths observed in sunspot variations, especially those near 11 and 180 yr (tables 2.1 and 2.2, respectively). In addition to the long-period resonances of the outer planets (table 2.2), Jose's (1965) work shows that the Sun rotates about the center of mass of the solar system with a period of 179.2 yr. Further, taking into account the relative masses, distances from the Sun, and orbital periods of all the planets, it can be shown that the gravitational (vector) force exerted by the planets on a fixed spot on the Sun varies cyclically with a period of 11.1 yr.

Table 2.1.—Short-Period Resonances of the Inner
Planets (from Sleeper, 1972)

Period	Earth Years
46 sidereal revolutions of Mercury	11.079
18 sidereal revolutions of Venus	11.074
(137 synodic revolutions of Moon)	(11.077)
11 sidereal revolutions of Earth	11.000
6 sidereal revolutions of Mars	11.286

Table 2.2.—Long-Period Resonances of the Outer
Planets (from Sleeper, 1972)

Period	Earth Years
6 sidereal revolutions of Saturn	176.746
15 sidereal revolutions of Jupiter	177.933
9 synodic periods, Jupiter-Saturn	178.734
14 synodic periods, Jupiter-Neptune	178.923
13 synodic periods, Jupiter-Uranus	179.562
5 synodic periods, Saturn-Neptune	179.385
4 synodic periods, Saturn-Uranus	181.455

If these two fundamental periods (11.1 and 179.2 yr) are used in equations (2.2) and (2.3), the resulting beat cycles have periods of 11.8 and 10.4 yr. Letting these two resultant frequencies beat together, two additional cycles emerge with periods of 89.5 and 5.5 yr. In other words, on the basis of planetary tidal theory, one could expect sunspot cycle lengths of (yr)

$$5.5$$
$$10.4, \ 11.1, \ 11.8$$
$$89.5$$
$$179.2$$

These numbers are quite similar to the spectral analysis results discussed in the preceding section (2.1.2) except that the triplet near 11 yr is displaced toward longer periods here. There have been suggestions that the apparent agreement between planetary tides on the Sun and sunspot cycles is fortuitous or is an artifact of the calculations (Okal and Anderson, 1975).

Planetary tides surely continued during the years of the Maunder sunspot minimum (Smythe and Eddy, 1977), but this observation merely shows that planetary tides do not cause the *absence* of sunspots and therefore they are not the root cause of sunspot generation. It is still an open question whether these tides might modulate the number, size, and frequency of occurrence of sunspots.

In summary, it is clear that attempts to project future sunspot variations from past behavior have met with difficulties. Also, models of the physical processes causing sunspot occurrence to change with time require further investigation before they can be utilized to supplement the projections. Therefore, even if a one-to-one correlation between solar activity and climate is established, predictions of future climate on the basis of sunspot number should be viewed with caution until the predictability of sunspots themselves is improved.

2.2 Solar Electromagnetic Radiation

Most of the energy from the Sun is in the form of electromagnetic radiation. Although the spectrum of this radiation extends from X-rays with wavelengths of 10 nm (1 nm $= 10^{-9}$ m) or less to radio waves of wavelengths 100 m and more, 99% of the energy is concentrated in the range 276 to 4960 nm, and 99.9% is in the range 217 to 10 940 nm (Thekaekara, 1974). In other words, all but 0.1% of the energy is found in the visible, infrared, and ultraviolet portions of the solar spectrum.

The manner in which solar radiation is related to weather and the manner in which the radiation changes as a function of solar activity are discussed in this section. For convenience, the visible and short wavelength (ultraviolet and X-ray) variations are treated separately (sec. 2.2.1 and 2.2.2, respectively). Solar flare occurrence is discussed in section 2.2.3, and the relative amounts of energy carried by solar radiation and the solar wind are compared in section 2.2.4.

2.2.1 Visible Radiation and the Solar Constant

It is generally considered that the radiant energy in the form of electromagnetic radiation from the Sun reaching the top of the atmosphere, referred to as "insolation" by meteorologists and "solar irradiance" by astronomers, is responsible for atmospheric circulation and consequent weather. One may regard the troposphere as a giant heat engine, with the source (heater) at the equator and the sink (cooler) at the poles. The temperature difference between the two drives the advective (horizontal) circulation, which is a mass transport of warm air toward the poles and cool air toward the equator.

This greatly oversimplified heat-engine model of the troposphere is maintained by insolation, because the solar energy flux available at the top of the atmosphere is proportional to the cosine of the angle of incidence. That is, the solar flux is maximum within $\pm 23°$ latitude of the equator (giving the highest temperature), and near the poles it is a factor of about 2.4 smaller. In the summer hemisphere, the integrated insolation per day is greater at the pole than at the equator. However, the stratosphere is warmer at the pole because of circulation rather than insolation effects.

The "efficiency" of the engine is directly proportional to the temperature difference between heater and cooler and inversely proportional to the temperature at the equator. According to approximate estimates (Brunt, 1952), the efficiency is on the order of 2%, meaning that 0.02 of the radiant (potential) energy arriving at the Earth is transformed into "the kinetic energy of atmospheric motion" (Monin, 1972).

The spectral distribution of this radiant energy at the top of the atmosphere (fig. 2.5) peaks in the visible range from about 400–700 nm. The integrated average rate of incoming radiation over all wavelengths, termed the solar constant, amounts to about $1.353(10^3)$ $W m^{-2}$ at normal incidence at the top of the atmosphere for average Sun-Earth distance (Thekaekara, 1974).

Estimates of this quantity vary, however, and a variety of recent high-altitude measurements by aircraft, rockets, and satellites above most of the intervening atmosphere show a dispersion of several percent (see the review by Fröhlich, 1977). Mitchell (1965), Abbott (1922), and others have suggested that a 1% change in solar constant is sufficient to cause profound alterations in atmospheric circulation. Moreover, Volland (1977a,b) has shown theoretically that a change of 0.1–0.3% can produce a measurable change in atmospheric pressure (sec. 6.1.1). Thus it is evident that we need much better monitoring of the solar constant and its possible variations than is now available.

In the first half of this century a great deal of study was devoted to changes in the solar constant (cf. Bigelow, 1915; Clayton, 1923); the most comprehensive study is that by the Smithsonian Institution Astrophysical Laboratory under the direction of C. G. Abbott during

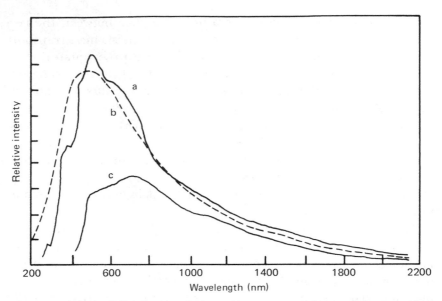

Figure 2.5. Spectral distribution of solar radiant energy at the top of the atmosphere (curve a) and after passing through the equivalent of 3 atm (curve c). The dashed curve (b) is the spectrum for a 6000 K black body. From Reifsnyder (1964).

the years 1902–1955 (see Roosen and Angione, 1975, and references therein). Although long-term changes in the solar constant associated with the sunspot cycle (cf. Abbott, 1958), and short-term fluctuations over days or weeks (Clayton, 1923) were reported, a firm belief that the solar constant is invariant has become established in some circles (Mitchell, 1965). The apparent fluctuations, it has been argued, are due to variations in atmospheric transmissivity rather than changes in source strength.

Utmost care has been taken to remove the possibility of atmospheric influences in the historical work; thus despite detractions it is worthy of mention. For example, based on measurements from 1905 to 1920, Abbott (1922) found a positive correlation between solar constant and sunspot number. With later data, Abbott (1958) showed a monotonic increase in solar insolation to a maximum change of 0.25% between 1940 and 1950, when the sunspot number was increasing from about 25 to 175. Öpik (1964) reanalyzed the Smithsonian data and verified long-period variations in the solar constant. Other independent work (Craig and Willett, 1951) also tends to support Abbott's conclusions.

The recent results from observations of the brightness of Neptune and Uranus at the Lowell Observatory in Flagstaff, Arizona, suggest that there may be variations in the solar constant (Lockwood, 1975). In regular monitoring it has been observed that at times the albedo of the major planets and their satellites changes systematically; this may be the result of a varying solar constant, but according to A. Hoag, Director of the Observatory (private communication, 1977), it could be produced by changes in the solar wind or the solar ultraviolet intensity.

A change of only a few tenths of a percent in the total energy radiated from the Sun is sufficient to cause profound meteorological changes; Mitchell (1965) suggested that such small changes do occur, and that they enter the atmospheric dynamic system through direct heating of the Earth's surface and the base of the atmosphere. In this sense, solar activity may be a signature for changes in the solar constant. The same latitudinal dependence as for normal heating by insolation would prevail; that is, the anomalous heating would be greatest at the equator and least at the pole during equinox, leading to an increase in temperature gradient with a consequent change in pressure gradient and accompanying changes in atmospheric circulation. Long-term changes in the solar constant would be associated with climate variations, and short-term fluctuations over days would cause weather changes.

From the foregoing it appears imperative that a measurement program above the atmosphere be undertaken to establish a precise value for the solar constant and determine whether it is actually constant. Aircraft measurements above most of the atmosphere have been made (Thekaekara, 1974), and there are plans to monitor the solar constant with spacecraft in the Solar Energy Monitor in Space (SEMIS) experiment (Thekaekara, 1975). This problem will also be addressed in connection with the Earth Radiation Budget (ERB) experiment.

2.2.2 Short Wavelength Variations

Since ozone is produced by UV radiation at wavelengths shorter than 242 nm, and the atmospheric ozone layer completely absorbs UV radiation between about 310 and 220 nm (Goldberg, 1954), variations in this portion of the solar spectrum are very important to the problem at hand. Here we are concerned with variability associated with the 11-yr solar cycle, the 27-day rotation period, the solar magnetic sector structure, and short-period phenomena (essentially solar flares). Unambiguous data on solar irradiance have only become available with the advent of rocket and satellite techniques, because ground-based measurements were always profoundly influenced by atmospheric absorption and scattering.

Rocket and satellite measurements have spanned the solar spectrum from the X-ray band through the extreme ultraviolet (EUV) to the near UV wavelengths in the vicinity of 300 nm. A division into wavelength categories is inappropriate for this discussion, but it should be kept in mind that, in general, UV radiation in the wavelength band 220–310 nm is principally related to ozone processes, and shorter wavelengths (EUV and X-rays) are responsible for ionospheric D and E region ionization processes above about 60 km altitude. The shortest-period phenomena are presented first.

Solar Flare Association: X-ray bursts associated with solar flares exhibit dramatic increases over preflare levels. In the great events of August 1–11, 1972, X-ray flux increases of greater than a factor of 100 were observed by the satellites Solrad (Dere et al., 1973) and OSO-7 (Datlowe and Peterson, 1973) in the wavelength ranges of 0.05–0.8 and 0.2–0.9 nm, respectively. For a less intense event, Wende (1969b) reported a factor of 5 to 10 increase in X-ray fluxes in the 0.2–1.2-nm channel on Explorer 33 and the 0.2–0.9-nm channel on Mariner 5, respectively, associated with the flare of July 25, 1967. This flux, of course, is small in reference to the total energy emitted by the Sun. The X-ray enhancements of August 1972 lasted for 4–18 hr, depending on wavelength, and, in general, the enhancements associated with solar flares decay over a period of several hours, depending on the severity of the event.

In the EUV part of the spectrum, Timothy and Timothy (1970) noted that there is a 25% increase in the flux of 30.4 nm (He II Lyα) associated with class 2B flares. The H Lyα line (121.57 nm) and wavelengths near it show enhancements of about a factor of 4 during flares (Friedman, 1960). Hall and Hinteregger (1969) found that the flare enhancements were most pronounced in the middle range of the band they observed (27–131 nm), and they related this to the ionization potentials of emitting solar ions responsible for the various wavelengths. The greatest increases occur on lines associated with ions with 30–50 eV ionization potentials.

Solar Magnetic Sector Boundary Passage: Since there are normally either two or four magnetic sector structure boundaries in the solar rotation, the next longest periodicity might be expected to be about 7–14 days. Obridko et al. (1974) statistically confirmed that solar proton flare activity tends to occur near sector boundaries and in the leading part of the sectors. Since short wavelength radiation enhancements are associated with solar flare eruptions, one may also expect a correlation between UV increases and sector boundary passage by the Earth.

From UV (120–300 nm) measurements on satellites Nimbus 3 and 4, Heath and Wilcox (1975) found enhanced UV irradiance coming from regions at solar longitudes corresponding to the feet of solar sector boundaries. The enhancements are more closely associated with central meridian (CM) crossing of the boundary on the solar surface than with sector boundary past the Earth (there is an approximately 4½-day lag between the former and the latter). This can be seen in figure 2.6, where the vertical dashed line at − 4½ days represents the time at which the sector boundary was near CM, and day 0 marks the time at which the boundary swept past the Earth. A similar pattern of

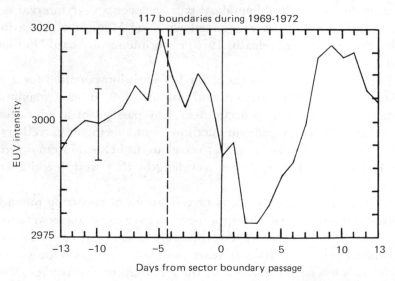

Figure 2.6. *Observed variation of average UV irradiance relative to observed solar sector boundaries. Day 0 is the day at which the boundary swept past the Earth, and the dashed vertical line is the time at which the same boundary was near the CM. The error bar is a typical standard error based on 117 boundary crossings. From Heath et al. (1975).*

behavior is seen in atmospheric vorticity with respect to sector boundaries in section 4.3.3. The time delay between CM crossing of an active region and the UV enhancement is given in figure 2.7. In crossing a boundary from a sector whose magnetic field direction is away from the Sun to one toward the Sun, the enhancements tend to occur just after CM passage. The data taken together without respect to sector polarity (the composite histogram in fig. 2.7) indicate that most UV enhancements as observed from near-Earth locations occur within ± 2 days of the CM passage of a sector boundary. This would seem to indicate that there is some "beaming" of the UV irradiance, and the energy flows out from the Sun in a cone angle with a full width of approximately 50° centered roughly on the heliographic longitude of the sector boundary. Otherwise, the active region giving rise to UV enhancements would affect the irradiance intensity as long as it were in view on the solar disk (about 13½ days).

Since it is an open question whether solar electromagnetic radiation or corpuscular emissions is the principal link between possible meteorological responses to solar activity, the Heath and Wilcox (1975) analysis of enhancements in the far UV solar irradiance in relation to solar sector boundary passage over a 5-yr interval is of interest. These data were observed with the Monitor of Ultraviolet Solar Energy (MUSE) (Heath, 1973) experiments on board Nimbus 3 and 4.

Two specific active centers of far UV emission persisted for a significant portion of the 5-yr interval, and in 1969, at least, maximum enhancements tended to occur near CM passage of a solar sector boundary. The magnitudes of maximum enhancements exceeded the annual variation in the far UV at wavelengths below 175 nm down to the H Lyα line, but at longer wavelengths they were less than the annual variation.

27-Day Recurrence: Various investigations of recurring magnetic storms and ionospheric absorption events over the years seem to indicate that 27-day recurrence tendencies are much more easily observed in sunspot minimum (ssmin) years than sunspot maximum (ssmax) years. This has been explained by the fact that, on the average, fewer active regions exist at any given time on the Sun in sunspot minimum years, and those present live for a number of solar rotations. In sunspot maximum years, however, new active regions are continually forming on the disk at random Carrington (solar) longitudes and have a tendency to die after one or two solar rotations; these would be superimposed on any existing long-lived active regions and tend to obscure any 27-day recurrence pattern.

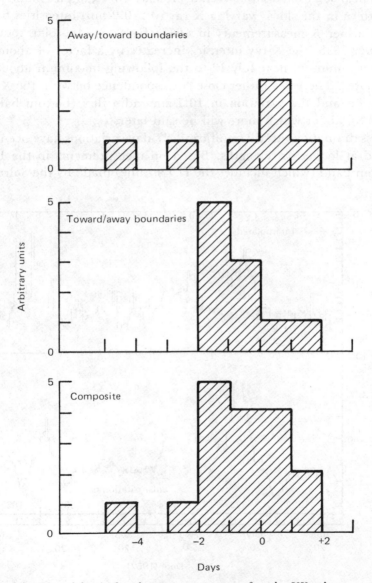

Figure 2.7. Time delay in days between occurrence of a solar UV enhancement and corresponding solar magnetic sector boundary CM crossing (day 0). Plus means advance; minus means lag. Directions are with reference to the Sun. From Heath and Wilcox (1975).

In spite of these earlier results, there appears to be a perceptible 27-day recurrence pattern in the variations in intensity of the solar spectrum at wavelengths shorter than about 300 nm, even during years near solar maximum. Wende (1969a), for example, found such a pattern in the slowly varying X-ray (0.2–0.9 nm) intensities based on Mariner 5 measurements in 1967 (fig. 2.8). In solar rotation number 1833, the X-ray intensity increases by a factor of about 10 from a minimum near July 12 to the following maximum about 15 days later. There is a rather close correspondence between the X-ray variation and the variation in 10.7-cm radio flux (bottom half of fig. 2.8), about which more will be said later.

Less dramatic, but still significant, 27-day variations have been observed at longer wavelengths. Based on measurements in the 104–135-nm band (which includes the H Lyα line) made by the Solrad 8

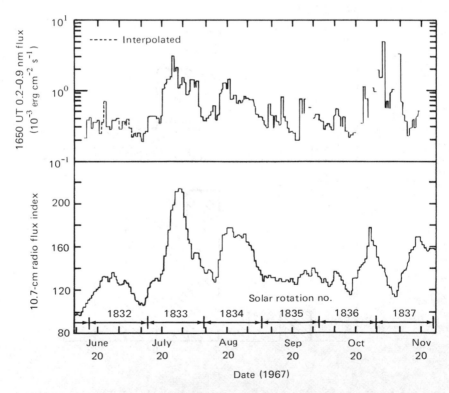

Figure 2.8. *Twenty-seven-day recurrence tendency of solar X-ray fluxes (0.2–0.9 nm) observed by Mariner 5 in 1967 for the hour of 1650 UT, compared with non-flare 10.7-cm radio fluxes measured at Ottawa (1640 UT) and Sagamore Hill, Massachusetts (1700 UT). From Wende (1969a).*

spacecraft during August to December 1967, Meier (1969) found intensity variations of 14–35% between the minima and maxima of given 27-day periods. Measurements made by OSO-3 in the wavelength range 27–131 nm (Hall and Hinteregger, 1970) indicate an increase of about 40% from minimum to maximum in a solar rotation. The increases in EUV were not uniform across the observed spectrum because of differences in the generation mechanisms on the Sun, and the strongest enhancements were found at the shorter wavelengths of less than 70 nm. In contrast to the solar flare-associated increases in EUV, Hall and Hinteregger (1969) found that those associated with a 27-day recurrence pattern seem to come from solar ions whose ionization potentials are high (~500 eV).

A short-lived experiment aboard the OV1-15 satellite provides additional evidence for a 27-day recurrence tendency (Prag and Morse, 1970). The wavelength intervals monitored were 30–115, 115–160, and 160–210 nm. The middle interval overlaps that used by Meier (1969). Unfortunately, the experiment only lasted for about one solar rotation period (July 13 to August 9, 1968), but it did reveal nonrandom variations which Prag and Morse attributed to the solar rotation period. Variations about the mean were more than 50% in the two longer wavelength channels and about 40% in the 30–115-nm channel. From the minimum UV flux observed near the middle of the experiment to maximum fluxes observed at the beginning and end of the experiment, an enhancement factor of at least 1.6 was found.

Heath (1973) pointed out that the large factor reported by Prag and Morse is probably not representative of the magnitude of 27-day variations, since it was based on a single solar rotation. Heath's (1973) results, based on MUSE observations over 13 solar rotations, showed a maximum increase of about 50% (from minimum to maximum irradiance in a single 27-day period) in the wavelength band 110–150 nm. This amount of increase is comparable to that reported by Meier (1969). The MUSE experiment results for the 13 solar rotations are given in figure 2.9, along with the corresponding magnetic activity indices, solar X-ray (0.8–2.0 nm), and 10.7-cm solar radio fluxes. The curves labeled A, B, and C are for UV channels of 110–160, 160–200, and 210–320 nm, respectively. The largest increase of 50% (in channel A on day 155 in 1969) was accompanied by an X-ray burst of about a factor of 4 increase, which is comparable to the findings of Wende (1969a).

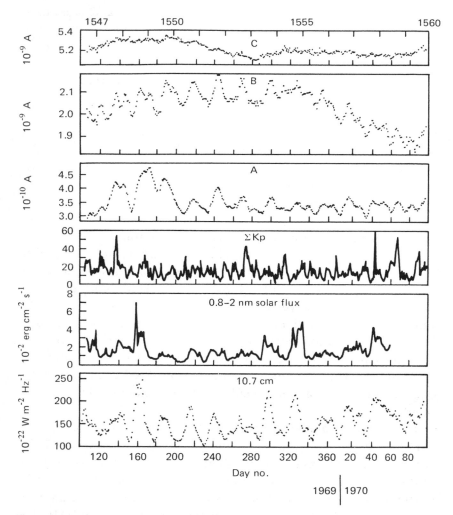

Figure 2.9. Time variation of MUSE sensor currents illustrating 27-day recurrence of UV enhancements, compared to magnetic index (ΣKp), solar X-rays, and 10.7-cm radio flux. The sensors cover the approximate wavelength ranges: A, 110–160 nm; B, 160–200 nm; C, 210–320 nm. From Heath (1973) and Heath et al. (1974).

The amount of 27-day variation in the UV spectrum appears to be a function of wavelength, as well as of the generation mechanism of the radiation, and in a general way the variability decreases with increasing wavelength. In the range 110–320 nm, Heath (1973) showed that the percentage change in a 27-day period decreases logarithmically with decreasing wave number (the reciprocal of wavelength), as illustrated in figure 2.10. No physical explanation of this relationship has yet been offered (Heath et al., 1974).

Over a solar rotation period, the minimum to maximum variation in irradiance in the band 120–300 nm can be at least 230 erg cm^{-2} s^{-1} (Heath and Wilcox, 1975). This may be sufficient to appreciably alter the ozone density and lead to changes in the atmospheric heat structure and alteration of circulation patterns.

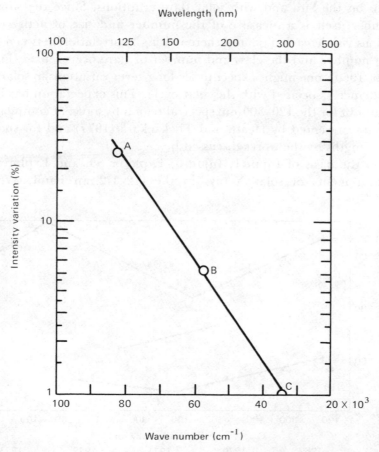

Figure 2.10. *Wavelength dependence of percentage UV variation per solar rotation (measured from min to max intensity) as derived from Nimbus 3 observations by Heath (1973). The points A, B, and C represent the ½-intensity points of the bands specified in figure 2.9. The wave number is the reciprocal of the wavelength.*

It was demonstrated by Heath (1973) that there are long-lived active regions during years near sunspot maximum, often two per solar rotation. From the MUSE experiment aboard Nimbus, Heath found two UV-emitting regions spaced about 180° solar longitude apart that persisted for at least 39 solar rotations (almost 3 yr), as is evident in figure 2.11. A third active region appeared late in 1970 and persisted through 1971 into the first half of 1972. The persistence of these features helps to strengthen the 27-day recurrence pattern.

Solar Cycle Variations: From the foregoing it is evident that the intensity of UV solar irradiance increases when there are active regions on the Sun and with solar flare eruptions. Since the sunspot number itself is a measure of the number and size of active solar regions visible each day, and there is a high correlation between sunspot number and the class and number of flare occurrences (Friedman, 1960), one might expect to see long-term variations in solar UV irradiance associated with the solar cycle. This expectation has been borne out for the 120–300-nm spectral region by a recent compilation of data presented by Heath and Thekaekara (1977) and for shorter wavelengths by the works discussed below.

On the basis of Injun 1, Injun 3, Explorer 33, and Explorer 35 measurements of solar X-rays in the 0.2–1.2-nm band, Wende

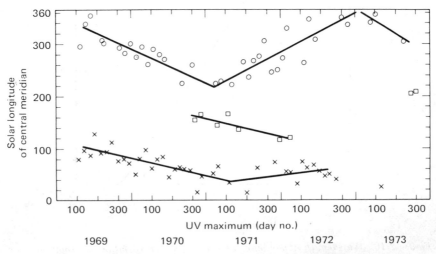

Figure 2.11. Carrington longitude of the central meridian on days of observed solar UV maximums. Different symbols represent different regions on the basis of groupings in longitude. From Heath and Wilcox (1975). (An earlier version of this plot was given by Heath (1973).)

(1969a) found at least a factor of 5 decrease going from sunspot maximum to sunspot minimum (see fig. 2.12). As is evident in figure 2.12, the X-ray intensity follows the solar cycle variation of 10.7-cm radio flux; this is mentioned later in this section.

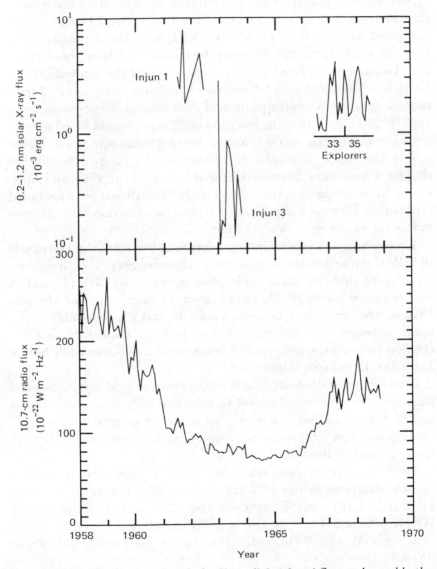

Figure 2.12. Solar cycle variation of solar X-ray (0.2–1.2 nm) flux as observed by the satellites Injuns 1 and 3 and Explorers 33 and 35, compared with variation in 10.7-cm radio flux. The fluxes are averaged in monthly intervals. From Wende (1969a).

Rocket measurements from August 1961 to November 1968 by Hall et al. (1969) with a scanning spectrometer covering the range 23–127 nm also showed a strong solar cycle dependence. From sunspot minimum in 1964 to sunspot maximum in 1968, Hall et al. (1969) reported that increases of factors of 10, 8, and 3 were seen on the wavelengths 28.4, 33.5, and 62.5 nm, respectively. These are lines associated with the ions Fe XV, Fe XVI, and Mg X, respectively. Over the whole range (23–127 nm) the increase was a factor of about 1.5. Timothy and Timothy (1970) reported that the intensity of the He II Lyα line (30.4 nm) follows very closely the variation in Zurich sunspot number. An extrapolation of their measurements in the years 1967–1969 suggests that the intensity of 30.4 nm would be a factor of 2 greater in sunspot maximum than sunspot minimum years. Heath (1974) also noted that solar irradiance in the range 120–300 nm showed a minimum intensity in the minimum year 1964 and maximum intensity in the years 1969–1970. Heath earlier concluded (1973) that there is a significant 11-yr cycle variation of solar irradiance on wavelengths near 175 nm.

There is still some question regarding the phasing of the 11-yr cycle in EUV compared to the sunspot cycle. Hinteregger (1977), for example, showed that the end of cycle 20 as measured by EUV (17 and 58 nm) occurred on April 20, 1975, about 14 months before the July 1976 sunspot minimum between cycles 20 and 21. This EUV minimum coincides with the minimum in 10.7-cm radio flux, but the relation between the two types of emission differed drastically before and after the sunspot minimum.

Correlations With Solar Radio Flux: Since several meteorological parameters have been observed to correlate with solar radio bursts and 10.7-cm radiation, it is of interest to note that there is a good correlation between solar radio noise and enhancements in the UV and X-ray spectra of the Sun.

The slowly varying component of the 0.2–1.2-nm solar X-ray flux follows variations in the 10.7-cm radio noise intensity in both the 11-yr (fig. 2.12) and 27-day cycle (fig. 2.8) periods, as shown by Wende (1969a). There is also a good correlation between X-rays (0.2–2.9 nm) and 2-cm radio flux bursts associated with flares (Wende, 1969b).

Hall et al. (1969) found that EUV variations, which were largest on wavelengths associated with highly ionized solar species, are correlated with 10.7-cm radio flux. As the 10.7-cm radiation intensity increased from 75 to 150 flux units over half a solar cycle, the EUV (23–127 nm) intensity increased by 50%. (One flux unit equals $1(10^{-22})$ W m^{-2} Hz^{-1}.) Specific coronal lines, that is, 28.4, 33.5, and 62.5 nm showed much larger increases. Hall and Hinteregger (1970) found a similar relationship over a 27-day solar rotation period; that is, the UV intensity in the band 27–131 nm increased by 40% when the 10.7-cm flux increased from 111 to 201 units.

A further study of the Hall (Hall et al., 1969; Hall and Hinteregger, 1970) data was made by Castelli and Richards (1971). They found that 65% of the EUV enhancements investigated were accompanied by solar noise bursts. Usually, but not always, the radio and EUV bursts began within about 15 sec of each other and were preceded by X-ray (<2 nm) enhancements by roughly 3–5 min. All the EUV events studied were associated with solar flares.

In an attempt to find an easily measurable parameter to monitor variations in solar EUV radiation of the *quiet* Sun, Chapman and Neupert (1974) correlated OSO-1 and OSO-3 data with ground-based measurements of 2800 MHz (10.7 cm) solar radio noise. The highest correlation found (.85 with 99% confidence) was between the intensity of the line at 33.54 nm and the radio flux intensity on frequencies of 2000, 2800, and 3750 MHz. Smaller, but still significant correlations of 0.80 and 0.70 were found with 1000 and 9400 MHz fluxes, respectively. An empirical formula was derived to describe the functional relationship between solar energy flux F (15–40 nm) in erg cm^{-2} s^{-1} and solar radio flux $F_{10.7}$ expressed in flux units;

$$F(15\text{--}40 \text{ nm}) = (0.98 \pm 0.24)$$
$$[1 + (0.0104 \pm 0.0044)F_{10.7}] \tag{2.4}$$

The error band in this equation represents the standard errors calculated from the data and does not include errors of calibration. This equation implies a much smaller quiet-time variability in EUV relative to the 10.7-cm flux than during solar active events.

Prag and Morse (1970) noted that their observations in the 115–160-nm band correlate well with 10.7-cm radio noise over a 27-day period, and all three of their channels (over the band 30–210 nm) showed a good correlation with a calcium plage region parameter of area times intensity of the region. Also, Meier (1969) reported a good correlation between H Lyα and 10.7-cm radiation. As previously mentioned, there is a similar 27-day recurrence pattern in 10.7-cm radiation and the UV intensities of channels A and B of Heath's (1973) experiments (see fig. 2.9) taken over the same time period.

2.2.3 Solar Flare Occurrence

The shortest-lived phenomenon is the solar flare, which usually occurs within a region encompassed by a large, magnetically bipolar sunspot group and lasts from a few minutes to a few hours. Its occurrence is defined by a sudden brightening of the H Lyα line, and it is usually accompanied by an enhancement in X-ray emission. Prior to January 1, 1966, flares were classified in importance by a scale running from 1 − to 3 + according to their intensity, area covered, and duration. The least important flares (importance 1) are the most numerous, and the great flares (importance 3) constitute only about 2% of the total observed. Since January 1, 1966, flare classification has followed the "dual importance" scheme adopted by the International Astronomical Union (IAU). This scheme consists of a whole number from 1 to 4 followed by a letter. The number is assigned according to the area of the flaring region at the time of maximum brightness; the larger numbers correspond to larger areas. The letter designation is either F (faint), N (normal), or B (brilliant). The designation SB is for a bright subflare and corresponds roughly to importance 1 on the old scale. The importance of the flare is assigned by each observatory on the basis of individual experience and is thus only qualitative.

The occurrence frequency of small flares is positively correlated with the 11-yr cycle, and, although the frequency of major flares also tends to peak at sunspot maximum, they can occur at any time. There is some evidence for a double peak in major flare occurrence, the second one appearing a few years after sunspot maximum. This secondary maximum may have important ramifications for Sun-weather relationships; for example, the secondary peak observed in meteorological microseism occurrence observed by Zatopek and Krivsky (1974) (discussed in sec. 3.1.7) may be related to flare activity. There is a tendency for flares to occur near solar magnetic sector boundaries (Obridko et al., 1974; Dittmer, 1975).

The X-ray and UV energy from flares arrives at the Earth in about 8 min and is known to produce intense ionization in the upper atmosphere (D-region heights), which is manifested by radiowave fadeout and sudden cosmic noise absorption, among other things (Ratcliffe and Weekes, 1960).

Additional details of solar flare characteristics and occurrences are available in a good short review by Smith and Gottlieb (1975) and in books by Smith and Smith (1963) and Svestka (1976).

2.2.4 Solar Wind Energy and the Solar Constant

In arguments against the possibility that solar activity can cause any appreciable change in atmospheric circulation or the weather, the vastly greater amount of energy provided by solar insolation (compared to that contributed by ultraviolet and X radiation, the solar wind, solar corpuscular streams, and magnetic field) is usually invoked. The calculations are generally made for the total cross-sectional area of the globe and do not take into account the possibility that some of the various types of energy may be preferentially dumped into areas smaller than the total disk and that they may dominate all other energy sources in unique regions of the upper atmosphere. This section explores possible modifications to the "relative energy" argument proposed by Dessler (1975) which would be imposed by preferential energy deposition from the solar wind into restricted areas of the globe. A slightly different approach has been taken by Willis (1976), who also gives estimates of the comparative amounts of energy delivered to the Earth's atmosphere by solar protons, galactic cosmic rays, auroral particles, and magnetospheric electric fields.

To gain an estimate of the global amount of insolation, it is customary to simply multiply the solar constant by the area of Earth's disk facing the Sun. The total amount is about $1.7(10^{17})$ W. In Dessler's (1975) view, about half of it is available to the atmosphere; the other half is lost through the Earth's albedo. (The usual value for average albedo, however, is 0.36.) According to Sidorenkov (1974), about 2% of it goes to drive the atmospheric engine; thus about $3(10^{15})$ W is utilized by atmospheric circulation. For comparative purposes, however, the estimated amount due to insolation can be revised, as discussed below.

Following Dessler (1975), the total solar wind and interplanetary magnetic field (IMF) energy incident at the top of the magnetosphere per unit time (U_s) can be estimated by

$$U_s = \pi r_m^2 (\tfrac{1}{2}\varrho V_s^2 + B^2/2\mu_o)V_s \qquad (2.5)$$

where $r_m = 12R_E$ $(7.65(10^7)$ m) is the radius of the magnetosphere in units of Earth radii; $\varrho = 8(10^{-21})$ kg^{-3} is the mass density of the solar wind; $V_s = 4(10^5)$ m s^{-1} is the solar wind velocity; and $B = 10$ gamma

41

$(10^{-8}$ tesla) is the strength of the IMF. The term μ_o is the magnetic permeability of empty space and has a value of $4(10^{-7})$ H m^{-1}.

With these nominal values, the total solar wind and IMF power incident at the top of the magnetosphere is about $U_s = 5(10^{12})$ W. During a magnetic storm the energy stored in the magnetospheric tail, about 10^{18} J, is dumped into the upper atmosphere in about 10^4 sec, so that about 10^{14} W is dissipated into the upper atmosphere. Dessler considers this 10^{14} W to be a maximum estimate of solar wind energy per unit time (U_s max) available for modifying meteorological systems. Calculations by Cole (1965) and Svalgaard (1975b) indicate that the amount of power dissipated into the ionosphere alone during a geomagnetic storm is on the order of $3(10^{10}$ to $10^{11})$ W, which is only a small fraction of the total dissipation. In order to affect weather, some of the energy must somehow reach the stratosphere or troposphere.

For comparison, Dessler considered the minimum amount of solar radiation (U_{EM}) available on global basis in winter: that is, he assumed that snow and cloud cover may increase Earth's albedo to 0.9 (i.e., 90% of the radiant energy is reflected back into space), and the polar cap itself would be in darkness. Under these conditions the power available from the solar constant would be $6(10^{15})$ W, and the ratio U_s max/U_{EM} $(10^{14}/6(10^{15}))$ would be $1.7(10^{-2})$. This "might be just barely large enough to do some good," according to Dessler.

Such gross comparative arguments are, unfortunately, misleading. As we have already seen, the annual average amount of radiant energy incident near the pole is only about 0.4 of that at the equator. It is this difference that leads to the generally higher temperatures and pressures in low compared to high latitudes and drives the average atmospheric circulation. Departures from average would be brought about by changes in the pressure and temperature gradients imposed by a redistribution of energy input into the polar and equatorial regions. This might be brought about by either a transient change in solar constant (if indeed there are any) or by a preferential dumping of energy into the polar regions by solar corpuscular emission, magnetospheric particle precipitation, and the like.

Another point generally ignored in comparative arguments is the basic fact that no solar radiant energy is incident on the night side of the Earth (or even on the day side in polar latitudes in winter), and it is here where charged particles may most easily enter the upper and middle atmosphere at high latitudes through the magnetospheric tail. The relative fraction of corpuscular and magnetic energy is then large compared to zero insolation, but whether the absolute amount is sufficient to produce changes in the lower atmosphere where weather takes place remains to be seen.

To make a more realistic comparison than Dessler's, it is necessary to consider that the solar wind energy is dumped mainly in a rather narrow circumpolar latitude belt near the auroral zone. Assuming this belt to be 10° wide centered at 65° latitude, then its area on the sunlit side of Earth to be multiplied by the solar constant is $9.35(10^6)$ km^2, and the solar constant itself must be multiplied by approximately 0.42 to account for the slant incidence of the radiant flux. With an albedo of 0.9 for winter, as Dessler assumed, the available solar radiant energy per unit time over this area would be $U_{EM} = 5(10^{14})$ W with the Sun at zenith. The available power from the solar wind (10^{14} W, averaged over the life of the event) dumped into this narrow circumpolar belt would then amount to 20% of U_{EM} rather than 1.7%. Further, on the night side the solar wind energy would constitute the total amount available from external sources (there being no radiant energy) and, being 20% as large as the normal energy input from the solar constant, could very well be large enough to have an effect. The possibility of an effect will become clear in section 4.2, where it will be seen that some pressure changes in high latitudes correlate with magnetic disturbances.

2.3 Solar Corpuscular Radiation

Along with enhanced bursts of UV (especially H Lyα radiation) and X-ray emission constituting major solar flares (importance 2 and greater), copious quantities of high-energy (10–200 MeV) relativistic electrons and protons are emitted from major active spot groups at the same time. The particles travel a bit slower than the electromagnetic energy (UV and X-ray) and arrive in the vicinity of Earth about 1 to 2 hr after the flare eruption. The corpuscular proton radiation enters the upper atmosphere in the polar cap region and produces the familiar polar cap absorption (PCA) events first identified during the International Geophysical Year (IGY) (Reid and Collins, 1959).

Protons emitted by the Sun are often referred to as "solar cosmic rays." To delineate between the cosmic rays of galactic origin discussed in section 2.4 and those of solar origin, the term solar protons is used. Solar protons constitute the principal component of the "solar corpuscular streams" emitted from regions of flare activity which occur spasmodically and from M-regions (coronal holes) which exhibit a 27-day recurrence tendency. Because their direct effect on the neutral atmosphere is much greater than other components of the corpuscular streams, the remainder of this section concentrates on their characteristics in terms of energy spectra, time and space variations, and the morphology of their effects on the atmosphere. For this the terms solar protons and corpuscular emissions or variations thereon will be used interchangeably.

Based on PCA observations, the corpuscular emission may last for 1–5 or 6 days (Bailey, 1959). Direct observations of solar particle fluxes by satellite have confirmed the relatively long duration of corpuscular emission following major flares (cf. Domingo et al., 1973; Lanzerotti and Maclennan, 1973). The energy of the solar protons is such that they penetrate to altitudes of 30 km and less and produce the enhanced ionization responsible for radiowave absorption of the PCA. Recent rocket measurements in the Antarctic (Greenhill et al., 1972) indicate that solar protons from flare-associated eruptions can penetrate directly to at least the 9-mb level at high latitudes on the day side. In intense, long-lasting events, direct entry of the solar protons to the upper atmosphere can extend equatorward as far as about 50° geomagnetic latitude (Besprozvannaya, 1962).

Almost all PCA events (as an indirect detector of intense solar corpuscular radiation) are associated with a geomagnetic storm sudden commencement (SSC) and geomagnetic storm (Hakura and Goh, 1959). The SSC and subsequent storm occurs about 20 hr after the beginning of the PCA. Not all major flares are accompanied by corpuscular emission, but those that are (referred to as proton flares) almost always are also accompanied by type IV solar radio noise bursts. Type IV events are solar emissions occurring over a broad band of radio frequencies. They begin coincident with the flare but continue for many hours afterward.

In recent years the detection of solar protons arriving at the Earth have been made by rocket and satellite (e.g., Lanzerotti and Maclennan, 1973; Domingo et al., 1973; Engelmann et al., 1971; Imhof et al., 1971; Van Allen, 1971; Pomerantz and Duggal, 1973). The inferences from earlier PCA observations have been largely confirmed, and additional characteristics, especially regarding energy spectra, have been identified.

A second source of solar proton emission is the so-called M region (McDonald and Desai, 1971), a magnetically active region on the Sun that has no agreed upon visual distinguishing characteristics. The coronal "holes" (Munro and Withbroe, 1972) visible on solar images made in the extreme UV and soft X-ray portions of the spectrum are a source of high-speed corpuscular streams (Rickett et al., 1976) and may in fact constitute the classical "M-region" (Timothy et al., 1975; Zirker, 1977). Such regions may persist for up to 8 or 10 solar rotations, and each time one of them crosses the CM, the Earth is exposed to the corpuscular radiation. Geomagnetic storms triggered by this exposure are known as recurrent storms because they repeat with a 27-day periodicity in association with successive CM crossings of an active M (for Maunder)-region. A similar pattern is exhibited by radiowave absorption events (Ratcliffe and Weekes, 1960). The intensity and duration of recurrent storms are usually smaller than those of the geomagnetic storms following major proton flares. These recurrent absorption events are not classed as PCA events.

The direct solar origin of energetic electrons precipitating into the upper atmosphere of the Earth is less clear, since the magnetosphere usually has a profound influence on the acceleration and dumping processes controlling energetic electron distributions. This is probably true also for relativistic electron precipitation (REP) events which seem to correlate poorly with solar activity and do not seem to be clearly related to geomagnetic disturbances (Thorne, 1977). Furthermore, except for REP-type events, electron precipitation processes cannot affect the middle atmosphere directly, since almost all the associated energy is deposited above 80 km altitude. However, because electron precipitation events are usually related to geomagnetic activity, which in turn is induced by solar activity, and because the precipitating electrons may affect the lower atmosphere through the production of secondary bremsstrahlung X-rays which can penetrate down to the lower depths, they must be considered. This consideration is reserved for discussion in chapter 6.

Any complete investigation of meteorological responses to solar corpuscular radiation must take into account at least the main characteristics of both the primary and secondary corpuscular radiation and their association with other solar and geophysical phenomena. Only in this way will the physical mechanisms relating solar activity and meteorological phenomena finally be identified and understood. A number of chronological listings of PCA events covering the years

1955–1976 are available for possible correlations with meteorological phenomena. Among them are those by Castelli and Barron (1977), Cormier (1973), Pomerantz and Duggal (1974), Shapley and Kroehl (1977), Svestka and Simon (1975), and Zmuda and Potemra (1972).

2.3.1 Solar Cycle Dependence

The sunspot cycle dependence of solar proton events has been inferred largely from PCA occurrences and associated intense geomagnetic storms. Although such events can occur any time during an 11-yr sunspot cycle, there is a definite preference for occurrence in years at and near sunspot maximum. In the second half of 1958 (July–December), for example, at least 22 PCA events were identified by Hill (1963), 12 of which lasted for more than 24 hr each. In contrast, in the sunspot minimum year 1964, no PCA events were reported (Cormier, 1973). Dessler (1975) suggested that the rate of occurrence of PCA (solar proton) events is $7\frac{1}{2}$ times greater during sunspot maximum than sunspot minimum years. Another way to infer solar proton events was developed by Castelli et al. (1967), using spectral signatures of solar radio noise bursts. If the flux density spectral curve at the time of maximum is U-shaped, the radio burst is likely to be associated with energetic proton emission. Here U-shaped is defined as high intensity exceeding 1000 flux units near 3-cm wavelength, a minimum in the decimeter range and rising again to ~1000 flux units in the long-meter-wavelength band. With this criteria Castelli and Barron (1977) listed proton events from 1966 to 1976 wherein there were 14 events in 1969 (ssmax year) and only one in 1975 (ssmin year). The 11-yr variation of the daily average value of 10.7-cm (2800-MHz) solar radio flux is in phase with the sunspot cycle (cf. Dodson et al., 1974), which is compatible with the findings of Castelli and Barron.

Recurring solar proton events detected at intervals of 27 days by recurrent geomagnetic storms are observed principally in years of low sunspot activity. These events may be associated with solar magnetic sector structure (cf. Sec. 2.5); their disappearance in years of maximum sunspot activity may indicate that the sector structure is frequently altered by the eruption of new active centers so that a fixed sector structure does not persist for as many 27-day solar rotations as it does in solar minimum years. Of the 81 PCA-associated solar radio bursts listed by Castelli and Barron (1977), about 27% emanated from the solar (Carrington) longitude sector 150°–180°, 19% came from the $60°-90°$ sector, and the remainder were more or less evenly distributed in all other solar longitudes. These results are suggestive of preferential longitudes that would lead to a 27-day recurrence tendency even in solar maximum years.

2.3.2 Solar Proton Spectra

Spectral determinations of solar protons have been made both as a function of rigidity (Freier and Webber, 1963) and energy. The magnetic rigidity R of a solar proton or cosmic ray particle defines the ability of the particle, with momentum p and electronic charge Ze, to penetrate a magnetic field of strength B, and can be expressed as

$$R = pc/Ze \tag{2.6}$$

where p is in units of BeV/c, and c is the velocity of light. Rigidity is expressed in units of volts or billion volts (BV), which should not be confused with the energy units of electron volts (eV) or BeV. (Jokipii (1971) gives a much more elegant discussion of cosmic ray magnetic rigidity than is required here.)

The momentum in turn is

$$p = m_o v/(1 - v^2/c^2)^{½} \tag{2.7}$$

where m_o is the rest mass and v the velocity. For $v \ll c$, equation (2.7) reduces to the familiar form $p = m_o v$. The momentum of a particle determines its resistance to a change in direction of motion. In the presence of a magnetic field the force tending to change the particle's direction of motion is proportional to the particle charge. Thus it is evident from equation (2.6) that the rigidity is a useful term for comparing the penetration into the Earth's magnetic field of cosmic particles with different charges, such as alpha particles (helium nuclei) and protons (hydrogen nuclei).

The particle kinetic energy is of interest for determining its penetration depth into the Earth's atmosphere. The kinetic energy is

$$E = m_o c^2 [(1 - v^2/c^2)^{-½} - 1] \tag{2.8}$$

and when $v \ll c$, this reduces to $E = ½ m_o v^2$.

From equations (2.6)-(2.8), it can be seen that the relationship between rigidity and kinetic energy is

$$R = (1/Ze)(E^2 + 2m_o c^2 E)^{½} \tag{2.9}$$

When $m_o c^2$, the rest energy, and E are in MeV, R is in MV.

The magnetic shielding of cosmic rays or high-energy protons entering the Earth's atmosphere is generally expressed in terms of the cutoff rigidity, which is a function of the particle's arrival direction and the magnetic field strength. The term is defined as the lowest rigidity a particle can possess and still penetrate through the magnetic field to the Earth's surface (Shea et al., 1965). It is usually specified for the vertical arrival direction.

The relationship between geomagnetic latitude and vertical cutoff rigidity, based on calculations by Shea et al. (1965) is plotted in figure 2.13. It holds for quiet magnetic conditions only; during storms, the cutoff rigidity may be significantly altered because of magnetic field changes. Although the cutoff rigidity for a given latitude usually decreases during storms, there is evidence that it sometimes increases instead (Barcus, 1969b). During both disturbed (Barcus, 1969a) and quiet periods (Smart et al., 1969; Smart and Shea, 1972) there is a diurnal variation in geomagnetic cutoff. This means that the particle

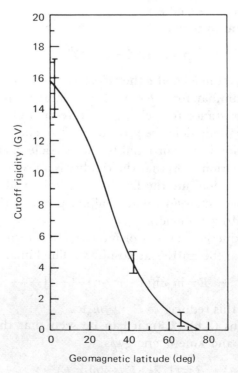

Figure 2.13. Cosmic ray vertical cutoff rigidity as a function of geomagnetic latitude. From calculations by Shea et al. (1965).

energy required to reach a fixed geomagnetic latitude is higher during daytime than nighttime (e.g., at Ft. Churchill the cutoff rigidity
is 150 MV and about 20 MV, respectively), and that a particle of fixed
energy can penetrate at lower geomagnetic latitudes at night. In
addition, the curve illustrated (fig. 2.13) is subject to variations with
geomagnetic longitude. Fluctuations in calculated cutoff are larger
near the equator than at high latitude because of longitudinal effects,
as indicated by the vertical bars. For strict accuracy the rigidity must
be computed for each point on the Earth's surface, but the curve
illustrated is a useful guide.

From the above it is evident that the effects of energetic particles
from solar events on the Earth's atmosphere will depend on the
energy or rigidity spectrum of the particles. A number of attempts
have been made to fit analytical expressions to the measured energy
and rigidity spectra of solar protons.

Power law representations of the differential number density have
been made in terms of

$$dJ/dR = K_1 R^{-n_1} \qquad (2.10)$$

or

$$dJ/dE = K_2 E^{-n_2} \qquad (2.11)$$

where dJ is the particle number density per unit rigidity (dR) or
energy (dE) interval. It was pointed out by Freier and Webber (1963)
that, although this form can be used reasonably well over narrow
rigidity (or energy) intervals, n_1 (or n_2) varies with rigidity (energy)
over wide spectral intervals, and it also varies with time during an
event. The integral spectrum can be expressed (Freier and Webber,
1963) as

$$J(>R) = J_o \exp(-R/R_o) \qquad (2.12)$$

or

$$J(>E) = J_o \exp(-E/E_o) \qquad (2.13)$$

where $J(>R \text{ or } >E)$ is the integral number density or flux of all the
protons with rigidities greater than R or energy greater than E. In
equation (2.13), E_o is often referred to as the folding energy of the distribution. The terms J_o and R_o (E_o) may vary from event to event, and
R_o (E_o) may vary with time in an event. Again, over wide spectral
intervals, determinations of R_o or E_o may be different for measurements in different parts of the spectrum.

49

Drawing on data from PCA absorption and rocket and balloon particle measurements to obtain a wide range of rigidity, Freier and Webber (1963) deduced solar proton rigidity spectra for four PCA events, as illustrated in figure 2.14. Note the change in spectral shape due to the differences in J_o and R_o from one event to another. At the lower rigidities the number density reflects the effects of geomagnetic cutoff. Here the point of importance is that the spectral characteristics of solar protons vary from one event to another; thus one cannot make a simple determination of the extent to which a postulated flare occurrence might affect meteorological phenomena.

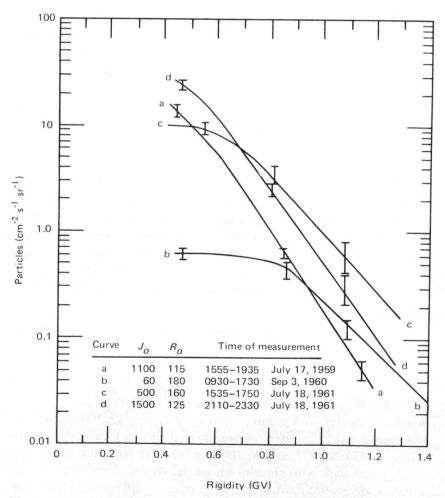

Curve	J_o	R_o	Time of measurement	
a	1100	115	1555–1935	July 17, 1959
b	60	180	0930–1730	Sep 3, 1960
c	500	160	1535–1750	July 18, 1961
d	1500	125	2110–2330	July 18, 1961

Figure 2.14. Solar proton rigidity spectra for four events measured at Minneapolis. From Freier and Webber (1963).

Satellite measured differential spectra (from OV1-18) expressed in terms of solar proton energy have been deduced by Imhof et al. (1971) and Engelmann et al. (1971), among others. Data from these two sources will suffice to illustrate spectral characteristics. Low-energy (< 60 MeV) spectra obtained during three different events in 1969 are shown in figure 2.15. At the times of measurement the satellite was over the polar cap at altitudes between 466 and 583 km.

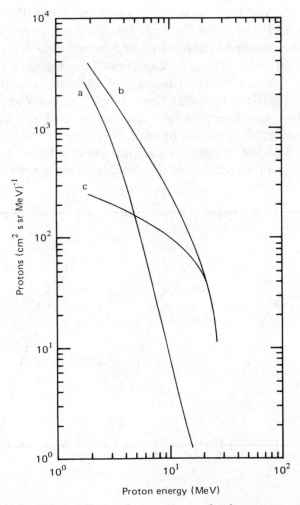

Figure 2.15. Solar proton differential energy spectra for three proton events in 1969. (a) 18.1 hr, June 10. (b) 4.3 hr, April 13. (c) 19.6 hr, Nov. 2. From Imhof et al. (1971).

The spectrum for June 10, 1969, (curve a) decreases more rapidly with increasing energy than the other two spectra, and the spectrum for April 13, 1969, (curve b) is the same as that for November 2, 1969, (curve c) above about 20 MeV, but has greater intensity at the lower energies. The curves should not be extrapolated to energies higher than those measured, since the slope of the spectrum changes with increasing energy. This is obvious in the spectra to 300 MeV deduced by Engelmann et al. (1971) as shown in figure 2.16. These are solar proton spectra obtained by the ESRO 2 satellite on three successive passes over the northern polar cap at altitudes of 750–950 km following eruption of a class 2B flare on February 25, 1969. The passes were separated in time by about 1 hr 40 min, with the first pass covering the period 1048–1101 UT. The "peak" spectra were taken with the satellite near an invariant latitude of 65°; the "trough" spectra are for 75° invariant latitude. These labels become clear in figure 2.17, in which the detector count rates are plotted as a function of latitude. Further discussion of figure 2.17 is given in the next section.

In figure 2.16 the straight lines are least-square fits to the observational data, and the count rates are normalized because of differences

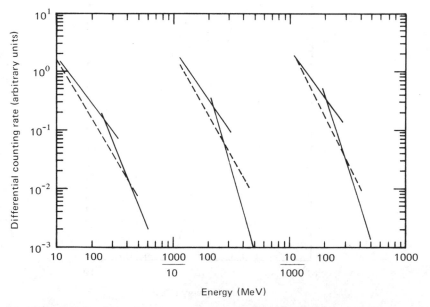

Figure 2.16. Solar proton energy spectra measured on three successive passes over the polar cap by ESRO 2 on February 25, 1969. Solid curves are peak spectra; dashed, trough spectra. From Engelmann et al. (1971).

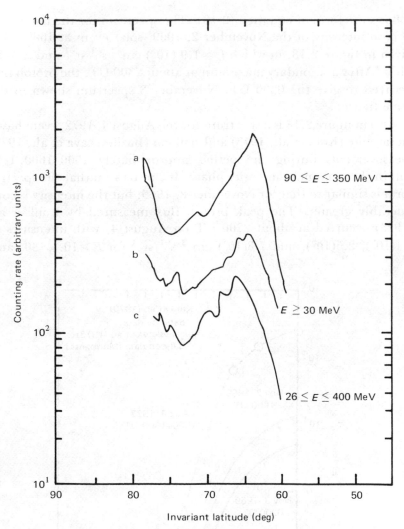

Figure 2.17. ESRO 2 proton detector uncorrected count rates in three different energy channels as a function of invariant latitude. From Engelmann et al. (1971).

in response of the detectors at different energy levels (see Engelmann et al., 1971, for details). These spectra show that the solar proton intensity drops by about two orders of magnitude between 20 and 300 MeV.

Proton integral energy spectra for representative solar events occurring in the period 1965–1969 have been reviewed by Zmuda and Potemra (1972), who showed that the integral spectral shape usually follows the form of equation (2.13). The spectrum for the maximum proton intensity of the November 2, 1969, solar event at 1600 UT is given in figure 2.18, in which $J_o = 1.9\,(10^3)$ cm^{-2} s^{-1} sr^{-1} and $E_o = 29$ MeV. After a secondary maximum at about 2300 UT, the proton flux decayed to give the 0300 UT, November 3 spectrum shown in the same figure.

Also in figure 2.18 is a spectrum for the August 4, 1972, event based on satellite (Kohl et al., 1973) and balloon (Bazilevskaya et al., 1973) measurements during the period approximately 1500–1600 UT, within the maximum intensity phase. It can be seen that the spectral form is similar to that for November 2, 1969, but the intensity is considerably greater. The peak proton flux measured by Kohl et al. (1973) occurred at about 2200 UT on August 4, with intensities of $1.1(10^6)$, $2.5(10^5)$, and $7.8(10^4)$ cm^{-2} s^{-1} sr^{-1} for $E > 10$, > 30, and

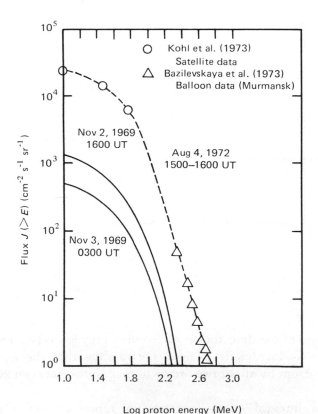

Figure 2.18. Measured integral proton spectra for the August 4, 1972, and November 2, 1969, solar flare events at selected times.

> 60 MeV, respectively. The spectral equation for these data is satisfied by $J_o = 8.0(10^5)$ cm^{-2} s^{-1} sr^{-1} and $E_o = 25.8$ MeV.

2.3.3 Latitudinal Variations

The entry of solar protons into the atmosphere is principally a high-latitude phenomenon. However, the latitude cutoff is sensitive to the initial energy of the proton; with increasing particle energy the cutoff moves equatorward. Maximum entry of the solar protons occurs in the vicinity of the auroral oval, and the cutoff latitude lies equatorward of the oval.

These features are apparent in figure 2.17, in which count rates from three different integral detectors on ESRO 2 are shown as a function of invariant latitude. No corrections have been applied to derive absolute count rates; differences in magnitude between the three curves are immaterial to this discussion. The point of importance is that the count rates peak near 65° invariant latitude. Equatorward of the peaks the count rates fall off rapidly.

Poleward of the peaks, the count rates are still well above cosmic ray background, but a "trough"—relatively lower rates—is evident around 75° invariant latitude. Spectra taken from the peak and trough regions were given in the previous section.

Latitude cutoff effects for relatively low-energy electrons, alpha particles, and protons are illustrated in figure 2.19, adapted from Imhof et al. (1971). The measurements were made during the solar proton event of April 13, 1969. The electrons (curve a) drop off sharply at about 63° invariant latitude, the count rate decreasing by an order of magnitude, but then flatten out to about 59°, where the count rate drops abruptly off scale. The alpha particles (curve b) exhibit the most gradual cutoff, ending at 59°. The remaining curves, for protons of energies 1.68–19.6 MeV, illustrate the equatorward shift of the cutoff latitude with increasing particle energy.

As we have seen, the spectra change from one solar proton event to another. The events with the hardest spectra (i.e., those with relatively more high-energy particles), influence the atmosphere at the lowest latitudes.

2.3.4 Time History of a Solar Proton Event

From early PCA observations it has been inferred that solar proton events begin within a few hours after the eruption of a major solar flare and persist for periods from less than 1 day to more than 5 days,

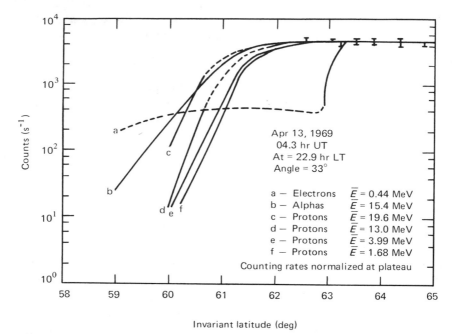

Figure 2.19. Latitude cutoffs for solar protons, electrons, and alpha particles for the event of April 13, 1969 (from Imhof et al., 1971). There may be some contamination of count rate due to precipitating particles.

depending on the severity of the event. More direct measurements of solar protons by satellite detectors have confirmed the durations of events and, in addition, provide a time history of the event in progress.

A variety of measurement data concerning the solar proton events of August 1972 have been made available (Coffey, 1973); the reports by Kohl et al. (1973), Pomerantz and Duggal (1973), Yates et al. (1973), Lanzerotti and Maclennan (1973), and Domingo et al. (1973) are of particular interest.

The measurements of Kohl et al. (1973) serve to illustrate the time variations of solar protons of energies greater than 10, 30, and 60 MeV in the period August 2–13, 1972. These data, from IMP 5 and IMP 6, are given in figure 2.20 along with notations of flare occurrences and magnetic storm sudden commencements. At the time of each flare its intensity (1B, 2B, 3B) and the solar position of its occurrence (east or west longitude) are noted in the figure. The period August 2–13 contains several overlapping events; the most important

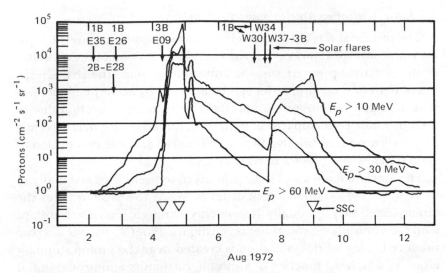

Figure 2.20. Solar proton fluxes measured by IMP 5 and IMP 6 during August 1972 solar events (from Kohl et al., 1973). Flare times are shown by arrows labeled with flare importance (e.g., 1B) and solar longitude of occurrence (degrees E or W).

are the one peaking late on August 4 following the 3B flare earlier in the day and the one peaking on August 8–9 following the 3B flare on August 7. The peak fluxes at about 2200 UT, August 4, for the three energy channels are given in table 2.3 along with the integrated fluxes from ~0700 UT on August 4 to ~1500 UT on August 7.

Table 2.3.—Peak and Integrated Proton Fluxes in August 1972 (from Kohl et al., 1973)

Proton Energy (MeV)	Peak Flux (protons $cm^{-2}\, s^{-1}\, sr^{-1}$)	Integrated Flux (protons cm^{-2})
>10	$1.1(10^6)$	$2(10^{10})$
>30	$2.5(10^5)$	$8(10^9)$
>60	$7.8(10^4)$	$2.4(10^9)$

The amount of ionization produced by these fluxes is discussed in the next section. The manner in which the ionization alters atmospheric conductivity is described in section 3.4.1, and in section 6.6 it is shown that the introduction of excess ionization and alteration of the conductivity may lead to the development of thunderstorms.

2.3.5 *Air Ionization Due to Solar Protons*

The principal ways in which solar protons might ultimately couple into meteorological processes is through the alteration of the chemical or the electrical properties of the atmosphere. Since the characteristics of both of these properties can be affected by atmospheric ionization, it is appropriate to outline the effects on air ionization due to solar protons. For comparison, ionization rates due to galactic cosmic rays are introduced briefly, although a more complete description of cosmic ray effects follows in section 2.4.

The ionization effects of solar protons have been discussed in detail by Reid (1974), so brevity is in order here. As the protons enter the atmosphere, they gradually lose energy through ionizing collisions with the atmospheric constituents, giving up about 35 eV per ion pair produced. Most of the ionization is created near the proton stopping altitude, which is a function of atmospheric density and proton initial energy. In an approximation of Reid's method, we may express the ion-pair production rate Q as a function of height as $Q = J(>E) \times Q_s(E)$, where $J(>E)$ is the integral flux density $(\text{cm}^{-2}\,\text{s}^{-1}\,\text{sr}^{-1})$ of protons with energies greater than E, and Q_s is the specific ionization rate (i.e., the number of ion pairs per second produced by a single proton) at the stopping altitude h for a proton with energy E. As can be seen in figure 2.21, the stopping altitude decreases and the specific ionization rate increases with increasing proton energy. The additional ionization contributed at altitude h by protons with energies greater than E on their way through that level is roughly compensated for by the use of the integral spectrum in the simplification used here.

The resulting Q curves for the three proton spectra given in figure 2.18 are illustrated in figure 2.22, along with several others for comparison. Curve 1 for the maximum phase of the proton event of November 2, 1969, compares reasonably well with the Q profile (not shown) computed by Zmuda and Potemra (1972) using more rigorous methods, implying that the simplification used here is adequate for the argument.

Further support for this adequacy is given by the comparison of curves 2 and 3 in figure 2.22. Curve 2 was computed by the present method using the spectrum of figure 2.18 for the August 4, 1972, 1500–1600 UT period. Curve 3 was calculated for August 4, 1972, 1508 UT, by Reagan and Watt (1976) using their "proton" computer code with proton energies 0.1–100 MeV. At and above 35 km altitude, curves 2 and 3 agree within ± 25% or better. The Reagan and Watt

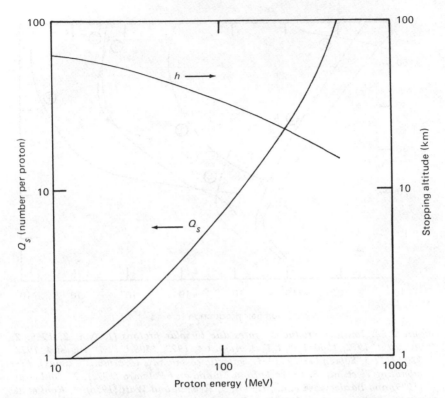

Figure 2.21. Specific ionization rate (ion-pair production per proton (left scale)) and proton deposition height (right scale) as a function of proton energy. From the data of Reid (1974).

curve stops at 33 km because of their truncation of the proton energy spectrum at 100 MeV, and the neglect of the higher-energy particles leads to production rates that are too low at the lower heights. Curve 2 includes all proton energies up to 550 MeV, the upper limit of the Soviet balloon measurements (Bazilevskaya et al., 1973).

The peak of the August 4 event at 2200 UT as defined by measurements by Kohl et al. (1973) produced the largest ion-pair production rate (fig. 2.22, curve 4) of any of the events investigated. Curve 5 was derived from proton data by Bryant et al. (1962) for the September 29, 1961, event. Their peak fluxes, for $E > 130$, > 340, and > 600 MeV best follow a power-law spectral shape given by $J(>E) = J_o E^{-1.5}$; therefore curve 5 may not be very accurate. It is included in figure 2.22 only to demonstrate that, during intense events, ionization enhancements due to solar protons may be manifest at altitudes down to and perhaps below 10 km height.

59

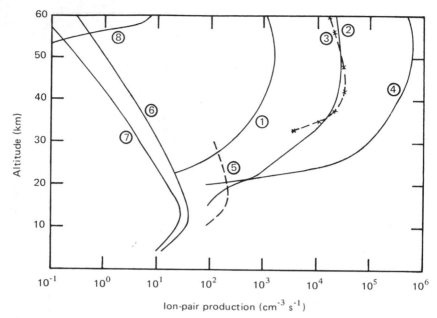

Figure 2.22. Ion-pair production rates due to solar protons (1, Nov. 2, 1969; 2, August 4, 1972, 1500–1600 UT; 3, August 4, 1972, 1508 UT; 4, August 4, 1972, 2200 UT; 5, September 29, 1961), galactic cosmic rays (6, ssmin; 7, ssmax); precipitating electrons, 8. Curve 1, from Zmuda and Potemra (1972); 2, Kohl et al. (1973) and Bazilevskaya et al., (1973); 3, Reagan and Watt (1976); 4, Kohl et al. (1973); 5, Bryant et al. (1962); 6, 7, Webber (1962); 8, Larsen et al. (1976).

It is evident that injections of solar protons produce ionization above 20 km considerably in excess of the normal quiet background production rate provided by galactic cosmic rays in both sunspot minimum (curve 6) and sunspot maximum (curve 7) years. These two curves, from Webber (1962), demonstrate the solar cycle variation in cosmic ray ion production at a magnetic latitude of about 70°. There is also a latitudinal variation in cosmic ray intensity (and hence cosmic ray ion-pair production rates, which peak near the tropospause). The intensity is minimum at the equator and increases nearly two orders of magnitude until about 60° geomagnetic latitude, where it becomes relatively flat (Neher, 1967; 1971). Significant cosmic ray decreases (Forbush decreases) occur during large geomagnetic storms, which may, but need not, be associated with solar proton flares.

During major solar proton events, a maximum reduction in cosmic ray flux of 30% at ground level is not uncommon, and Pomerantz and Duggal (1973) reported a 50% decrease for the August 4, 1972, event. The recovery to predisturbance level can take from one to several days (McCracken, 1963). This decrease is manifest from the ground up to balloon altitudes, and the fractional decrease near 15 km altitude appears to be 15–20% greater than at ground level (Webber and Lockwood, 1962). Also, weaker decreases occur with the passage of solar magnetic sector boundaries past the Earth. Corresponding variations can therefore be expected in the ion-pair production rates due to cosmic rays at altitudes below 20 km. The reduction is thought to take place because the solar proton event modifies the interplanetary magnetic field, which in turn modulates the galactic cosmic ray flux. A similar modulation mechanism explains the solar cycle variation in the intensity of galactic cosmic rays.

A typical profile of the ionization due to the energetic component of precipitating electrons associated with poststorm outer belt drizzle (Larsen et al., 1976) is illustrated in figure 2.22 (curve 8), where Q was derived from electron data over Ottawa, Canada. The ionization rate generally exceeds that due to cosmic rays only at altitudes above about 60 km (cf. Zmuda and Potemra, 1972), but occasionally can be significant to about 55 km. Enhanced ionization may be produced at lower heights by X-ray bremsstrahlung associated with auroral electrons or by relativistic electron precipitation (REP) events. These possibilities are not discussed in detail here because of the current feeling that single event processes of this type cannot compete with PCA energetics. However, in chapter 6 some new and intriguing ideas involving these radiations are considered.

2.4 Galactic Cosmic Rays

Cosmic rays originating in the galaxy are almost isotropically distributed in the vicinity of the Earth, and their intensity varies with time due to modulation processes occurring in a region within about 50 astronomical units (AU) of the Sun (Fulks, 1975). There is a small but discernible diurnal variation in intensity due to the slight anisotropy. Their range of energy, from tens of MeV to hundreds of GeV, allow them to penetrate into the atmosphere and produce secondary radiation (e.g., muons and neutrons) which reaches all the way to the surface of the Earth. Perturbations in intensity are also introduced by the Earth's magnetic field and by the atmosphere. Thus the cosmic ray intensity changes with the 11-yr and longer-term solar cycles, altitude of measurement, terrestrial magnetic latitude, and cosmic ray particle energy, and there are short-term variations related to solar outbursts (such as Forbush decreases) and to changes in solar magnetic sector structure. The intensity variations have been studied using neutron monitor count rates of the secondary neutrons produced by primary cosmic rays in the atmosphere, ionization chamber measurements, and measurements of the air ionization rates due to primaries and secondaries.

2.4.1 Solar Cycle Dependences

Variations of the average ground-level cosmic ray intensity with the 11-yr sunspot cycle are well documented and show a clear inverse correlation (Forbush, 1954). An example of this is given in figure 2.23, in which the normalized neutron monitor count rate from Climax, Colorado, is compared with monthly smoothed Zurich sunspot number over two solar cycles.

There is an approximately 20% decrease in count rate from solar minimum year 1954 to maximum year 1958. Note that in the smaller sunspot maximum year 1968, the cosmic ray decrease is only 12–15% below the previous solar minimum year. Data from Kent and Pomerantz (1971) indicate that at middle latitudes (55° geomagnetic) the

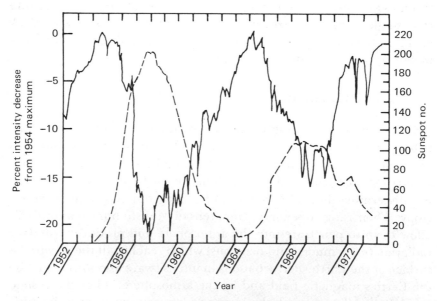

Figure 2.23. Solar cycle variation of cosmic ray intensity (solid curve) and sunspot number (dashed curve) over two solar cycles. From Fulks (1975).

count rate is about 21% lower at solar maximum, but near the equator it is only 7% lower.

The Climax cosmic ray intensity peaks approximately two-thirds of a year later than the time of sunspot minimum occurrence, but the amount of lag seems to be slightly different at different stations (Fulks, 1975).

Nonlinear changes in the cosmic ray energy spectrum over a solar cycle produce a so-called hysteresis effect, as illustrated in figure 2.24. Here the proton flux for energies 40–90 MeV is plotted against the Climax monthly average neutron monitor hourly count rate for years surrounding the 1969/1970 solar maximum years. The asymmetry in the response of low-energy cosmic rays ($\lesssim 100$ MeV) to solar cycle modulation causes the hysteresis loop evident in figure 2.24. The character of the loop changes when cosmic ray electrons with energies of 600–1250 MeV are considered, as can be seen in figure 2.25. A different view of solar cycle effects on cosmic ray energy spectra is given in the next section, where it can be seen that the lower energies have a greater solar cycle variability than the high energies.

The ionization rate due to cosmic rays exhibits an 11-yr cycle dependence which is more pronounced at high altitudes than near the surface. At Thule, for example, the ratio of ionization rate between 1958 (ssmax) and 1954 (ssmin) at an atmospheric depth of 200 $g\,cm^{-2}$ (approximately 12 km altitude according to appendix A) is about 1.4, but at 20 g cm^{-2} (26 km) it is about 2.2, as illustrated in figure 2.26. Further discussion of the altitude dependence of cosmic ray ionization is given in section 2.4.4.

In addition to the 11-yr cycle dependence, longer-term solar-associated periodic and nonperiodic variations in cosmic ray intensity have also been found. A 22-yr variation of small amplitude ($\sim 0.07\%$) has been identified in the so-called W component of the diurnal anisotropy, which is a streaming from the asymptotic direction 128° east of the Sun-Earth line (Forbush, 1973; Pomerantz and Duggal, 1974). The maxima occur in sunspot minimum years following a positive maximum in the Hale double sunspot cycle, e.g., in 1944 and 1964.

Nonperiodic variations with much larger amplitudes have been deduced from carbon 14 analysis of tree rings (sec. 2.1). During the Spörer and Maunder sunspot minimum periods, the C^{14} abundance and hence the cosmic ray intensity was 10% or more above the norm, and during the twelfth century Grand Maximum in sunspot

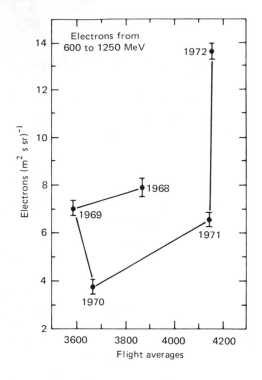

Figure 2.24. Hysteresis loop for cosmic ray protons of 40–90 MeV energies. Average primary proton flux is plotted against monthly average of Climax hourly neutron count rates. From Fulks (1975).

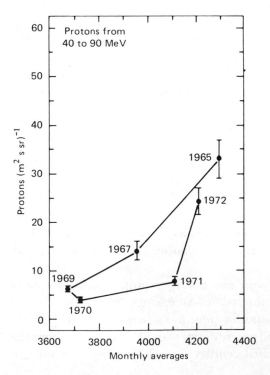

Figure 2.25. Same as for figure 2.24 but for primary electrons plotted against Climax neutron monitor averaged over the time periods of the electron-measurement rocket flights. From Fulks (1975).

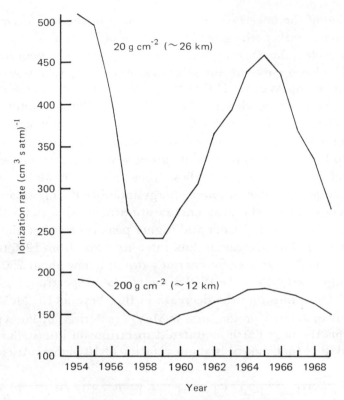

Figure 2.26. Ionization rate due to galactic cosmic rays at atmospheric depths of 20 and 200 g cm^{-2} corresponding to altitudes of approximately 26 and 12 km, respectively, for 1954–1969. From Neher (1971).

activity it was 10% or more below the norm (see also fig. 2.3). There may also have been minima in cosmic ray intensity associated with sunspot maxima in 860 and 960 AD (Schove, 1955; Stuiver, 1961). The cosmic ray maximum corresponding to the Maunder minimum is generally referred to as the DeVries fluctuation, after its discoverer.

2.4.2 Cosmic Ray Energy Spectra

Primary spectra of cosmic ray particles have been derived from balloon and satellite observations, and all are generally normalized to the flux at the top of the atmosphere. Low-altitude measurements thus contain uncertainties introduced by the extrapolation technique, which depends on knowledge of the residual atmosphere between the measurement height and the top of the atmosphere. For our purpose, resolution of the uncertainties or refinement of the measurements is unnecessary; rather, the gross features are of interest.

Solar cycle influence on primary proton spectra is evident in figure 2.27. The lower curve for the solar maximum year 1968 was derived by Lezniak and Webber (1971) from IMP 4 and Pioneer 8 satellite measurements. They derived the 1965 (near solar minimum) curve from balloon, IMP 3, and OGO-1 observations. The significantly lower intensity of primary protons during a solar maximum year compared to 1965 is worthy of note; it can be seen that the lower energies are much more affected than those above about 500 MeV.

The larger decrease in lower energy intensity during solar maximum tends to shift the peak energy upward, to about 500 MeV in 1968, compared to a broader and higher peak centered at about 300 MeV in 1965. The decrease in flux intensity going from 1965 to 1968 is a factor of 2 or greater for energies at and below about 250 MeV.

A compressed view of the 1968 primary proton spectrum is given in figure 2.28 to illustrate the decrease in flux beyond 10^3 MeV. The peak flux of about 1 proton $(m^2\,s\,sr\,MeV)^{-1}$ as derived by Fulks (1975) represents the near-Earth modulated spectrum; in interstellar space the peak flux (not shown) is about a factor of 10 higher. At energies

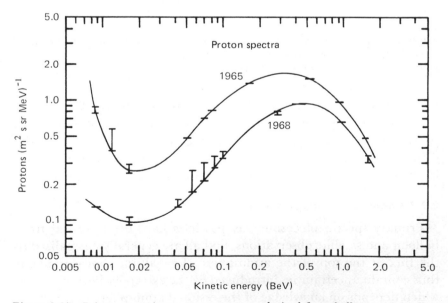

Figure 2.27. Primary cosmic ray proton spectra derived from balloon and satellite measurements in 1965 and 1968. From Lezniak and Webber (1971).

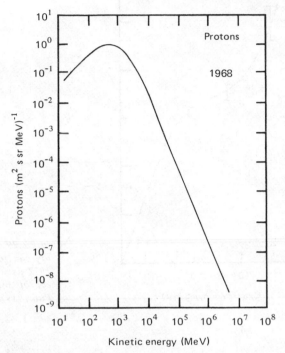

Figure 2.28. Primary galactic proton energy spectrum for 1968 as derived by Fulks (1975).

greater than 10^4 MeV, there appears to be no solar modulation detectable near the Earth. The energy spectrum for alpha particles (not shown) is similar to the proton spectrum, but the peak flux is only 0.1 of the proton flux.

Spectra for cosmic ray electrons at the top of the atmosphere also exhibit a substantial solar cycle modulation. The spectrum for a relatively low sunspot number year (1972) is illustrated in figure 2.29. This spectrum was derived by Fulks (1975) from various balloon and satellite measurements. For comparison, the primary electron spectrum for 1968 as adapted from the data of Fulks (1975) is given in figure 2.30. As with protons, there seems to be little solar cycle modulation of cosmic ray electrons with energies greater than about 10^{10} eV. Comparison of the spectra in figures 2.29 and 2.30 reveals the variation in spectral shape at the lower energies with changing solar activity. Similar primary electron spectra are given by Marar et al. (1971).

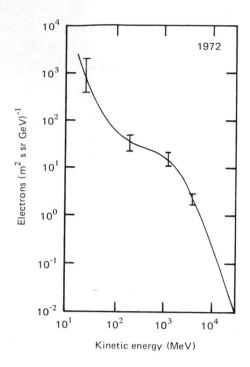

Figure 2.29. Primary cosmic ray electron spectrum for 1972 derived from a variety of measurements by Fulks (1975).

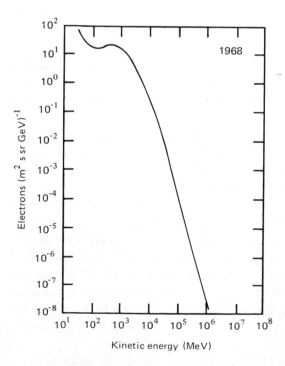

Figure 2.30. Primary cosmic ray-electron spectrum for 1968. From Fulks (1975).

2.4.3 Latitudinal Variations

Latitude surveys of cosmic ray ionization have been made by Neher (1967), Kent and Pomerantz (1971), Shea et al. (1965), Manzano and Winckler (1965), and Lockwood et al. (1975).

The latitudinal dependence as derived by Neher (1967) from 1965 measurements of air ionization is illustrated in figure 2.31. Note that ion production increases from the equator to about 50°–60° geomagnetic latitude, where it breaks to form a "knee." The knee moves to higher latitudes at the smaller pressure levels (greater heights). Poleward of the knee, the curves are flat because of decreased magnetic rigidity effects in the nearly vertical geomagnetic field. At a pressure level of 5 g cm^{-2} the knee is at 63° geomagnetic latitude in the low sunspot year of 1965. In 1958 the knee occurred at 56° geomagnetic latitude at the same pressure level (Neher, 1967), indicating that rigidity effects vary through the solar cycle. It should be noted also that the latitudinal effect on the vertical distribution of ion-pair production can be seen in figure 2.32 (from Gish, 1939).

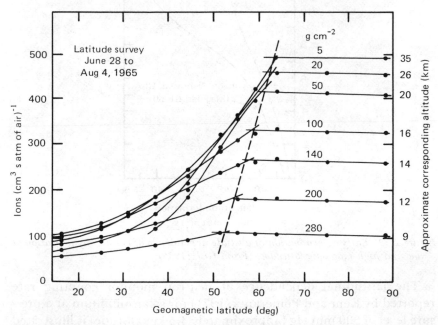

Figure 2.31. Latitudinal dependence of air ionization due to galactic cosmic rays at atmospheric depths from 5 to 280 g cm^{-2} (from Neher, 1967). The dashed line marks the "knee."

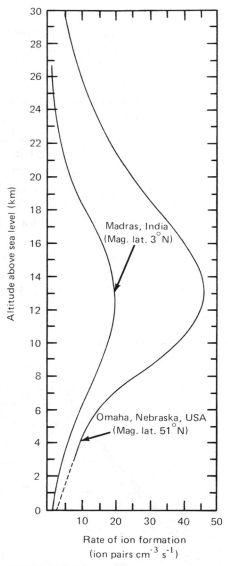

Figure 2.32. Early determination of altitude dependence of cosmic ray ionization at low and high magnetic latitudes. From Gish (1939).

The latitudinal dependence of neutron monitor counting rate reported by Kent and Pomerantz (1971) for solar minimum at a pressure level of 500 mm Hg (approximately 3.5 km altitude) is illustrated in figure 2.33. The knee occurs at about 2 GV, corresponding to approximately 54° geomagnetic latitude, comparable to the findings of Neher (1967). Error limits assigned to the curve in figure 2.33 stem

70

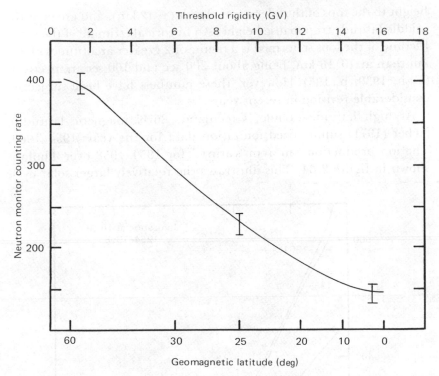

Figure 2.33. Latitudinal and cutoff rigidity dependence of cosmic ray neutron monitor count rate. From Kent and Pomerantz (1971).

from uncertainties in pressure correction to the neutron monitor count rates and calculated cutoff rigidities. For convenience the corresponding geomagnetic latitude derived from figure 2.13 is indicated on the abscissa. The count rate at the knee (54°) is nearly a factor of 3 greater than that at the equator.

2.4.4 Altitude Dependence of Cosmic Ray Ionization

Maximum ion production from cosmic rays takes place at altitudes from about 12 to 20 km, corresponding to atmospheric depths of approximately 150 to 50 $g\,cm^{-2}$, respectively, depending on season, phase of solar cycle, and latitude. An early determination of the height dependence of cosmic ray ionization has been given by Gish (1939) for magnetic latitudes of 3°N and 51°N (fig. 2.32).

At the higher latitude, ion-pair production peaks at 13 km altitude; near the magnetic equator the maximum is broader in altitude and peaks at about 12 km altitude. The maximum at any latitude is usually referred to as the Pfotzer maximum. The peaks correspond in height to the tops of thunderstorm clouds (~ 12 km), and are near the middle latitude tropopause height. An historical estimate of the mean lifetime of the ions so formed is a factor of 2 greater at altitudes of 2–5 km than at 10–16 km, being about 200 sec and 100 sec, respectively (Gish, 1939, p. 195). However, these numbers have been subject to considerable revision in recent years.

At high latitude (Thule, Greenland, 86°N magnetic latitude), Neher (1971) summarized ionization data for the years 1954–1969. The ion production rate $(cm^3 s atm)^{-1}$ for 1954–1958 over Thule is shown in figure 2.34. This illustrates the relatively larger solar cycle

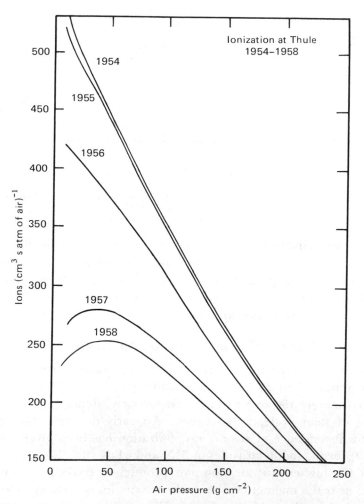

Figure 2.34. Altitude dependence of cosmic ray ionization over Thule at different phases of the sunspot cycle. From Neher (1971).

dependence at high altitudes (low pressures) compared to low altitudes. However, being normalized to a standard atmosphere, the data in this figure mask the peak ion-production height. The data were therefore "denormalized" by the multiplicative factor (pressure $(g\ cm^{-2})/1030\ (g\ cm^{-2}\ atm^{-1})$) for plotting in figure 2.35. To convert to altitude in kilometers, the approximate relationship given in appendix A was used.

In figure 2.35, for the sunspot minimum years of 1954 and 1964, and maximum years 1958 and 1969, the altitude dependence of cosmic ray ionization is clearly evident. In the minimum sunspot years

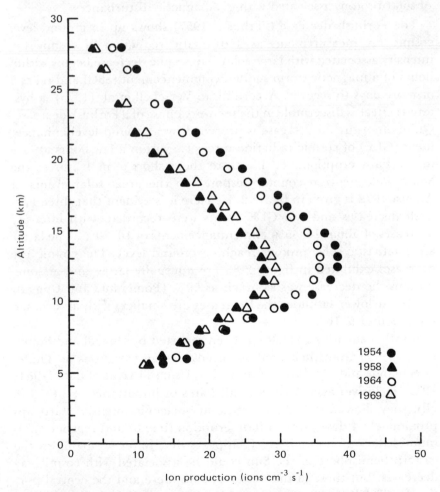

Figure 2.35. Ion-pair production due to cosmic rays as a function of altitude over Thule at sunspot maximum (1958, 1969) and minimum (1954, 1964). Calculated from the data of Neher (1971) using the atmospheric density model of appendix A.

the peak altitude tends to be slightly higher than in maximum years, and the ionization rate at all altitudes is greater.

2.4.5 Short-Term Cosmic Ray Variations

The types of short-term variation in cosmic ray intensity summarized here are (1) decreases associated with geomagnetic storms following solar flares (Forbush decreases), (2) the 27-day recurrence tendency, and (3) variations with solar magnetic sector boundary crossings (see also sec. 2.5). These phenomena are observed principally in ground-based observations and do not include enhancements of solar protons associated with geomagnetic disturbances.

The Forbush decrease (Forbush, 1957) shows up in ground-level cosmic ray measurements as a dramatic reduction in cosmic ray intensity associated with large solar flares. The decrease begins within hours of a magnetic storm sudden commencement (SSC) and takes 5 or more days to recover. According to Verschell et al. (1975), a hysteresis effect is discernible in the recovery phase of a Forbush decrease. Quite often such a decrease is preceded by a ground-level enhancement (GLE) of cosmic radiation intensity, within a few hours after a major flare eruption. To illustrate these short-term features, the South Pole neutron counter response to the great solar events of August 1972 is given in figure 2.36. Here it is evident that three Forbush decreases and two GLE events were recorded, with intensity decreases of about 10-35% and enhancements of 10-20%. The latter are relativistic solar protons reaching ground level. The cosmic ray decreases exhibited in figure 2.36 are unusually large, and at some stations the decrease was as much as 50% (Pomerantz and Duggal, 1973). At lower latitudes the decreases are smaller, with an average reduction of 5-10%.

A rather surprising result has been reported by Duggal and Pomerantz (1977) from their analysis of cosmic ray variations at Thule, Greenland, and McMurdo, Antarctica. Using 11 years of data (1964-1974, inclusive) associated with all flares of importance ≥2 (379 in all), they showed that the decrease in nucleonic intensity starts approximately 4 days *prior* to flare eruption (day 0) and reaches minimum 4 days after the flare. It appears that flares occurring in the eastern hemisphere of the Sun could be associated with cosmic ray decreases, but those in the western hemisphere and the central portion (± 30° about the central meridian) cannot. This finding demon-

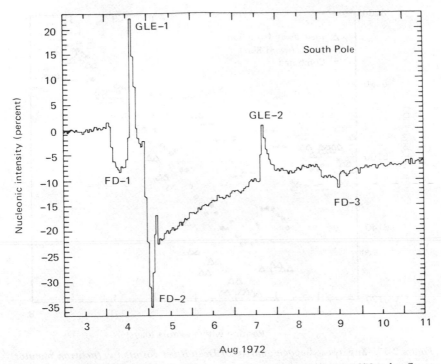

Figure 2.36. Response of South Pole neutron monitor to August 1972 solar flares, exhibiting ground-level enhancements (GLE) and Forbush decreases (FD). From Pomerantz and Duggal (1973).

strated that the flare process itself is not directly responsible for the Forbush decrease, although the latter appears to be related to some characteristic of the active region. The full significance of these results to Sun-weather relationships has not yet been established.

There is a 27-day recurrence tendency wherein the ground-level cosmic ray intensity maximizes about 1½ days after a geomagnetic activity minimum. The amplitude of the maximum is about 5% (Forbush, 1956), but the low-energy cosmic ray amplitude variation can be as much as 20% (Simpson, 1957). Since minimum geomagnetic activity occurs about 1 day prior to sector boundary passage (Shapiro, 1974), this would imply a maximum in cosmic ray intensity about ½ day after boundary passage. The implication is verified by the data of Wilcox and Ness (1965) presented in figure 2.37. With an average of four sectors per solar rotation, the second cosmic ray peak at day 7 in this figure is probably associated with the boundary passage following

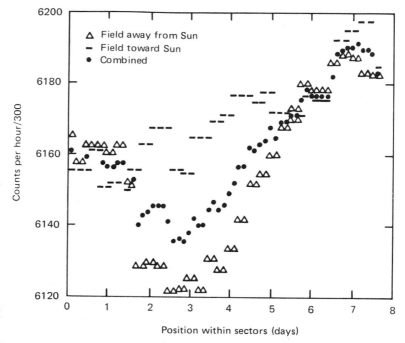

Figure 2.37. Superposed epoch analysis of Deep River cosmic ray (neutron monitor) count rate as a function of position within positive and negative solar sectors (Wilcox and Ness, 1965). Note the deep minimum in count rate occurring 2½ days into a positive sector.

the one at day 0. The minimum in cosmic ray intensity about 2½ days after day 0 corresponds in time to a maximum in geomagnetic activity as measured by Kp (Wilcox and Ness, 1965).

2.5 Solar Magnetic Sector Structure

The solar magnetic field (which is the source of the interplanetary magnetic field) is divided into characteristic sectors in which the magnetic polarity, directed either toward or away from the Sun, remains constant for several days at a time (Wilcox and Ness, 1965). A sample sector structure inferred from IMP 1 spacecraft observations is illustrated schematically in figure 2.38. The plus and minus signs around the periphery indicate interplanetary magnetic field (IMF) direction away from and toward the Sun, respectively, as measured every 3 hr at the spacecraft location. The IMF has four sectors in the illustrated 27-day rotation interval, separated by sharply defined boundaries at

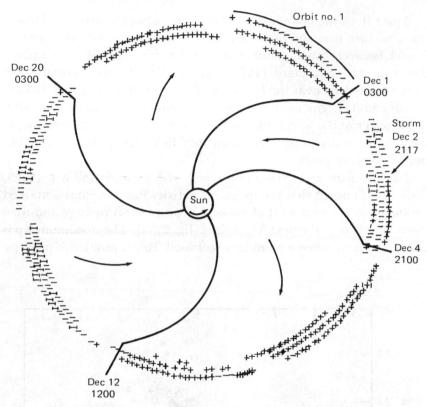

Figure 2.38. Solar magnetic sector structure as inferred from IMP 1 spacecraft observations (Wilcox and Ness, 1965). Plus signs (away from Sun) and minus signs (toward Sun) are 3-hourly measurements of interplanetary magnetic field direction, and arrows in the four sectors indicate predominant direction of the field.

which the field polarity reverses within a few hours. At times there are only two sectors.

The field polarity is apparently connected to the Sun, and as it rotates, the field also rotates so that the sectors and boundaries sweep past the Earth. Wilcox and Colburn (1969, 1970, 1972) used magnetometer data from Explorers 33 and 35 to list magnetic sector boundary (MSB) passages for the years 1962–1970, and Svalgaard (1972) extrapolated the tabulation of MSB passages back to 1926 with ground-based magnetometer data. Correlations between MSB passage and meteorological phenomena are discussed in section 4.3, in which it will be seen that some strikingly good correlations have been uncovered in recent years.

Apart from the boundary passage itself, other features of solar sector structure may shed light on the reasons for positive correlations found between other parameters of solar activity and the weather. For example, Svalgaard (1973) suggested that solar proton flares occur most often near the foot of MSBs on the Sun, magnetic sudden storm commencements have a marked tendency to occur near MSB passage across the Earth, high solar wind velocities and densities occur at times near a passage, and high IMF field strengths are often observed at those times.

Also, Wilcox and Ness (1965) and Wilcox and Colburn (1969, 1970, 1972) noted that the magnetic activity index Kp has a marked tendency to rise to a level of about 3 near an MSB passage and then decay slowly over the next 3 or 4 days (fig. 2.39). The maximum Kp is about the same when a boundary is crossed from a positive to negative

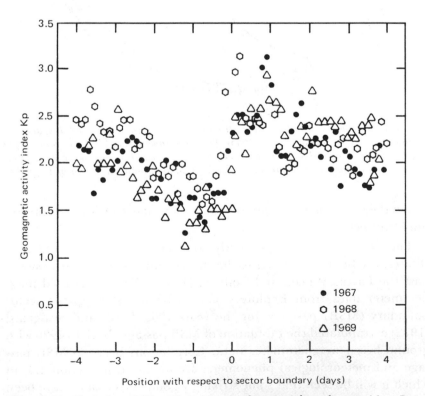

Figure 2.39. Variation of Kp with respect to solar sector boundary position. Boundary sweeps past the Earth on day 0. From Wilcox and Colburn (1972).

sector or from a negative to positive sector (Wilcox and Ness, 1965). These enhancements have a tendency to recur every 27 days, and Hirshberg and Colburn (1973) suggested that these recurrent magnetic storms may be more related to fast solar wind streams than to sector structure. It appears, however, that all three are interrelated.

Long-term variations in solar sector structure may also have a bearing on the sometimes peculiar tendency for extremes in meteorological phenomena to lead or lag the sunspot cycle by 1 or 2 years (ch. 3). Wilcox and Scherrer (1972) utilized the data from Svalgaard (1972) to confirm an annual variation in the predominant polarity of the IMF first suggested by Rosenberg and Coleman (1969). This is a small modulation on the "ever-present" (Wilcox, 1968) sector structure and is imposed by the fact that from December 7 to June 7 the southern polar region of the Sun is tipped toward Earth, whereas in the other half-year the northern polar region is so oriented. The predominant polarity of the IMF should be the same as that of the solar polar region tipped toward Earth and thus should reverse around June 7 and again around December 7. It does so within a few days. The complexity of the sector structure shows a semiannual variation (Sawyer, 1974), with more sectors per solar rotation in May and June and again in November and December. This is probably related to the annual variation in predominant polarity.

The physical basis of the sector structure can be understood in terms of a phenomenological model suggested by Schultz (1973) and by Svalgaard et al. (1974). A large-scale current sheet separating the positive and negative sectors imposes a warping of the heliomagnetic equator; thus, relatively speaking, the Earth is sometimes above that equator and sometimes below it as the Sun rotates. When the extension of the tilt in the current sheet (sector boundary) rotates by the Earth, the IMF polarity is observed to reverse. The model has also been used to explain long-term variations in cosmic ray intensity (Svalgaard and Wilcox, 1976).

On the average, the phase of the annual variation changes about 2⅔ yr after sunspot maximum (Wilcox and Scherrer, 1972). That is, for about 10 consecutive years the predominant field direction is positive between December 7 and June 7, and then the phase changes so that the polarity is predominantly negative for that period. Wilcox and Scherrer suggest that this phase change is related to the double sunspot cycle, which, as will be seen in section 3.2, seems to relate better to some climatic changes than does the 11-yr cycle.

2.6 Geomagnetic Activity

The geomagnetic storm is a phenomenon that occurs in the near-Earth environment in response to solar activity. Detection and measurement of such storms thus constitutes an indirect indicator of solar activity. The use of geomagnetic data as a solar indicator is encountered often in Sun-weather studies; this section describes the various magnetic activity indexes in use and the concept of "sudden commencement" geomagnetic storms.

It is an historical fact that the intensity of geomagnetic activity varies in phase with the 11-yr cycle (Sabine, 1852; Stagg, 1927; Chapman and Bartels, 1940). Violent fluctuations sustained over a period of one to a few days constitute geomagnetic storms, the occurrence of which correlates with other solar variables in addition to active sunspot regions. Such storms usually follow the eruption of solar flares; they are correlated with the emission of enhanced solar corpuscular radiation, and the recurrent variety is associated with M-regions and MSB passages (sec. 2.5). Geomagnetic substorms occur with magnetic activity of a few hours duration and are more localized in auroral latitudes. Both storms and substorms are associated with magnetospheric disturbances, visual aurora, radiowave absorption, and other related phenomena.

2.6.1 Indices of Measurement

Variations in semiquantitative indices of magnetic activity are indicative of solar disturbances; thus it is perhaps not surprising that a number of Sun-weather correlative studies have used magnetic activity as the intermediary indicator. A variety of indices have been utilized in these studies; a description of the more common ones follows. These include Kp, Ap, Ci, and Cp, which are measures of global magnetic activity, and the indices K, C, AE, Dst, and Q, which reflect more localized activity. A new measure of global magnetic activity is the aa index introduced by Mayaud (1972, 1973, 1975). A good introduction to the derivation and reporting of the older magnetic indices is given by Davies (1965, pp. 30–35), and Mayaud (1972) describes the new aa index fully; thus only the briefest description is necessary here. A critical discussion of the quantitative reliability and suggested use of magnetic indices is given by Rostoker (1972).

C and Ci: At each participating magnetic observatory, the daily magnetic records of the Earth's magnetic field strength and direction are examined for fluctuations. A qualitative judgment is made of the intensity and duration of any field perturbations present, and a daily character figure, C, is assigned using only the three whole numbers 0, 1, 2 for quiet, moderately disturbed, and greatly disturbed, respectively (Fleming, 1939, p. 42).

The daily C values from all collaborating observatories are averaged together to the nearest tenth to yield the "international daily character figure," Ci. The index Ci thus has 21 gradations, from 0.0 representing the quietest days to 2.0 for the most disturbed days, on a global basis.

Criticisms of the index Ci include the point that a qualitative judgment which may vary from one observer to the next is used for the local index C, and for long-term studies, the number of participating observatories has varied over the years. In 1906, when Ci was established, the number was 30, and by 1938 it was 53 (Fleming, 1939); backward extrapolation of Ci to the nineteenth century was made with 10 or fewer stations (Mayaud, 1973); thus early values, especially prior to 1880, are extremely suspect.

K, Kp, Cp, and Ap: The local index K is assigned to each 3-hourly interval of universal time, 00–03, 03–06 UT, and so on, on the basis of the largest excursion of magnetic field strength on all three magnetometer orthogonal elements. The index takes on integer values from 0 to 9, where 0 is most quiet and 9 is most disturbed. The minimum excursion (or range) required for $K = 9$ varies from 300 gamma (1 gamma = 10^{-5} gauss or 10^{-8} tesla) at low-latitude stations to 2000 gamma at stations in the auroral zones.

The elimination of local influences at 12 selected stations lying between geomagnetic latitudes of 48° and 63° in both northern and southern hemispheres yields standardized values of K, the mean of which is denoted Kp, the "planetary 3-hr index" (Davies, 1965). Tabulations of Kp go back to the year 1932.

The two daily world indices Cp and Ap are derived from the eight 3-hourly Kp values. The planetary character figure Cp ranges from 0.0 to 2.0 in steps of 0.1 (like Ci), and it is approximately logarithmically proportional to the ranges defining Kp. The index Ap is more linearly related to these ranges.

Dst.: This index was originally devised by Sugiura (1964) to describe ring current variations during the International Geophysical Year (IGY). It is derived from disturbance variations in the H component at magnetic observatories selected for equal longitude spacing and low-latitude locations where both auroral- and equatorial-electrojet effects are minimal. Dst is thus a measure of equatorial geomagnetic activity due to the ring current alone. Details of the derivation have undergone several changes (Rostoker, 1972), so only the latest Dst set should be used for Sun-weather correlations. For consistency, this set is based on data from the same four low-latitude stations and derivation criteria for all years from 1957 through 1977 (M. Sugiura, private communication, 1978). It is available from the World Data Center for Solar-Terrestrial Physics, Boulder, Colorado.

AE and Q: These two indices have apparently not yet been used in investigations of weather responses to solar activity, and both are measures principally of magnetic activity in and near the auroral zones. The index AE (for auroral electrojet) is closely related to magnetospheric processes and is particularly useful in studies of auroral substorms (Davis and Sugiura, 1966). It is defined by using only the H (horizontal) component of the perturbation field at auroral zone magnetic observatories selected to give uniformly spaced coverage in longitude. The westward electrojet current imposes a negative perturbation in H, whereas the eastward current gives a positive ΔH; the difference betweeen maximum positive (AU) and maximum negative (AL) perturbations, scaled at 2.5-min intervals, constitutes AE (Rostoker, 1972).

The index Q is another indicator of auroral zone magnetic activity scaled at 15-min intervals, but it has been largely supplanted by AE and is not discussed further.

Interactions between the interplanetary magnetic field and the geomagnetic field that produce magnetospheric disturbances affecting Kp and AE have been reviewed by Burch (1974), who showed that an IMF having a southward-directed component correlates best with variations in these two indices. These "southward turning" IMFs are associated with earthward displacement of the subsolar magnetopause and equatorward displacements of the polar cusps (Hill and Rassbach, 1975).

aa: For several long-term geophysical studies, especially analysis of relationships between magnetic activity and climate changes, it would be desirable to extend tabulations of Kp to years before 1932. The effort involved to scale old magnetic records from the 12 standard stations to do this has been prohibitive, so Mayaud (1972) has devised the *aa* index as a measure of global magnetic activity based on two antipodal middle latitude stations. Mayaud (1972, 1973, 1975) personally scaled 100 years (1868–1967) of magnetic records from Greenwich, England, and Melbourne, Australia, and their successor stations, to obtain 3-hourly K indices which he then transformed into amplitude *ak* in gammas. The mean *ak* of the two stations is the *aa* index.

Daily, monthly, and annual means of the *aa* index tabulated by Mayaud (1973) for the years 1868–1967 represent the longest-span collection of homogeneous magnetic data available. For the overlapping years with Kp (1932 forward), it has been shown that *aa* is compatible, and the earlier years of the latter index may therefore be used with equal confidence. To date apparently no correlations between *aa* and meteorological phenomena have been reported.

The *aa* index shows an annual variation that is statistically repeatable over the entire 100-yr data base within a few percent (Mayaud, 1972). The minimum and maximum for each antipodal station occur near the local winter and summer solstices, respectively (Mayaud, 1972; Rourke, 1965; Wulf, 1971), in correspondence to the phase changes in predominant polarity of the interplanetary magnetic field (sec. 2.5). Good correlation is also obtained between *aa* and the 11-yr and longer secular solar cycles, to the extent that Mayaud (1972) predicted extremely low annual magnetic activity for the two solar minima occurring in 1975 and about 1986.

2.6.2 Storm Sudden Commencements

A special case of geomagnetic storms is the type that begins suddenly, heralded by a rapid rise of a few to as much as 100 gammas in magnetic intensity within about 4 min (Mayaud, 1975) simultaneously over most of the globe. Known as an SSC storm, it often follows a polar cap absorption event (Reid and Leinbach, 1959), beginning about 20 hr after eruption of the PCA-producing major solar flare.

The characteristic SSC signature (rapid rise and subsequent increased intensity), thought to be a geomagnetic response to an interplanetary magnetic shockwave, is followed within a few hours by the main phase of the storm, in which Kp reaches values from about 6 to 9. The storm can last from less than one day to several days.

An SSC storm often occurs within a few hours of magnetic sector boundary passage (Wilcox and Colburn, 1972); the annual number of storms is positively correlated better with annual sunspot number than with the *aa* annual index (Mayaud, 1975), and, perhaps surprisingly, it shows almost no 27-day recurrence tendency. Recurrent geomagnetic storms do tend to recur with the solar rotation interval, but in contrast their beginning is gradual rather than sudden, and the maximum Kp value reached is less than that in most SSC storms. Like the SSC variety, however, they are positively correlated with the 11-yr cycle and with MSB passage.

The morphology of SSC storms may have an important bearing on studies of meteorological responses to solar activity. Whereas there is a variable time lag between solar flare occurrence and the development of a geomagnetic storm, and past correlative studies have often been vague as to when the storms in question began (Roberts and Olson, 1973a), it appears that utilization of the precise beginning time of SSC storms would be advantageous. Further, for long-term correlations there now exists a homogeneous list of 2462 SSC occurrences in the 100-yr period 1868–1967 (Mayaud, 1973).

3 Long-Term Climatic Trends

Climatological trends associated with the long and short cycles of sunspot activity have been studied by a number of investigators using data spanning more than two centuries. The quest for this elusive association began even before Schwabe discovered the sunspot cycle for the Western world in 1843 (sec. 2.1.1). As noted by Eddy (1976), the famous scientist Herschel suggested in 1801 that the price of wheat in London was indirectly controlled by sunspots based on his personal observations that less rain fell when there were few spots. In most cases the statistical significance of the historical results cannot be evaluated at this late date. Their value is therefore open to question, but some are nonetheless included in this chapter to illustrate the variety of results available as well as to provide a perspective for more recent analyses.

The two most common parameters used to define climate have been rainfall and temperature, and these have been utilized in many of the Sun-weather studies. The results of some of those studies are summarized in sections 3.1.1 and 3.1.3. Indirect indicators of rainfall such as snowfall, lake levels, and river flooding have been correlated with sunspot number; these variables are of more direct interest to hydrologists than to climatologists (Wallis, 1977), but it may be too much to hope that simple correlations with sunspots will improve the predictability of winter water storage through snow accumulation, runoff amounts, and ground water supply. Reported correlations are included in this chapter as a matter of general Sun-weather interest.

Surface pressure, both at individual stations and averaged by zones, has been a popular parameter to correlate with sunspot number, and pressure systems and winds as well as storm tracks have also been investigated. These considerations are reviewed in sections 3.1.5, 3.1.6, and 3.1.7. If relationships with solar activity are to be found with any one of the atmospheric parameters (rainfall, temperature, or pressure), they should be discernible in all, since these quantities are inextricably intertwined in the atmospheric weather machine.

In some locations, pressure, temperature, and rainfall amounts seem to be better correlated with the Hale cycle than the Schwabe cycle, and this is especially true of droughts in the United States; these are discussed in section 3.2.

The topic of correlation breakdowns and/or reversals, which may be indicative that all Sun-weather correlations are merely fortuitous, or which may alternatively contain clues as to the physical mechanisms (however obscure) in linking solar activity to weather and climate, is treated separately in section 3.3.

Atmospheric electricity is a factor in some atmospheric processes associated with weather, notably thunderstorm occurrence, so its possible responses to solar activity should be considered as background for physical mechanisms. The basic relations of atmospheric electric quantities, especially the potential gradient, air conductivity, and thunderstorm occurrence and their reported correlations with long-term solar activity, are discussed in section 3.4.

Speculations that the stratosphere, especially through the ozone layer, might enter into Sun-weather relationships by providing a possible shielding mechanism for modifying weather or climate heightens the importance of studies concerning ozone response to solar activity. These studies are reviewed in section 3.5, which also contains a basic discussion of the regular variations in atmospheric ozone.

3.1 Sunspot Cycle Correlations

In this section we review studies that attempt to relate the 11-yr sunspot cycle to such climatic variables as rainfall and its indirect indicators (i.e., flooding and lake levels), atmospheric temperature, atmospheric pressure and winds, and storm tracks.

3.1.1 Rainfall

The correlation between sunspot numbers and annual rainfall may be positive, negative, or nonexistent, depending on where the meteorological measurements are made. For example, in equatorial latitudes the correlation is positive, as shown by Clayton (1923) with rainfall data from Fortaleza and Recife, Brazil; Bathurst and Mombasa, Africa; and Batavia, Java, using the superposed epoch method for analysis. Weighted running averages of total annual rainfall at these stations in relation to sunspot maximum and minimum years, shown in figure 3.1, reveal that, on the average, more rain falls dur-

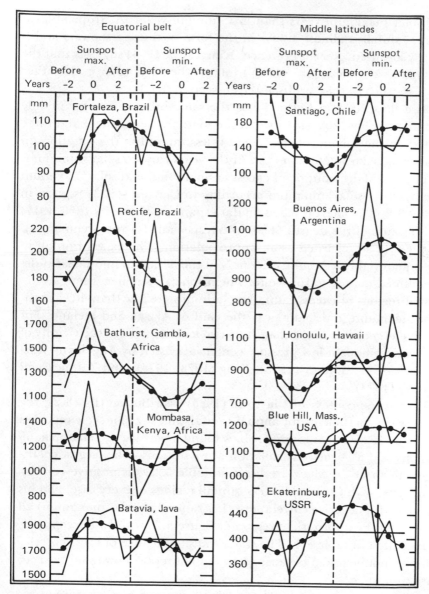

Figure 3.1. Mean rainfall in relation to sunspot maximum and minimum years at equatorial and middle latitude stations for the years 1860–1917. The solid lines are annual means; dotted curves are weighted 5-yr running means plotted on the center year to smooth out short-term fluctuations (Clayton, 1923). The vertical dashed lines indicate that the curves are discontinuous between the max and min portions.

ing solar maximum years than in minimum years. At tropical locations, rainfall is almost always in the form of thundershowers and is
highly localized. Recent evidence (King et al., 1974) suggests that the
rainfall at Fortaleza (4°S, 39°W) follows the 22-yr solar cycle rather
than the 11-yr cycle, as discussed in section 3.2.1.

Also illustrated in figure 3.1 is the same information for middle
latitude stations (20°–40°), two in the southern hemisphere and three
in the northern hemisphere. There is less rainfall in these stations in
years near solar maximum than in the years close to solar minimum.

The global distribution of excess annual rainfall at solar maximum
compared to solar minimum according to Clayton (1923) is given in
figure 3.2. The chart is based on data spanning the years 1860–1917,
but because of the dearth of stations (especially for the ocean areas),
it can only be regarded as an approximation. The excess rainfall in
the equatorial belt is quite evident, but the deficit in middle latitudes
is confined mainly to the western hemisphere. Further, there are revealed regions of excess rainfall at latitudes greater than 40° at sunspot maximum, especially near the Gulf of Alaska and Iceland. For
later reference it is noted that these two locations are in the vicinity of
the semipermanent low-pressure centers discussed by Angell and Korshover (1974), Bradley (1973), King (1973, 1974), and Zatopek and
Krivsky (1974).

Within the context of Clayton's (1923) distribution (fig. 3.2), the
correlation coefficients for annual rainfall and sunspot cycle reported
by Shaw (1928) are of interest. Shaw found a positive correlation at 69
stations and a negative correlation at 81 stations. The largest coefficients reported by Shaw are listed in table 3.1. His positive correlations agree with Clayton's excess rainfall regions in every case, and his
stations with negative correlations (less rainfall at solar maximum) all
fall within the appropriate region of figure 3.2, with two exceptions,
as indicated in table 3.1. The statistical significance of these correlations cannot be tested because Shaw did not report how many years of
data were used.

Among more recent results available for comparison with these
early findings are those of Bowen (1975) for annual rainfall at Hobart
(43°S, 147°E) and Cairns (15°S, 146°E), Australia. Bowen's analysis
of data for 1880–1960 gives a positive correlation for rainfall and sunspot number at Hobart, in agreement with Clayton's chart (fig. 3.2).
At Cairns, however, Bowen's correlation is negative and opposite to
Clayton's result.

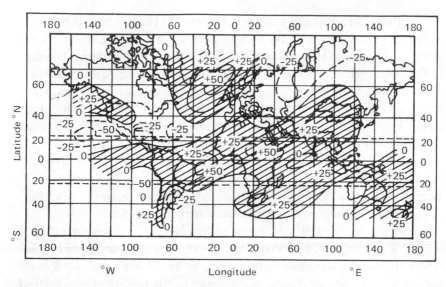

Figure 3.2. Global distribution of annual rainfall difference (in centimeters) between sunspot maximum and minimum; shaded area is greater rainfall at maximum. Based on data from 1860 to 1917. From Clayton (1923).

Table 3.1.—Correlation Between Annual Rainfall and Sunspot Cycle (from Shaw, 1928)

Station	Geographical Location		Correlation Coefficient	Agreement with fig. 3.2
Bathurst, Gambia	13.2°N	16.5°W	+ .51	Yes
New Caledonia	21.3°S	164.2°E	+ .3 to + .4	Yes
Wellington, New Zealand	41.2°S	174.5°E	+ .3 to + .4	Yes
Bahia, Brazil	11.1°S	43.0°W	+ .3 to + .4	Yes
Durban, Natal	29.5°S	31.0°E	+ .3 to + .4	Yes
St. Louis, Senegal	16.1°N	16.3°W	+ .3 to + .4	Yes
Leh, India	34.1°N	77.4°E	+ .3 to + .4	Yes
Victoria, Canada	48.3°N	123.3°W	+ .3 to + .4	Yes
Edmonton, Canada	53.3°N	113.5°W	− .50	Yes
Punta Arenas, Chile	53.1°S	70.5°W	− .43	No
Ekaterinburg, USSR	56.5°N	60.4°E	− .3 to − .4	Yes
Tokyo, Japan	35.4°N	139.4°E	− .3 to − .4	Yes
Albany, NY, USA	42.4°N	73.5°W	− .3 to − .4	Yes
Suakin, Sudan	19.0°N	37.2°E	− .3 to − .4	No
Newcastle, Jamaica	18°N	77°W	− .3 to − .4	Yes
Alice Springs, Australia	23.4°S	133.6°E	− .3 to − .4	Yes
Eyre, Australia	32.2°S	126.2°E	− .3 to − .4	Yes
Pelotas, Brazil	31.5°S	52.2°W	− .3 to − .4	Yes

To jump ahead in the story a bit, Bowen (1975) pointed out that Hobart's rainfall is governed by low-pressure systems off the southern ocean, which leads to wet winters and relatively dry summers. Clayton (1923) found that, for stations along the southern coast of Australia, the amount of winter rainfall is positively correlated with the sunspot cycle, whereas summer rainfall is the opposite. Cairns, on the other hand, being dominated by tropical cyclones moving southward down the Queensland coast, has almost no winter rainfall.

Bowen (1975) indicated that a Russian study found a positive correlation for Archangel, USSR and a negative one for Athens, Greece. Beirut, Lebanon (34°N, 36°E) also has a negative correlation (King, 1973). These results are in agreement with figure 3.2.

For seasonal rainfall variations with solar cycle, Clayton's (1923) work is less complete. However, he did point out that at interior, continental, middle latitude stations such as Salt Lake City, USA, and Hopefountain, South Africa, winter rainfall is negatively correlated and summer rainfall positively correlated with the solar cycle. At some coastal stations, such as Capetown, South Africa; the Pacific coast of Canada; the Pacific coast of Chile (40°–50°S); the southern coast of Australia; and New Zealand, the winter correlation is positive and the summer correlation is negative (see table 3.2).

According to the results of King (1973), who used the Wales-Smith (1973) analysis of monthly rainfall totals at Kew, England (51°N, 0°E) for the 274-yr period 1697–1970 to investigate solar cycle influence, Kew falls into the category of a coastal station. That is, the driest

Table 3.2.—Correlation Between Seasonal Variation of Excess Rainfall in Various Geographic Regions and 11-Yr Sunspot Cycle. Plus Sign Indicates Greater than Average Rainfall at Sunspot Maximum (from Clayton, 1923)

Geographic Region	Correlation Winter	Correlation Summer
Interior continental	−	+
Midlatitudes (e.g., Capetown, South Africa; Pacific coast of Canada and Chile (40°–50°S); southern coast of Australia; New Zealand	+	−

winters tend to be associated with low sunspot numbers, and the driest summers occur during solar maximum years. Spring rains at Kew tend to have the same correlation as summer rains. Apart from these conclusions, however, King (1973) felt that the solar cycle variation of rainfall at Kew is not very distinct.

King also noted that winter rainfall over parts of northern Africa and northern India is much reduced during solar maximum years, in accordance with their interior, continental, middle latitudinal zones ranging from 40° to 80°N.

Annual excess precipitation as a function of 11-yr sunspot cycle has been investigated by Xanthakis (1973) for 10°-wide latitudinal zones between 40° and 80°N. His results can be compared only roughly with Clayton's chart (fig. 3.2), because Xanthakis averaged his zonal data over rather wide longitudinal bands. In the polar zone (70°–80°N), using data from stations at longitudes from 156°W to 80°E spanning the years 1912–1960, excess rainfall showed a consistently high positive correlation (+ .77) with the 11-yr sunspot cycle. In this latitudinal band it can be seen in the chart that an average of Clayton's results over the same longitudinal width in the polar zone would be positive (that is, excess rainfall occurring in solar maximum years); thus Xanthakis' finding is in agreement. In the next lower band (60°–70°N) at longitudes from 40°E to 165°W and 6° to 177°E, with data from 1882–1960, the correlation was again consistently high, but negative (− .71). In this case the longitudinal width is too great to permit even a rough comparison.

In the latitudinal zone 50°–60°N within the longitude band 176°W eastward to 160°E covering Canada and Alaska (176°–55°W), Europe, and Asia, Xanthakis found a strong negative correlation (− .67) for the period 1893–1913, but then there was a sudden reversal, and from 1914 to 1960, the correlation was strongly positive (+ .74). Further discussion of the reversal is given in section 3.3.2. Again, the longitudinal extent is too great to allow comparison with figure 3.2.

Excess rainfall in the middle latitude band (40°–50°N) in the longitude range 124°W to 162°E was highly correlated with the 11-yr cycle between 1885 and 1960, but the sign reversed abruptly several times during the period. Discussion of this band is deferred to section 3.3.2.

In contrast to the apparently significant correlations reported by Xanthakis, Gerety et al. (1977) failed to find any linear relationship between sunspot numbers and annual precipitation at individual stations, even though the data base they used contained the Xanthakis data base as a subset.

Another analysis of essentially the same data was made by Dehsara and Cehak (1970) using a superposed epoch technique similar to that of Clayton (1923). They found that some individual-station rainfall totals were significantly correlated with sunspots, but others were not. On a global basis, a tendency was noted for the precipitation "cycle" to lead the sunspots by a quarter cycle. Their conclusion was that ". . . even investigations using a large number of stations with relatively long series of observations cannot support the idea of a direct influence of solar activity on meteorological elements on a large scale." The results of Dehsara and Cehak are in a form convenient for updating Clayton's chart (fig. 3.2). In the North American sector, about half of the recent results are compatible with the distribution in figure 3.2. Additional work is required to check the global agreement.

3.1.2 Indirect Indicators of Rainfall

In the higher middle latitudes, winter precipitation is often in the form of snow rather than rain, and there have been a few studies of the correlation of snowfall with solar cycle. An early one is that by Clayton (1923), who analyzed annual snowfall data from Blue Hill Observatory, Milton, Massachusetts for 1886–1917, and Sierra, California for 1878–1900. At Blue Hill, on the basis of 5-yr running means, maximum snowfall ($\sim 25\%$ above average) occurs about 1 yr before sunspot maximum, and minimum snowfall (20% below average) at sunspot minimum (see fig. 3.3). This positive correlation for winter precipitation is in keeping with Blue Hill's location near the Atlantic coast. At Sierra the trend is less clear (fig. 3.3), but there is an indication of higher snowfall amounts about 1 yr after solar maximum. The annual means at these two stations show a greater variability, but at Blue Hill there is still an indication of positive correlation with sunspot number.

Other indirect indicators of rainfall include water level in lakes and river flooding. The correlation coefficient of the mean annual water level of Lake Victoria and sunspot number is $+.88$ (Shaw, 1928). This implies an excess of rainfall at sunspot maximum for the region of Lake Victoria (2.0°S, 32.2°E), in agreement with Clayton's distribution (fig. 3.2) showing excess rainfall in equatorial regions. The

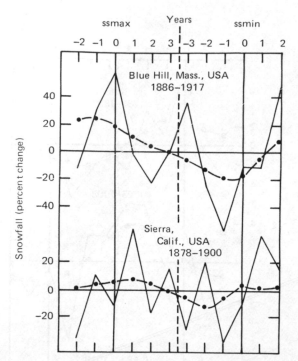

Figure 3.3. Snowfall amounts at sunspot maximum and minimum, expressed as percentage of average amount. Solid lines are annual means; broken curves are 5-yr weighted running means (Clayton, 1923). The vertical dashed lines indicate that the curves are discontinuous between the ssmax and ssmin portions.

strength of the Lake Victoria correlation deteriorated considerably after 1930 (King, 1975) and is discussed further in section 3.3.2.

Also in the equatorial belt is the Nile River, which flows out of Lake Victoria. The mean height of this river in Egypt for the years 1737–1908, almost two centuries, was analyzed by Clayton (1923) in relation to sunspot activity. For his first group of data (1737–1800), he found maximum heights about 1 yr after sunspot maximum and minimum heights about 1 yr before sunspot minimum (fig. 3.4). In the second data set (1825–1908) the maximum river height lagged sunspot maximum by about 2 yr. This variation again implies greater rainfall in the equatorial belt in years near solar maximum. A correlation of + .36 was found by Shaw (1928) between Nile flooding and sunspot number.

The Parana River flowing into the Rio de la Plata at 34°S, 58.5°W, near Buenos Aires, Argentina, is located in a middle latitude region

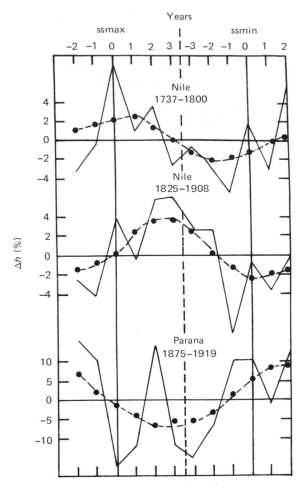

Figure 3.4. Mean percentage change in heights of Nile and Parana Rivers in sunspot maximum and minimum years. Solid lines, annual means; broken curves, 5-yr weighted running means (Clayton, 1923). The curves are discontinuous between the ssmax and ssmin portions, as indicated by vertical dashed line.

exhibiting less rainfall at sunspot maximum than minimum (fig. 3.2). Accordingly, the mean height of the river is higher at sunspot minimum (fig. 3.4), when more rain falls. The Ohio River near Cincinnati (39.1°N, 84.3°W) is an interior continental middle latitude river; in spring and early summer months of solar maximum years the mean height is greater than in minimum years, but during the remaining seasons this correlation is less clear (fig. 3.5).

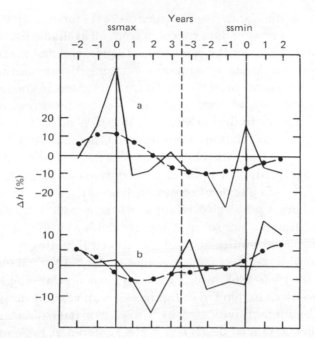

Figure 3.5. Mean percentage change in height of Ohio River at Cincinnati in sunspot maximum and minimum years. Solid lines, annual means; broken curves, 5-yr weighted running means (Clayton, 1923). (a) April–June 1871–1908. (b) July–March 1871–1908. The curves are discontinuous between ssmax and ssmin (vertical dashed line).

In summary, it appears that annual rainfall could exhibit a dependence on the 11-yr sunspot cycle in many areas of the world. There is a pronounced trend of greater rainfall during solar maximum years in equatorial latitudes ($\pm 20°$), less in middle latitude regions ($\sim 20°$–$40°$), and again more at latitudes greater than about 40°. The global distribution given by Clayton in 1923 (fig. 3.2) still holds true in most areas in light of more recent analysis (see sec. 3.3.2). Finally, the amount of rainfall is greatly influenced by the movement of pressure systems (Winstanley, 1973; Bowen, 1975); this topic is discussed in section 3.2.6.

3.1.3 Surface Temperature

Attempts to correlate air temperature at the Earth's surface with sunspot cycle have produced mixed results. The correlation with the 11-yr cycle may be positive (maximum mean temperatures at sunspot maximum) or negative, depending on the geographic region and time span of the data base. Köppen (1914), for example, utilized long-term temperature data collected from all available sources in the world to show that, for the years 1804–1910, the global mean annual temperature was lower at sunspot maximum than at sunspot minimum. This negative correlation held true in subsets of the data organized into tropical and north and south extratropical regions, and it verified his earlier findings (Köppen, 1873). Walker (1915) found a similar negative correlation. According to Clayton (1923), "Köppen's results have been confirmed by a number of investigators and are now generally accepted," an opinion shared years later by Craig and Willett (1951). On a scale of centuries, however, global temperatures appear to have a positive correlation, wherein extended cold periods coincide with minimum sunspot activity (Eddy, 1976).

Further general confirmation of the historical finding of a negative correlation with the 11-yr cycle is available. Global annual mean temperatures for 1880–1968, which includes years overlapping Köppen's (1914) data base, are plotted in figure 3.6, with years of sunspot maximum and minimum indicated by arrows. For later discussion, sunspot numbers averaged over 11-yr cycles centered at cycle maximum year are included. In almost every case, minimum temperatures occur at or quite near solar maximum years, and vice versa. The worst ex-

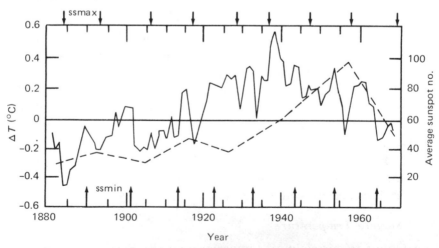

Figure 3.6. Northern hemisphere annual mean temperatures for 1880–1968 (solid line), compared to 11-yr mean of annual sunspot numbers plotted on center (maximum) year (broken line). Years of ssmax are indicated by arrows at top, ssmin years by arrows at bottom. From Budyko (1969) and National Academy of Sciences (1975, p. 148).

ceptions occur in the most recent data; the solar minimum of 1964 coincides with a temperature minimum rather than a maximum. This recent apparent reversal of correlation may be related to a longer-term trend in solar activity and is referred to again in section 3.3.1.

Clayton (1923) reanalyzed Köppen's data on the basis of annual and 5-yr running means of the departure from the average temperatures in equatorial, north temperate, and south temperate regions, with the results illustrated in figure 3.7. In the equatorial zone, based on data for 1804–1910, the range of temperature variation between sunspot maximum and minimum was about 0.4°C, with the minimum temperature occurring near the maximum of the 11-yr solar cycle. The annual mean departure has a range of slightly more than 0.5°C. In the north temperate zone (also data for 1804–1910), the negative correlation is quite clear, and the 5-yr running mean departure from sunspot maximum to sunspot minimum is about 0.2°C (0.4°C in the annual means). In the south temperate zone, based on a shorter data base (1841–1910), the range is about 0.3°C. It can be seen in figure 3.6 that the fluctuations of northern hemisphere annual mean temperatures between successive sunspot maxima and minima have a range of about 0.3°–0.4°C, similar to Köppen's results.

Spectral analysis of annual mean temperature data spanning 84 yr to 1968 from 226 stations (10 in North America) has revealed a somewhat smaller amplitude of 0.1°C (Currie, 1974), but the associated cyclical period was 10.6 ± 0.3 yr, in agreement with the shorter 11-yr sunspot cycle for this century. However, even a 0.1°C temperature change is sufficient to cause major climate changes in some borderline regions of the Earth if there is also a north-south temperature gradient (Bryson, 1974).

Currie's (1974) maximum entropy spectral analysis results support the earlier work of Landsberg et al. (1959), who had found spectral peaks at 2, 5, and 11 yr in the temperature data at Woodstock College in Maryland. Landsberg and Kaylor (1977) subjected Tokyo (direct and indirect) temperature data spanning the years 1443–1970 to both maximum entropy spectral analysis and fast Fourier transform (FFT) analysis, and obtained "quite consistent values" between the two types of analysis. Notable periodic peaks were found in the spectral intervals of 2.0–2.2, 2.7–3.0, 5–6, 8–12, 18–23, and >80 yr, with center periods of 2.1, 2.85, 5.5, 10, 20.5, and >80 yr. A similar analysis of Eastern United States winter temperatures showed peaks near

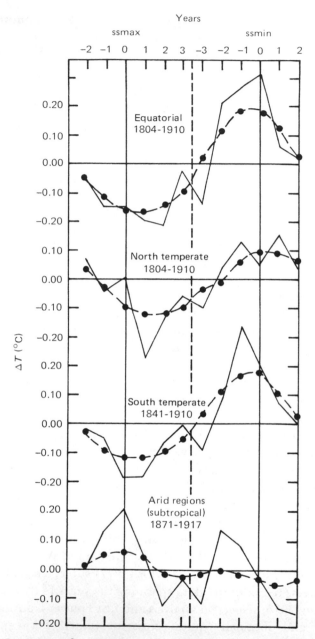

Figure 3.7. Departures of temperature from normal for different regions of the globe in sunspot maximum and minimum years. Solid line, annual mean; broken curve, 5-yr weighted running mean. The curves are slightly discontinuous between the ssmax and ssmin portions. From Clayton (1923).

3, 5, 11, and 22 yr, although the two latter peaks associated with sunspot cycle lengths were less prominent (Landsberg and Kaylor, 1976). Also, Mason (1976b) used central England monthly mean temperatures for 1659-1973 and found prominent spectral peaks at 2.1, 3.1, 5.1, 14.5, 23, and 76 yr.

Shaw (1965), on the other hand, used the Blackman and Tukey (1958) method of power spectrum analysis on 12-mo running averages of temperatures in New York City (years 1822-1956), central England (1698-1955), and the Netherlands (1735-1944) and found no periodicities that could be related to the solar cycle. A critical discussion of the application of spectrum analysis to geophysical data by Anderson and Koopmans (1963) and Brier (1961) indicates that spectral peaks of random noise (e.g., round-off and measurement errors) in the data superimposed on the phenomenological peaks of interest commonly lead to a flat spectrum, and physically significant peaks are often missed in this type of analysis. Also, in a rebuttal to Shaw's (1965) paper, Mitchell and Landsberg (1966) used the same New York City data (summer period) and included cross-spectrum analysis in addition to the simple power spectrums employed by Shaw to show that meaningful spectral peaks do emerge. (The Mitchell-Landsberg work may help to satisfy the call by Gerety et al. (1977) for more cross-spectrum analyses.) Considering the additional evidence, especially the recent findings of Currie (1974), Mason (1976), and Landsberg and Kaylor (1977), it appears that Shaw's (1965) conclusion that an 11-yr relationship between sunspots and temperature does not exist has not been proven.

In arid regions the temperature correlation with sunspots was found to reverse (bottom curve of fig. 3.7), and the range was about 0.1°C between maximum and minimum sunspot years. This reversal led Clayton (1923) to conclude that rainfall is an important element in determining the inverse correlation found in tropical and temperate latitudes. Without the rainfall in those regions, the temperature would probably be higher at sunspot maximum than minimum.

For specific locations, a positive correlation for annual temperatures and sunspots was found at only 18 stations (not specified) by Shaw (1928), and the largest coefficient was + .27 at Auckland, New Zealand. Auckland is not, however, in an arid region. Similarly, King et al. (1974) showed a positive correlation at London over two complete 11-yr cycles (1938-1958), as is evident in figure 3.8. On the

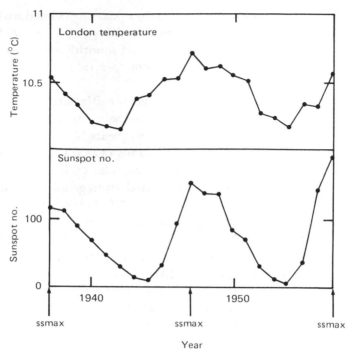

Figure 3.8. Five-year running mean of annual mean temperatures at London compared to annual mean sunspot number. From King et al. (1974).

other hand, a negative correlation, in agreement with the results of Köppen (1914) and Clayton (1923), was found at 76 stations, the largest being $-.58$ at Pelotas, Brazil. Seventeen stations had negative correlation coefficients of $-.3$ or greater (table 3.3). Insufficient data are available to determine the statistical significance of the reported correlations.

In addition to variations in temperature with the 11-yr cycle (and the 22-yr cycle as discussed in sec. 3.2), there are longer-term fluctuations that appear to be associated with solar activity. In the hemispheric temperature data plotted in figure 3.6 for the years 1880–1968, there was a warming trend from about 1880 to 1940, followed by a cooling trend to the end of the curve in 1968. This behavior could be evidence of a 90-yr cycle as envisioned by Mitchell (1965). The total range of increase in annual departures from the mean temperature between 1884 and 1938 is more than 1°C; discounting the extrema gives a range of about 0.5°C, the same order as found for

Table 3.3.—*Correlation Between Annual Temperatures and Sunspot Number (from Shaw, 1928)*

Station	Geographical Location		Correlation Coefficient
Auckland, New Zealand	36.5°S	174.5°E	+ .27
Pelotas, Brazil	31.5°S	52.2°W	− .58
Recife, Brazil	8.1°S	34.6°W	− .45
Winnipeg, Canada	49.6°N	97.1°W	− .55
Agra, India	27.2°N	78°E	− .43
Brisbane, Australia	27.3°S	153.1°E	− .42
Calcutta, India	22.3°N	88.2°E	− .44
Hong Kong	22.2°N	114.2°E	− .45
Sydney, Australia	33.6°S	151.2°E	− .49
Victoria, Canada	48.3°N	123.3°W	− .3 to − .4
Tashkent, USSR	41.2°N	69°E	− .3 to − .4
Newcastle, Jamaica	18°N	77°W	− .3 to − .4
Santiago, Chile	33.3°S	70.4°W	− .3 to − .4
Baghdad, Iraq	33.1°N	44.2°E	− .3 to − .4
Batavia, Illinois, USA	41.5°N	88.2°W	− .3 to − .4
Bombay, India	18.6°N	72.5°E	− .3 to − .4
Cordoba, Argentina	30.2°S	64°W	− .3 to − .4
Yakutsk, USSR	62.1°N	129.5°E	− .3 to − .4
Sydney, Canada	46.1°N	60.1°W	− .3 to − .4

11-yr excursions. There appears to be an antiphase relationship between the warming/cooling trend and the 11-yr averages of sunspot number, although this is an arguable point. If true, however, it would imply a negative (or at least a negative lag) correlation between solar activity and temperature over the secular span from 1880 to 1968. On the other hand, since the long-term temperature peak in 1940 precedes the peak in sunspot number in 1958 by 18 yr, it could well be suspected that there is no relationship between the two variables. Before accepting such a suspicion as fact, longer-term data should be considered.

The findings of Eddy (1976) are a case in point. His masterful argument leaves little room to doubt the reality of the "Grand Maximum" period of sunspot activity spanning the years 1100–1250 AD or the Spörer and Maunder minimums in 1460–1550 and 1645–1715, respectively (see sec. 2.1). But what is their importance to the present

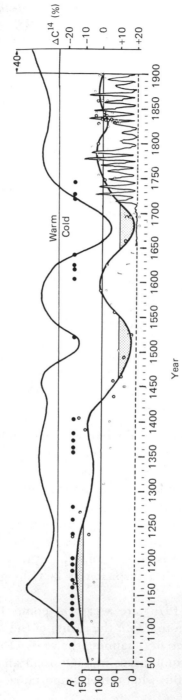

Figure 3.9. Relationship between winter severity in Paris and London (top curve) and long-term sunspot variations as reproduced from figure 2.3. The winter severity index is shifted 40 yr to the right to allow for cosmic-ray-produced C^{14} assimilation into tree rings (see p. 18). From Eddy (1976, 1977).

subject? The Maunder minimum coincides exactly in time with the coldest part of the "Little Ice Age" in the seventeenth century, and the Spörer minimum coincides with its second coldest dip in the fifteenth century (fig. 3.9). The Little Ice Age is generally considered to span the years 1430–1850, based on temperature and related data from North America and Western Europe (National Academy of Sciences, 1975). It was a time of glacial advances and retreats in the Alps, Scandinavia, and Iceland (Brooks, 1951). The prolonged period of maximum sunspot activity occurred at about the same time as the warm climatic optimum of the twelfth and thirteenth centuries when Greenland was settled and wine grapes grew in England (Lamb, 1972).

Analysis of Tokyo winter temperatures for 1443–1970 by Landsberg and Kaylor (1977) showed the coldest period to be between 1489 and 1528, which is within the time frame of the Spörer minimum. However, no notable variation was found during the Maunder sunspot minimum. These results suggest a positive correlation between sunspot number and temperature, and thereby argue against the negative correlations with the 11-yr cycles found for more recent times. The lack of notably cold Tokyo temperatures during the Maunder minimum underscores the frustrations of trying to find unambiguous relationships between sunspots and climate. (Differences in regional responses to solar activity may be partly responsible for the contradictory state of affairs in this subject.)

3.1.4 Indirect Indicators of Temperature

In this section we summarize investigations of indirect measurements of temperature and their correlation with secular changes in solar activity. The indicators are the amount of ice in high latitudes (which is also dependent on precipitation), the number of icebergs seen in the Antarctic Ocean, and growing season. Observations of the number of months per year that ice was present on the coast of Iceland for the period 1791–1906 were analyzed by Clayton (1923) for 11-yr solar cycle influence. Using annual and 5-yr running means he showed (fig. 3.10) that the average number of months for ice on Icelandic shores was 2.4 near sunspot maximum and 2.0 near minimum. The annual mean (curve c) shows greater variability, but still suggests more ice at solar maximum than at minimum. Since one can expect the ice to be present longer in cooler years, Clayton's result

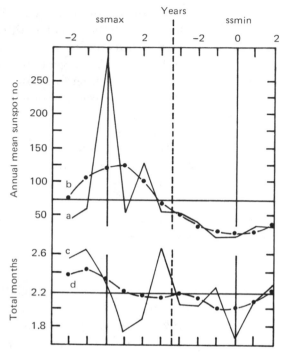

Figure 3.10. Mean annual number (curve a) and 5-yr running mean of means (curve b) of icebergs sighted in Antarctic waters for the period 1890–1912 in years of sunspot maximum and minimum. Mean number of months ice present on Iceland coast per annum (curve c), and 5-yr running mean of months (curve d), based on the period 1791–1906. The curves are discontinuous between the ssmax and ssmin portions. From Clayton (1923).

implies a negative correlation between surface temperature and sunspot number. It would be interesting to pursue this idea further with satellite data.

Although the data on iceberg sightings cover a relatively short period of time (1890–1912), there is a suggestion of a positive correlation between the annual number of icebergs in the Antarctic Ocean and sunspot cycle (fig. 3.10). One must be cautious with this sort of data, because it may be only an indication that more ships operated in Antarctic waters during solar maximum years than minimum years for an entirely unrelated reason. Further, because of the many factors that influence the number of icebergs (e.g., ocean temperature, age and condition of the parent ice), this finding of a possible response to solar activity serves as a good example of a misleading correlation.

King (1973) defined growing season as that portion of the year in which the air temperature 0.25 m above ground exceeds 5.6°C. His analysis of Gloyne's (1973) data for Eskdalemuir, Scotland over the years 1914–1971 indicates that the growing season tends to be longest about 1 yr after solar maximum and is about 25 days longer than in years near solar minimum. The season length depends almost entirely on the beginning date in spring rather than the ending date in autumn, with the implication that the solar cycle influences spring temperatures much more than those in autumn. How this relates to annual mean temperature is not readily apparent, but it is plausible to assume that the latter would tend to be higher in years with long growing seasons. If so, it would appear that the correlation of annual mean temperature with sunspot cycle at Eskdalemuir is positive, as it is in (fairly) nearby Kew, England, and these two locations are anomalous with respect to the trend of northern hemispheric annual mean temperatures.

3.1.5 Atmospheric Pressure

Direct correlations of sunspot cycle and surface atmospheric pressure at specific locations were made mostly in the first decades of this century. It was argued quite early (e.g., Hanzlik, 1931) that the effects of solar activity on weather might be more visibly manifest in variations of pressure systems, their intensities, locations, and the winds generated by them. This section therefore summarizes the direct correlations to establish historical perspective, and the next section (3.1.6) treats the dynamic effects of the pressure variations.

To analyze long-term solar effects on surface pressure, Clayton (1923) utilized 5-yr running means to cancel out shorter-term variations caused by other complex meteorological variables. The data base used, from 1858 to 1920, included 6 sunspot maximum years and 5 minimum years. From the difference between 5-yr means at sunspot maximum and sunspot minimum, global distributions of average pressure variation were obtained for annual, summer (June–August), and winter (December–February) periods, as illustrated in figure 3.11. The contour lines are in steps of 0.5 mb, and positive differences (higher pressure at sunspot maximum) are shaded in the figure.

Several general features of these distributions are of interest. For example, when the number of sunspots is greater, there is a tendency

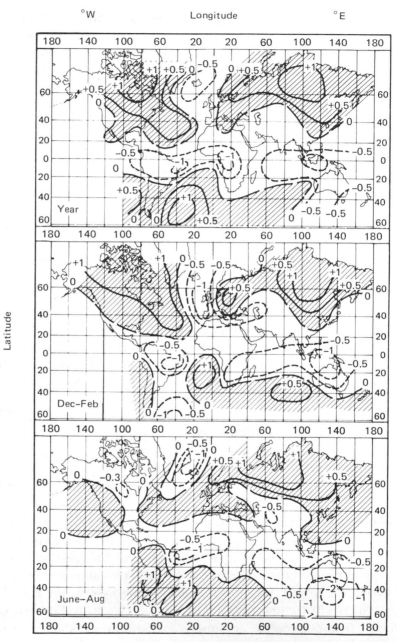

Figure 3.11. Distribution of mean pressure differences between sunspot maximum and sunspot minimum for the whole year (top), December–February (middle), and June–August (bottom). Contours are spaced at 0.5 mb, and positive differences (higher pressure at ssmax) are shaded. From Clayton (1923).

for the pressure to be high over the continents in local winter (December–February, northern hemisphere; June–August, southern hemisphere) and over the oceans in summer. On an annual basis (top map) a positive difference is found over the continents poleward of about 20° latitude and a negative difference over equatorial latitudes. In the annual averages, the decrease in pressure at sunspot maximum is especially noticeable in humid regions of the Earth, such as the area north of Australia, the Gold Coast of Africa, and northeastern Brazil. The behavior in regions of particular meteorological importance should be noted: the "semipermanent" low-pressure region in the vicinity of Iceland tends to have lower pressure at sunspot maximum than in sunspot minimum annually and in each season. The "semipermanent Aleutian low" (roughly centered at 55°N, 180°E) was not adequately covered by observations in those early years. Pressure in the "semipermanent Bermuda high" (mid-Atlantic region about 30°N) is higher during sunspot maximum than sunspot minimum both annually and seasonally.

The correlation between annual sunspot number and annual average surface pressure was computed by Shaw (1928) for 87 locations. A positive correlation (higher pressure at sunspot maximum) was found for 39 stations, the 10 highest of which ($>+.24$) are listed in table 3.4. The remaining 48 stations had negative correlations, 15 of which were greater than $-.27$ (table 3.4). Again, the statistical significance of these correlations cannot be ascertained, but they are obviously weak and imply pressure control dominated by influences other than sunspot number. There is generally good agreement between these results and Clayton's annual distribution in figure 3.11. The only two exceptions, Para and Blumenau, Brazil, are both located near a dividing line between excess and deficient pressures at sunspot maximum across the South American continent; thus on a global scale this discrepancy is not serious.

It is evident in the global distributions of pressure differences (fig. 3.11) that there is a general tendency for the pressure to be lower at sunspot maximum in equatorial latitudes and higher in temperate latitudes. This tendency is clearly evident in figure 3.12 for the annual pressure difference in both northern and southern hemispheres. The higher average pressure in sunspot maximum years at high latitude was also noted by Wexler (1950), and it suggests a mass displacement of air toward the higher latitudes in years of high solar activity, as concluded by Willett (1965).

Table 3.4.—Correlation Between Annual Sunspot Number and Surface Atmospheric Pressure (from Shaw, 1928)

Station	Geographical Location		Correlation Coefficient	Agreement with fig. 3.17
Pelotas, Brazil	31.5°S	52.2°W	+ .36	Yes
Santiago, Chile	33.3°S	70.4°W	+ .35	Yes
Galveston, Texas, USA	29.2°N	94.5°W	+ .30	Yes
Honolulu, Hawaii, USA	21.2°N	158.0°W	+ .24 to + .30	No data
Sydney, Canada	46.1°N	60.1°W	+ .24 to + .30	Yes
Albany, New York, USA	42.4°N	73.5°W	+ .24 to + .30	Yes
Ekaterinburg, USSR	56.5°N	60.4°E	+ .24 to + .30	Yes
Hong Kong	22.2°N	114.2°E	+ .24 to + .30	Yes
Para, Brazil	20.2°S	44.4°W	+ .24 to + .30	No
Buenos Aires, Argentina	34.2°S	58.3°W	+ .24 to + .30	Yes
Capetown, South Africa	33.5°S	18.3°E	− .47	Yes
Zanzibar, Tanzania	6.1°S	39.1°E	− .46	Yes
Blumenau, Brazil	26.5°S	48.6°W	− .43	No
Bombay, India	18.6°N	72.5°E	− .27 to − .38	Yes
Calcutta, India	22.3°N	88.2°E	− .27 to − .38	Yes
Madras, India	13.1°N	80.2°E	− .27 to − .38	Yes
Colombo, Sri Lanka	6.6°N	79.5°E	− .27 to − .38	Yes
Leh, India	34.1°N	77.4°E	− .27 to − .38	Yes
Port Darwin, Australia	12.3°S	131.0°E	− .27 to − .38	Yes
Rio de Janiero, Brazil	22.5°S	43.2°W	− .27 to − .38	Yes
Brisbane, Australia	27.3°S	153.1°E	− .27 to − .38	Yes
Adelaide, Australia	34.5°S	139.1°E	− .27 to − .38	Yes
Alice Springs, Australia	23.4°S	133.6°E	− .27 to − .38	Yes
Batavia, Illinois, USA	41.5°N	88.2°W	− .27 to − .38	Yes
Derby, West Africa	25.6°S	27.2°E	− .27 to − .38	Yes

Above 40° latitude (fig. 3.12), the pressure difference exhibits a minimum in local winter in both northern (December–February) and southern (June–August) hemispheres, which means that the pressure is less at sunspot maximum than at sunspot minimum in this region. The identification of this latitudinally narrow minimum, centered at about 55°N in the northern hemisphere, is an important result because its existence implies that low-pressure troughs can develop more often in years of high solar activity. It anticipates by half a century the findings of Roberts and Olson (1973a,b), which are discussed in section 4.2.3.

The puzzling tendency for atmospheric pressure to be positively correlated with the 11-yr sunspot cycle in some geographic areas and negatively correlated in others is now recognized to be in part a mani-

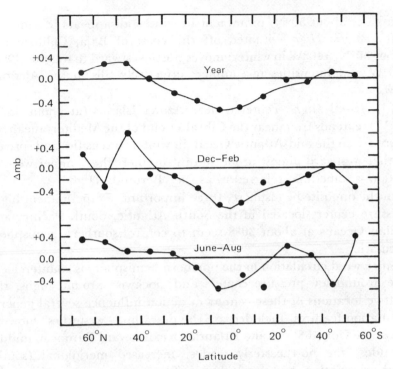

Figure 3.12. Latitudinal dependence of mean pressure difference between sunspot maximum and sunspot minimum. From Clayton (1923).

festation of standing planetary waves (King et al., 1977). Details of this important new result are discussed in section 6.1.1 in connection with an intriguing causal mechanism proffered by Volland (1977a,b).

3.1.6 Pressure Systems and Winds

The general circulation of the atmosphere is controlled largely by "centers of action," or large semipermanent high- and low-pressure belts distributed around the Earth. Among the most important of these in the northern hemisphere are the following:

(a) *Icelandic Low*—situated over Iceland, southern tip of Greenland, and extending to the Canadian Arctic over Baffin Island; with some variation in intensity, extent, and location of center, it persists year round.

(b) *Aleutian Low*—centered over tip of Aleutian Islands between the east coast of the Siberian Kamchatka Peninsula and the Gulf of

Alaska at about 50°N; prominent in winter, disappears in summer.

(c) *Pacific High* — situated off the coast of Baja, California at about 30°N, 140°W in winter; moves northwestward to roughly 40°N, 150°W and intensifies in summer; effectively fills in the Aleutian Low.

(d) *Azores High* — centered near Azores Islands (at about 35°N, 25°W), extends from near the Gibralter end of the Mediterranean Sea westward to the mid-Atlantic Ocean in winter; intensifies and spreads further westward almost to Florida in summer (the summer western section is sometimes referred to as the "Bermuda High").

In the opposite hemisphere, three important semipermanent high-pressure centers located in the South Atlantic, South Pacific, and Indian Oceans at about 30°S seem to control southern hemisphere circulation.

Since wind circulation in the northern hemisphere is counterclockwise around low-pressure centers and clockwise around highs, the relative locations of these centers of action influence several general circulation features. Included are the prevailing "westerlies" blowing across the United States and Atlantic Ocean toward Europe in middle latitudes, the northeasterly trades, increased meridional (south-north) circulation, and development of low-pressure troughs near the Aleutian and/or Icelandic Lows.

Apart from normal seasonal variations in the centers of action, there is some evidence for additional, long-term fluctuations. Directly addressing the Aleutian and Icelandic Lows and the Azores and Pacific Highs, Angell and Korshover (1974) utilized pressure maps from 1899 to 1967 to investigate long-term fluctuations in their latitude, longitude, and intensity.

There was a slight indication (not statistically significant, according to Angell and Korshover) that the west longitudinal edge of all four centers of action were farther west at sunspot minimum than at sunspot maximum. The latitude of the Aleutian Low was found to be higher at sunspot minimum than at sunspot maximum, a finding that was statistically significant (correlation of $-.24$ with a 95% confidence level). Other than this, Angell and Korshover felt that "from a purely statistical point of view, there is no convincing evidence of a relationship between sunspot number and location or pressure of centers of action."

However, their results showed that both the Azores High and the Icelandic Low gradually migrated northward between 1889 and 1940

and then began moving southward and eastward. This pattern parallels the behavior of northern hemisphere annual mean temperatures
during the same time span (see fig. 3.6), which may be an indication
of an association with the 80- or 100-yr secular trend in solar activity.

The secular migration of the Icelandic Low has been observed in a
different way and over a longer time span than the above, by Mitchell
(1965). Mitchell utilized data from Lamb (1963) to show how the
40-yr running-mean longitude of the semipermanent low-pressure
trough at 55°N (the Icelandic Low) varied with time from about 1780
to 1959, as illustrated in figure 3.13. This result, unfortunately, is not
directly comparable to that of Angell and Korshover (1974) because
of the 40-yr running mean and the fixed latitude reference. The
trough at 55°N gradually shifted eastward (fig. 3.13) from about 1889
to 1939 and then began moving westward. The time of reversal agrees
with that of Angell and Korshover, and, according to Mitchell, the
trend is evidence for a secular solar cycle influence with an 80- or

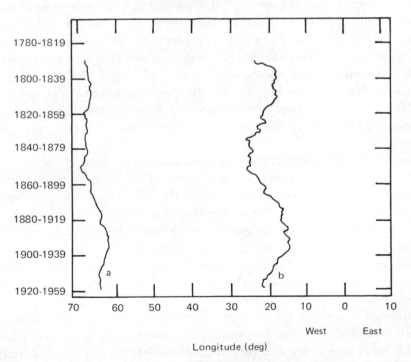

*Figure 3.13. Longitudes of semipermanent surface pressure trough (curve a) and
high-pressure ridge (curve b) in July in the Atlantic sector at 55°N, based on 40-yr
running means from about 1780 to 1959. From Mitchell (1965).*

111

90-yr period. King (1974) noted the same westward shift between 1933 and 1951 in the 300-, 500-, and 700-mb trough data of Palmen and Newton (1969). King related this long-term variation to the westward drift of the Earth's magnetic pole. A similar periodicity is observable in the longitude of the ridge of high pressure off the Atlantic coast of Europe at 55°N (fig. 3.13). This ridge is associated with the Azores High further south.

On a shorter-term scale, Bradley (1973) investigated the western portion of the Icelandic Low extending over northern Canada. For July only, average pressure contour maps were prepared for the two periods 1955–1963 and 1964–1972. The first of these two periods had an average sunspot number of 105, and the second had 63; sunspot activity for the maximum year 1958 was nearly twice as great as that in the maximum year 1969. In the earlier period the July mean map was dominated by a trough of low pressure over Baffin Bay and southern Baffin Island just north of Frobisher Bay; the trough center was at approximately 65°N, 60°W. In the latter period, when solar activity was less on the average, the low was displaced northward and westward, and its center was at about 80°N, 86°W, north of Resolute Bay. This 1500-km westward displacement from periods of high (1955–1963) to lower (1964–1972) solar activity is in agreement with the aforementioned indication noted by Angell and Korshover (1974). Bradley also noted that the pressure gradients across the Canadian Archipelago were much stronger in the lower-activity years, implying increased movement of air across the region from the north.

As mentioned earlier, the clockwise circulation around the Azores High produces northeasterly trade winds. This wind system may extend all the way to the eastern end of the Mediterranean Sea, especially in summer, when the Azores High has its greatest intensity and extent. Etesian winds belong to the same system and are a prominent feature of the summer weather pattern in Greece. The occurrence frequency (number of days per year) of Etesian wind in Athens shows a remarkable correlation with the 11-yr sunspot cycle (Carapiperis, 1962). This is evident in figure 3.14, in which the occurrence frequency for the years 1891–1961 is compared with annual sunspot number. Maximum and minimum Etesian wind occurrences coincide with solar maximum and minimum in almost every case. The only exception occurred in the early 1920s, when the wind minimum lagged the solar minimum by about 2 yr. Also discernible in figure

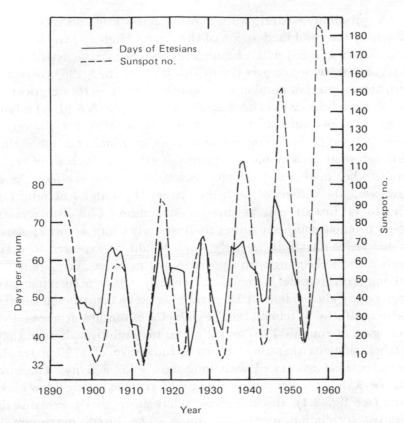

Figure 3.14. Annual occurrence frequency of Etesian winds in Athens for the period 1891–1961. From Carapiperis (1962).

3.14 is a longer-term trend wherein the occurrence frequency increases from about 1900 to the middle or late 1940s and then falls off again.

The cross-correlation coefficient between Etesian wind annual occurrence and annual sunspot number is approximately $+.6$, significant to a confidence level greater than 99.9% according to the standard z test (Mendenhall and Scheaffer, 1973, p. 421). From this behavior of Etesian winds as a function of sunspot number one might infer that the Azores High is more intense and extensive or that its center is further east in solar maximum years than it is in minimum years. The latter inference favors the indication found by Angell and Korshover (1974) that the longitude of the Azores High is displaced westward at sunspot minimum.

113

The prevailing westerly wind blowing across England is controlled largely by the combined action of the Azores High and the Icelandic Low. Lamb's (1965) data of annual occurrence frequency (days per year) of westerly winds over the British Isles for 1873–1963 correlated with annual sunspot number gives a coefficient of $-.18$, significant at the 90% confidence level because the data sample ($N = 91$ yr) is fairly large. This low but statistically significant negative correlation between westerlies over England and sunspot number implies that, although solar activity has a measurable effect on such wind occurrence, other meteorological processes have a greater effect. As we have seen, the centers of both the Azores High and Icelandic Low tend to lie further east at sunspot maximum. This displacement would promote southerly rather than westerly winds across England, so that fewer days with westerly winds would be expected in maximum years, in keeping with the computed negative correlation.

Long-term (secular) trends in westerly wind occurrence over England are also evident. A 10-yr running mean constructed through Lamb's data by Mitchell (1965) exhibits a minimum at about 1880 and again at roughly 1960 and a broad maximum peak near 1920. Mitchell suggests that the pattern is indicative of a 90-yr secular trend, possibly associated with long-term solar activity. The circa 1920 peak, however, occurs around an 11-yr cycle having a low maximum (see fig. 2.1); this antiphase relationship partly explains the negative correlation mentioned above. The broad maximum in occurrence frequency in the 1920s agrees with the closest approach to England of the high-pressure ridge in the North Atlantic (fig. 3.13), whereas the 1880s minimum corresponds to a more westerly position of the ridge at that time.

3.1.7 Storm Tracks

In addition to the semipermanent centers of action governing the general circulation, there are transient low- and high-pressure systems (cyclones and anticyclones, respectively) which may move over considerable distances and persist for up to several weeks. The storm tracks followed by these systems are influenced by the centers of action (Brown and John, 1977), and, if the positions of these centers are affected by solar activity as suggested in the previous section (3.1.6), one might expect that the storm tracks would vary with the sunspot cycle. That they well may is demonstrated in this section.

There is evidence that some low-pressure storm systems may circle the globe in approximately 1 week. In the northern hemisphere the cyclones tend to travel in a more or less eastward direction, guided by the circumpolar jet stream. They are generally responsible for the stormy weather (especially in winter) in northern middle to high latitudes, and their travel is confined to a latitude band of approximately 30°-60°. The polar jet stream meanders eastward within this band. Details of the formation of the lows (cyclogenesis) and highs (anticyclogenesis) are beyond the scope of this book, but may be found in a good meteorology textbook (e.g., Donn, 1965).

The prevailing cyclonic storm tracks across the North Atlantic Ocean tend to be displaced equatorward during periods of high sunspots (Helland-Hansen and Nansen, 1920; Kullmer, 1933), which presumably indicates either that the guiding circumpolar jet stream is further south as well, or that there are larger-amplitude excursions of the circumpolar vortex. Brown and John (1977) found "a clear solar cycle dependence" in the mean latitude of surface depressions crossing a given longitude in the northeast Atlantic Ocean/northwest Europe sector during the winter months in the last five solar cycles. The average track crossing in the North Sea area is some 3° further southward at sunspot maximum compared to sunspot minimum, in full agreement with the historical conclusions of Helland-Hansen and Nansen, and Kullmer.

In the southern hemisphere, particularly Australia, stormy weather is produced by cyclones moving eastward across the continent toward New Zealand. In winter and spring the mean monthly tracks tend to lie further north (about 30°-35°S) than in summer and autumn (35°-40°S). The yearly latitudinal range of the tracks seems to vary in phase with the 11-yr solar cycle, being smaller than normal in sunspot minimum years and greater in sunspot maximum years (Kidson, 1925). Three-year means of the range deviations from normal over the 30-yr interval 1891-1921, illustrated in figure 3.15, clearly show maxima centered around the sunspot maximum years of 1893, 1906, and 1917. The relationship held true when the analysis was extended to the 1950s (Bowen, 1975). These results seem to imply that the cyclone tracks extend farther north (that is, equatorward) during sunspot maximum years, but further investigation of Kidson's work is needed to verify the implication. If true, it indicates that storm tracks in both northern and southern middle latitudes are displaced equatorward in sunspot maximum years. There is some indication of a 40-yr component in the latitudinal variation of storm tracks (Kullmer, 1943), which might be indicative of a 20-yr variation in the amplitude of the storm track 11-yr oscillations.

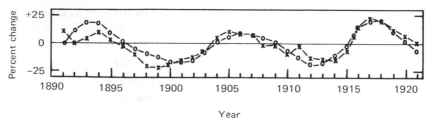

Figure 3.15. Departures of annual latitudinal range of anticyclones moving across Australia from generally west to east from normal range between 1891 and 1921. Data points: circles are 3-yr running means of range departures; x's are proportional to sunspot number. From Kidson (1925) and Bowen (1975).

According to Brown and John (1977), these storm track variations with respect to solar cycle may explain some of the conflicting "latitude effects" in rainfall that have been reported (see sec. 3.1.1).

Regarding the number of cyclonic storms generated with respect to solar cycle, Kullmer (1917) showed that the occurrence frequency of such storms in the northern and southern portions of the United States is greater in sunspot maximum years than in sunspot minimum years. In the central United States, however, the correlation is reversed.

A more recent study of cyclonic event occurrence in the United States and the entire North American continent (Reitan, 1974) for years 1951–1970 can be used to establish solar cycle influence, except that regional behavior in the United States is not available to compare with Kullmer's results.

Reitan counted the number of cyclonic events occurring in the months of January, April, July, and October for each year (1951–1970). He defined a cyclonic event as the passage of a cyclonic center (a low-pressure system lasting at least 24 hr) through a prescribed area. Each area is a rather small square, 740 km on a side; thus a large number of cyclones counted in a month can mean either more cyclones or a longer storm track for individual centers. The total number per year for the North American continent in all four months is shown in figure 3.16, along with the total for the United States. Comparing these curves with the sunspot number curves of figure 2.1, there appears to be an inverse correlation. Either appearances or statistical correlations can be deceiving, however, because, although the total occurrence curve has maxima near the sunspot minimum years of 1954 and 1964 and minima near the 1958 and 1969 solar maxima, the computed correlation coefficient of only −.05 indicates that the two phenomena are not correlated. Better

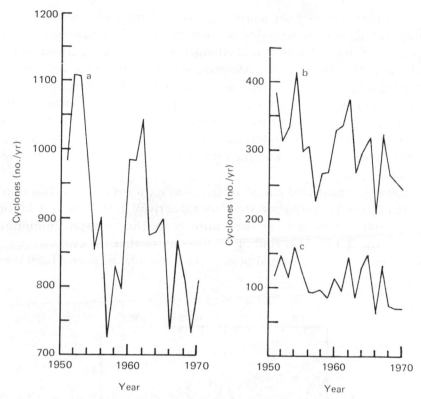

Figure 3.16. Number of cyclonic events per year counted by Reitan (1974) for the North American continent summed over the months January, April, July, and October (curve a), for the United States sector summed over the same four months (curve b), and for the United States in January only (curve c).

results obtain when only the United States sector total is considered; both visually and statistically the cyclone occurrence frequency is lower in sunspot maximum years than in sunspot minimum years (correlation coefficient −.42, with a confidence level of 94%).

To test for any effect of the 22-yr solar cycle, the data were separated into the positive years (1955–1964) and negative years (1951–1954 and 1965–1970); the correlation coefficients are −.49 and −.46, respectively. Thus there was no apparent 22-yr periodicity in occurrence frequency of cyclonic events in the United States.

The results of this exercise lead to the conclusion that, in the United States, fewer cyclonic storms occur in sunspot maximum years compared to sunspot minimum years. The possible significance of this in relation to the studies of Roberts and Olson (1973a,b) is examined in section 4.2.3.

Another way to study storm activity at remote distances over the oceans is through observation of "meteorological microseisms" (Zatopek and Krivsky, 1974). Rapid changes in the pressure patterns in the circumpolar caps and the associated activity at the polar front penetrating down to 40° latitude and less in the northern hemisphere are closely correlated with microseisms. In the European area microseisms are observed principally in winter and are believed to be caused by large-scale circulation features in the North Atlantic Ocean frontal zone between the low- and high-pressure ridges discussed in the previous section.

Zatopek and Krivsky used microseism data over almost two solar cycles (1948–1966) to show that frontal activity in the North Atlantic is greater during sunspot maximum years than sunspot minimum years (fig. 3.17). This finding is opposite to that for cyclonic event occurrence over the United States sector; on a hemispheric basis they

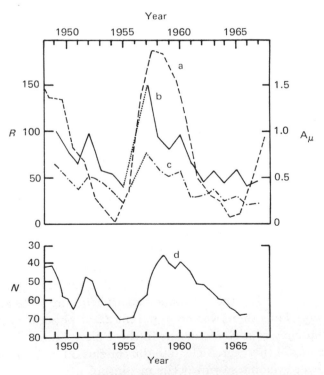

Figure 3.17. Comparison of microseism activity with solar activity and cosmic ray intensity. Curve a, sunspot number R; b, maximum smoothed microseismic amplitudes A_μ; c, annual mean microseismic amplitudes A_μ; d, cosmic ray intensity variation plotted on negative scale N. From Zatopek and Krivsky (1974).

would thus tend to cancel each other out, which might help to explain the lack of correlation between sunspot number and total cyclonic event occurrence found above.

For later investigation it should be pointed out that Zatopek and Krivsky suggested that the variations in microseism occurrence are more closely associated with variations in the intensity of cosmic rays than with sunspot number. Their argument for this association is discernible in figure 3.17. Note that, although microseismic activity is maximum in both sunspot peak years of 1948 and 1958 corresponding to minimum cosmic ray intensity, there is a secondary maximum in microseisms in 1951, corresponding to a secondary minimum in cosmic rays without a secondary maximum in sunspot number. To date, no physical mechanism to link cosmic radiation with North Atlantic frontal activity has been proffered, so additional study is required.

3.2 Correlations with the Hale 22-yr Solar Cycle

A significant number of studies indicate that some meteorological parameters correlate better with the double sunspot cycle than with the 11-yr cycle. The results of some of those studies are summarized in this section.

3.2.1 Rainfall

Although Clayton (1923) found that the rainfall annual total in Fortaleza, Brazil was positively correlated with the 11-yr sunspot cycle, more recent investigation of the data from 1865 forward seems to show that a better correlation was afforded by the 22-yr cycle (King, 1975). In figure 3.18 it can be seen that the annual total rainfall at Fortaleza varies in phase with the double cycle for the period plotted, and the modulation in rainfall amount is about 35% of the average annual total (King, 1975). After about 1925 the correlation changed phase; this is discussed in section 3.3.2.

Rainfall at three stations in South Africa in the region bounded by about 25.7°–28.2°S and 27.2°–30.3°E followed a 22-yr periodicity from 1910 to at least 1965, in phase with the double cycle (fig. 3.19). At these stations no phase reversal took place around 1925 as it did in Fortaleza.

The results of a study of rainfall characteristics at Adelaide, Australia (Cornish, 1936; 1954), show evidence of a dependence on the double sunspot cycle. The Cornish results, expressed as the date by which one-quarter of the annual total rainfall has fallen, have been shown

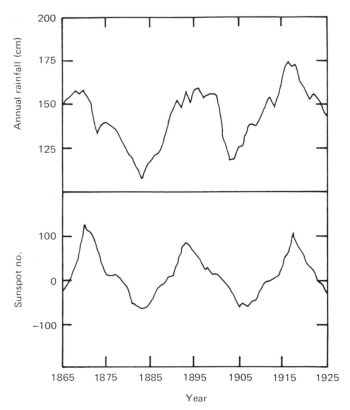

Figure 3.18. Smoothed annual total rainfall at Fortaleza, Brazil (4°S, 39°W) compared with the double sunspot cycle. From King (1975).

to be in antiphase with the double cycle (King, 1975), at least over the period 1844–1944. The earliest quartile date consistently fell in a year of minimum sunspot number following a maximum in the positive half of a Hale double cycle. For the southern hemisphere, e.g., along the south coastal region of Australia (34.6°S), rainfall in local autumn is negatively correlated with the 22-yr cycle. When the date for occurrence of the seventh octile (⅞ of the annual total) is considered, however, a marked deterioration of the correlation sets in near the year 1922 (discussed in sec. 3.3.2).

3.2.2 Droughts

Closely related to rainfall amounts is the occurrence of droughts. A drought is defined as a prolonged dry spell in a region in which rainfall or dewfall is normally expected but is absent or well below normal. The most celebrated drought regions in the United States are in

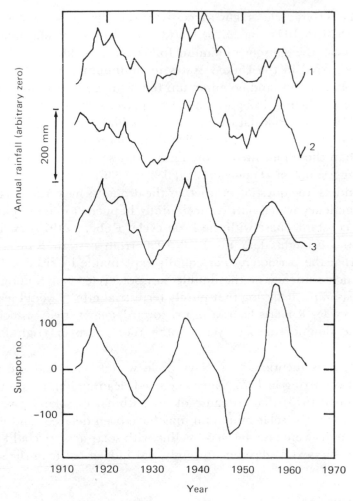

Figure 3.19. Smoothed annual total rainfall at three locations in South Africa compared with the double sunspot cycle. Curve 1, Rustenburg (26°S, 27°E); curve 2, Bethal (27°S, 30°E); curve 3, Dundee (28°S, 30°E). From King (1975).

the High Plains region and the midwestern states. The United States regions have been studied fairly extensively in relation to solar cycle, and Roberts (1975) recently reviewed the evidence for a connection between the two. Drawing on the works of others (Borchert, 1971; Marshall, 1972; Thompson, 1973), he showed that there has been a marked tendency for droughts to recur at intervals of 20–22 yr for the past century and a half in the High Plains region, and their occurrence has a constant phase with the Hale double sunspot cycle rather than the 11-yr cycle. Eight successive droughts in Nebraska from about 1820 to 1955 (fig. 3.20), as identified by tree ring data, occurred near the sunspot minimum following a negative maximum. None occurred in the United States in minimum years following a positive maximum, and no minimum following a negative maximum failed to produce a drought. The same pattern was evident in Marshall's (1972) rainfall data from the High Plains region (fig. 3.21), and there were no major, extensive droughts in the period studied other than those indicated in the figure. These findings support the early suggestions of Douglass (1919, 1928, 1936).

To address the question of whether the droughts have a 20-yr recurrence tendency which only coincidentally happens to be in approximately constant phase with the Hale cycle, Roberts (1975) analyzed additional drought data for 1850–1960 from eastern Kansas and found that the periodicity was equally explainable by either a 20-yr recurrence tendency or the double sunspot cycle. Not finding any good reason for believing that purely terrestrial effects would lead to a 20-yr cycle, Roberts leans a priori toward solar activity associated with the double sunspot cycle as the root cause of High Plains droughts.

As Roberts mentioned, a 21-yr cycle would have had the next drought occurring in 1973. None occurred, leading him to speculate (in October 1973) that, because of an outburst of solar activity in August 1972, the solar minimum may have been delayed, and if the next drought were also delayed, its link with solar activity could be a reality. The next Midwestern drought did indeed occur in the sum-

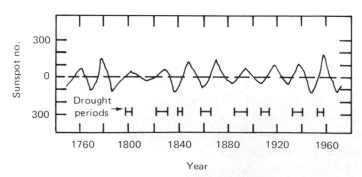

Figure 3.20. Occurrence of drought (from tree ring data) in western Nebraska compared to Hale 22-yr sunspot cycle. From Roberts (1975).

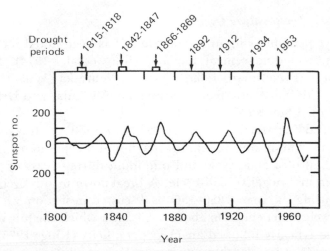

Figure 3.21. High Plains droughts (from rainfall data) compared to 22-yr sunspot cycle according to Marshall (1972). From Roberts (1975).

mer of 1974, followed by another in 1976 which continued into 1977, when the growing season rainfall was 40-90% below normal in the cornbelt region of the United States. Also in 1976, England and continental Europe suffered the severest drought in over 100 yr. As noted in chapter 2, the most recent sunspot minimum in the 11-yr cycle was not reached until 1976. These events strongly support an association between drought occurrence and the double sunspot cycle.

The most recent analysis of drought cycles in the United States and their relation to sunspots, as discussed by J. Murray Mitchell, Jr. at the IAGA/IAMAP conference in Seattle in 1977, provides still more evidence for a real connection. An annual index of the total area of the central and western United States that is affected by drought was derived by Mitchell et al. (1977) from tree ring data extending back to 1700. That index exhibits a strong cyclical behavior with a period averaging 22 yr in length, and various statistical tests have demonstrated a strong coherence with the Hale sunspot cycle. Mitchell concluded that "the consistency of these statistical relationships strongly implies a real causal connection between drought occurrence in the United States and long-term solar variability, that requires a physical explanation." He went on to predict tentatively that other continental regions of the world may show similar drought responses if the total area affected rather than the severity at individual stations is utilized for analyses.

3.2.3 22-Yr Temperature Cycles

A 22-yr periodicity in air temperatures has been noted for several locations, including central England (King et al., 1974), Boston, Massachusetts (Newman, 1965), Omaha, Nebraska (Willett, 1974), and the Middle Atlantic region (Maryland, Virginia, and Delaware) of the United States (Mather, 1974).

In central England during the period 1750–1880, the July temperature was maximum during years of maximum sunspot number in the positive half of a Hale cycle and minimum during years of sunspot maximum in a negative half-cycle. A breakdown in this cyclical behavior during the years 1830–1860 is discussed in section 3.3.1. The double-cycle effect ended in about 1880, after which the July temperatures more nearly followed an 11-yr periodicity (King, 1975).

The opposite relationship appears in Boston winter temperatures (Newman, 1965). That is, highest temperatures (average 3.8°C) were observed in the sunspot maximum years of a negative half-cycle and the lowest (2.7°C) in the peak years of a positive half-cycle. The variation in the variability of Boston winter temperature also showed a relationship with the 22-yr cycle. That is, extreme temperatures (both high and low) were found to be greatest in years marking sunspot minimum following a negative maximum.

In Omaha, Nebraska, the average summer temperatures (June, July, August) for the years 1871–1970 were nearly 1°C warmer at sunspot minimum following a negative maximum than at the minimum following a positive maximum. Since drought occurrences are marked by hot, dry temperatures, the cyclical behavior of the temperature at Omaha, in the cornbelt region, is consistent with the findings of Roberts (1975) and Mitchell et al. (1977) discussed in section 3.2.2.

3.2.4 Atmospheric Pressure

There is some evidence (Craig and Willett, 1951), based on early work by Hanzlik (1930, 1931), that long-term variations in global pressure patterns are more closely associated with the Hale double sunspot than with the 11-yr cycle. Decreasing zonal winds (e.g., westerlies in middle latitudes (35°–55°) of the northern hemisphere) associated with relatively higher pressures at high latitudes were observed near the maximum of a major (positive) half-cycle, and increasing zonal winds (low pressure at high latitudes) near the maximum of a negative half cycle.

Similar results have been found by the Russian investigators Maksimov and Slepcov-Sevlevic (1971), who reported that surface pressure is below average in high latitudes in maximum years of a negative half-cycle. The opposite pattern was found near sunspot maximum in positive half-cycles. These investigators also noted that the pressure at latitudes south of 40°N was above average in the maximum years of a negative half-cycle.

In a follow-up to the Maksimov and Slepcov-Sevlevic report, Miles (1974) analyzed the surface pressure at all available longitudes and latitudes 65°, 55°, and 45°N. For both 65°N and 55°N, the average pressure was higher at sunspot maximum in both positive and negative half-cycles and low at sunspot minimum; this behavior is characteristic of an 11- rather than a 22-yr periodicity. However, at 45°N latitude the annual average pressure for all longitudes was highest about 1 yr after sunspot maximum in a negative half-cycle, which is contrary to the Russian results.

Investigation of the pressure behavior in the neighborhood of the Icelandic Low (65°N, 40°W) by Miles (1974) revealed minimum pressure at sunspot maximum in a negative half-cycle, in agreement with the results of Maksimov and Slepcov-Sevlevic (1971) and Craig and Willett (1951). However, Miles felt that his results were only marginally statistically reliable.

It appears that if there is any solar influence on surface atmospheric pressures, it is manifested differently in different geographical regions and depends on longitude as well as latitude. This has been evident in studies of 11-yr periodicities in pressure (sec. 3.1.5) and also shows up in short-term correlations with solar flares (sec. 4.1.1) and magnetic activity (sec. 4.2.1). Averaging over all longitudes, as Miles (1974) did, may serve to obscure atmospheric pressure responses to solar changes.

In view of the conflicting results on 22-yr variations in atmospheric pressure, it may be best to concentrate on the 11-yr periodicity and short-term responses when searching for physical mechanisms linking atmospheric pressure changes and solar activity.

3.3 Correlation Reversals and Failures

In a number of cases it has been noted that correlations between meteorological parameters and sunspots have broken down or even reversed after the elapse of several solar cycles. In some cases this per-plexity is evident in the original investigations, and in others the reversal or breakdown was discovered only by later extensions with additional data by the same or other researchers. Faulty analysis is not the only possible source for the correlation breakdowns. The pos-sibility that solar conditions, not reflected by the sunspot number itself, might have undergone some secular change should be consid-ered. In addition, other meteorological forcing functions (e.g., polar ice cap area) unrelated to solar activity might switch from a minor to dominant role over long time periods.

It is therefore of interest to review the major instances of correla-tion reversal or breakdown to determine whether they might share a common time period, so that sensitive solar activity indicators other than sunspot number can be examined for the same time period. If physical mechanisms are to be found to link variable solar activity with possible meteorological responses, these breakdowns and rever-sals must be accounted for as well as the many significant correlations cited in this review. On the basis of the correlation failures, it might be argued that no physical relationships exist between the weather and the variable Sun, and the failures are due simply to long-term changes in the troposphere. On the other hand, it may be that the failures contain a vital key to an identification of a real link.

3.3.1 Temperature Correlation Failures

The apparent recent breakdown of the negative correlation be-tween global or hemispheric mean temperatures and the 11-yr cycle evident in figure 3.6 after 1958 has been noted by Starr and Oort (1973). They used over 10^7 data points to obtain the average monthly temperature of "the bulk (92%) of the atmospheric mass in the north-ern hemisphere" for each of the 60 months between May 1958 and April 1963. By subtracting the mean seasonal variation from the monthly values, they obtained "residuals," which showed a decreas-ing trend in temperature amounting to a drop of 0.6°C over the 5 yr. King (1973) carried the analysis a step further and compared the Starr and Oort results to the 12-mo running mean sunspot number for each month. The decrease in temperature closely followed the decrease in sunspot number from near solar maximum in May 1958 to near minimum in 1963. A trend toward a leveling out of the sun-spot numbers in 1962 and 1963 was matched by the bulk mass tem-perature. On a month-to-month basis the correlation was less striking; nevertheless, months in which the temperature was relatively high or low coincidentally varied with sunspot number. These short-term results imply a positive correlation, in keeping with the Little Ice Age results of Eddy (1976), but in contradistinction to those of Köppen (1914) for 11-yr variations of global temperatures.

An earlier correlation reversal in the July temperatures in central England was reported by King et al. (1974; see also King, 1975). In temperature data over the period 1750–1880, it was noted that the July values varied in phase with the double (22-yr) sunspot cycle up to about 1830, after which the decrease in temperature lagged the sunspot number decrease to such an extent that by 1840 it was out of phase by one-half of an 11-yr cycle. By 1860 the temperature was again in phase with the 22-yr cycle, but around 1880 the correlation broke down again. According to King (1975), the central England July temperatures have exhibited an 11-yr periodicity since 1880. These results would seem to indicate that something peculiar happened in the period 1830–1860 and again near the year 1880.

In the tropical region, Troup (1962) reexamined and extended the results of Köppen (1914), Walker and Bliss (1928), and Callendar (1961). Callendar considered tropical temperature data for the period 1873–1920. Troup subjected these earlier results to vigorous statistical tests and concluded that ". . . there is a reasonable statistical probability that tropical temperatures are lower at sunspot maximum than at sunspot minimum." This negative correlation applied to the period 1813–1920.

Table 3.5.—Correlation Coefficients Between Sunspot Number and Seasonal or Annual Tropical Temperatures Before and After Circa 1920 (from Troup, 1962)

Station	Season	Period 1	Period 2	Location
Samoa	Dec–Feb	−.44(1891–1917)	−.01(1925–1957)	12.3°S, 170°W
Colombo	March–May	−.33(1870–1918)	+.21(1921–1954)	6.9°N, 79.5°E
St. Helena	Dec–Feb	−.25(1893–1924)	+.32(1926–1954)*	16°S, 5.2°W
Port-Au-Prince	March–May	−.24(1888–1920)	+.16(1921–1947)	18.4°N, 72.2°W
Lagos	June–Aug	−.38(1892–1920)	−.29(1921–1950)*	6.3°N, 3.2°E
Trinidad	March–May	−.33(1862–1920)	+.24(1921–1953)*	10.8°N, 61.6°W
Djakarta	Dec–Feb	−.46(1867–1923)	+.10(1924–1953)	6.2°S, 106.5°E
Tropical zone*	Year	−.38(1871–1920)	+.23(1921–1950)	

*From the values of Callendar (1961); a positive linear trend has been removed from the temperature values for period 2.

For the entire tropical zone, the correlation coefficient for annual temperature and sunspot number (11-yr cycle) was $-.38$ up to 1920, but for the period 1921–1950, the correlation had reversed and the coefficient was $+.23$. Correlation coefficients for seven tropical stations before and after circa 1920 are listed in table 3.5.

Inspection of the coefficients in table 3.5 reveals that the seasonal correlation reversed at five of the seven stations, remained negative but with a smaller magnitude at one (Lagos), and became essentially zero at the other (Samoa). For tropical temperature and 11-yr sunspot variation, the anomalous period for reversal was in the early 1920s at most of the stations investigated by Troup (1962).

3.3.2 Precipitation Correlation Failures

Rainfall amounts appear to have been correlated with the Hale double sunspot cycle in at least two places, and in both locations a correlation reversal was observed. At Fortaleza, Brazil (4°S, 39°W), the correlation of annual rainfall with the 22-yr cycle was "strongly positive" from 1865 to 1925 (King et al., 1974; King, 1975), but then became negative.

In Adelaide, on the southern coast of Australia (Cornish, 1936), the number of rainy days in Australian winter exhibited a periodic variation with a period of 23 yr and amplitude of 30 days in the years 1839–1912, but from 1912 to 1933 this "law of changes" in Cornish's estimate broke down. Cornish (1954) then extended his investigation using Adelaide data for 1934–1950, inclusive, and analyzed the dates by which specified fractions of the annual total rainfall had been achieved. A strong secular variation was found in the dates for accumulated rainfall amounting to $\frac{1}{4}$ (lower quartile), $\frac{3}{8}$, $\frac{1}{2}$, $\frac{5}{8}$, $\frac{3}{4}$ (upper quartile), and $\frac{7}{8}$ of the annual total, as can be seen in figure 3.22.

King (1975) called attention to the strong correlation between Cornish's lower quartile curve (top of fig. 3.22) and the 22-yr sunspot cycle which persisted from 1844 to 1944. One should note with care King's treatment of sunspot number in making the comparison; his analysis indicates that the earliest dates by which one-quarter of the total rainfall was achieved occurred in sunspot minimum years following a maximum in the positive half of a Hale double cycle. This can be seen by comparing the center year of the earliest dates in the top curve of fig. 3.22 (that is, 1857, 1878, 1900, 1924, and 1943) with the years of sunspot minima plotted in figure 2.1.

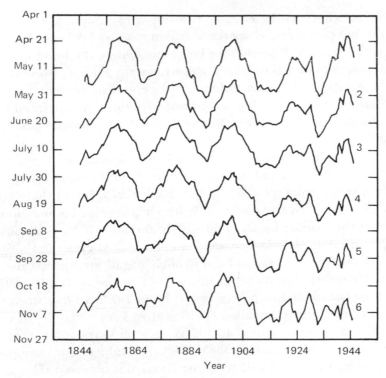

Figure 3.22. Ten-year means of the dates for octiles of rainfall year at Adelaide. Curve 1, date by which 1/4 (second octile) of annual rainfall occurred; 2, third octile (3/8 of total); 3, median or fourth octile; 4, fifth octile; 5, upper quartile (3/4 of total); 6, seventh octile. From Cornish (1954).

A similar periodicity persists at least down through the date marking half the total annual rainfall, but in proceeding on toward the seventh octile, a marked deterioration of the correlation sets in. Although Cornish (1954) suggested 1912 as the year of breakdown, figure 3.22 shows that a marked departure did not take place until a decade later, about 1922. From that year to 1944, when the analysis ended, there are relatively minor fluctuations in the data of seven-eighths rainfall occurrence which have slight, if any, relationship to the double sunspot cycle.

To digress for a moment, Cornish (1954) suggested that the apparent 22-yr cyclical variation in quartile date ". . . must be due to secular changes in the latitudinal paths of anticyclones (with their attendant cyclones) across southern Australia." As discussed in section 3.1.7, Bowen's (1975) results imply that the Australian cyclone

129

tracks are closer to the equator in sunspot maximum years. There would thus be less rain along the southern coast at Adelaide's location (34.6°S, 138.4°E); it would take longer to achieve the lower quartile of annual rainfall in those years. Unfortunately, Bowen's storm tracks oscillate with an 11- rather than 22-yr periodicity (except that the oscillations may have a 22-yr amplitude variation); we are faced with still another puzzling aspect in the problem of solar-climatic relationships.

The important point here is that at both Adelaide and Fortaleza a marked change occurred in rainfall patterns in the early 1920s.

On a wider geographic basis, Xanthakis (1973) found that excess rainfall occurs with an 11-yr periodicity when averaged over all longitudes in the latitude bands of 60°–70°N and 70°–80°N, as discussed in section 3.1.1. No evidence was found for a 22-yr cycle. In the 50°–60°N band, however, rainfall was strongly negatively correlated with sunspot number with a coefficient of −.67 in the years 1890-1913, and then the trend abruptly reversed. From 1914 to 1960, when the analysis ended, the correlation coefficient is +.74.

In the next lower band, 40°–50°N, several correlation reversals occurred in the interval 1885-1960, including one complete breakdown. In the 1905-1918 span, Xanthakis observed the excess rainfall to fluctuate slightly around a mean value with no significant correlation with sunspot number.

If the pattern of the global distribution of excess rainfall (e.g., that of Clayton in fig. 3.2) undergoes secular changes due to long-term variations in extraterrestrial or even purely terrestrial influences, averages over wide geographic expanses could very well exhibit correlation reversals with sunspot number. It appears that additional rainfall analysis along the lines of figure 3.2 might reconcile some of the discrepancies between the results of Xanthakis (1973), Gerety et al. (1977), and Dehsara and Cehak (1970). An important aspect of such future analyses would be a consideration of the latitudinal variation of storm tracks, as suggested by Brown and John (1977).

The final indication of a reversal or breakdown in the possible relationship of precipitation and sunspot number to be discussed here is an indirect observation. Shaw (1928) showed that the water level in Lake Victoria (approximately 2°S, 33°E) had a high positive correlation (coefficient = +.88) with sunspot number from the 1880s to the 1920s, but according to Bargman et al. (1965), the correlation broke down around 1930. Beginning circa 1950 the water level has been negatively correlated with sunspot number (King, 1975).

3.3.3 Pressure Centers, Winds, and Storm Frequency

As discussed in section 3.1.6, atmospheric circulation is largely controlled by (pressure) centers of action, one of which is the so-called Icelandic Low. A preliminary analysis reported by Schuurmans (1975) of winter weather types in Europe indicates that at times the longitude of the Icelandic Low is displaced eastward toward Scandinavia. His analysis (extending from 1888 to 1973) seems to show that the Icelandic Low is near Scandinavia more often in the 11-yr negative half of a Hale double cycle than it is in the positive half. However, when his results are compared with the double sunspot cycle in the manner illustrated in figure 3.23, it is evident that in the period 1923–1943, the occurrence percentage of winter storm types associated with an eastward displacement of the Icelandic Low changed very little. Thus the 22-yr longitudinal oscillation of the Icelandic Low temporarily disappeared for about two decades after 1922.

Schuurmans (1975) interpreted these occurrence-percentage results to mean that the Icelandic Low is farther west during the positive half of a Hale solar cycle. He also found weather types indicative of high pressure over the Iceland area more often in positive half-cycles, leading him to believe that a pressure oscillation exists that has a larger amplitude in positive compared to negative halves of the double cycle. In passing, it might be noted that the data in figure 3.23 for 1954–1963 and 1964–1973 indicate an eastward displacement of the Icelandic Low in winter from the first period to the second. In contrast, Bradley (1973) has shown that in July the displacement was in the opposite direction (sec. 3.1.6) between these two periods.

In view of Schuurmans' (1975) findings of an apparent 22-yr periodicity in the Icelandic Low position as indirectly evidenced by winter European storm types, it would be interesting to see a reanalysis of the Angell and Korshover (1974) investigation which found a marginal 11-yr correlation based on direct observation of the pressure patterns near Iceland (see also sec. 3.1.6).

Two additional cases of temporary breakdown or reversal are worthy of mention. First, the positive correlation between Etesian wind occurrence in summer over Greece and sunspot number (11-yr cycle) discussed in section 3.1.6 temporarily failed near the sunspot

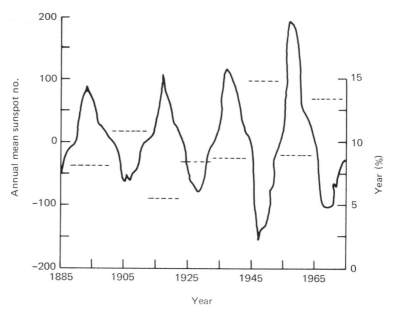

Figure 3.23. Percentage of time that the semipermanent Icelandic Low is displaced eastward toward Scandinavia compared to the double sunspot cycle. From Schuurmans (1975).

minimum year of 1922. Second, there was a ". . . remarkable reversal in the distribution of storm frequency in the U.S. . . ." associated with the Hale double cycle (Kullmer, 1943).

3.3.4 Summary of Reversals and Breakdowns

The years or periods of reversals and breakdowns in statistical correlations between sunspot number and meteorological or climatological parameters are summarized here to identify critical times that require additional scrutiny.

For global surface temperature, the correlation with the 11-yr sunspot cycle went from negative to positive in the period 1958–1963, and 1974–1975 data indicate that it may have subsequently returned to negative.

In central England in July, the surface temperature was in phase with the 22-yr solar cycle from 1750 to 1830 and again from 1860 to 1880. After 1880 this parameter has exhibited an 11- rather than 22-yr periodicity. The crucial periods for this parameter are accordingly 1830–1860 and the years near 1880.

Tropical temperatures were negatively correlated with the 11-yr cycle prior to the 1920s and then positively correlated to at least 1950. The crucial period is approximately 1920–1925.

Rainfall at Fortaleza, Brazil, being positively correlated with the 22-yr cycle from 1865 to 1925 and negative afterward indicates a crucial period in the 1920s decade. Also, rainfall at Adelaide, Australia had a negative correlation with the 22-yr cycle up to about 1922 and no apparent relationship afterward, which also points to a period of change in the 1920s.

Rainfall in the latitudinal band of 50°–60°N reversed its correlation with the 11-yr cycle from strongly negative prior to 1913 to strongly positive after that year. In the 40°–50°N band, there was a period of no apparent correlation between rainfall and the 11-yr cycle from 1905 to 1918 and then a series of reversals spanning the period 1928–1935.

The water level in Lake Victoria, an indirect indicator of tropical rainfall, was positively correlated with the 11-yr sunspot cycle from 1880 to 1930, became uncorrelated until 1950, and then showed a negative correlation. A critical period of 1930–1950 is thus indicated.

East-west oscillations in the position of the Icelandic Low with a 22-yr periodicity have been evident in winter storm behavior in Europe for the years 1888–1973, except for the period 1923–1943.

A strong positive correlation between Etesian wind occurrence in Greece and the 11-yr sunspot cycle has been in evidence for the span 1893–1961, except for a brief failure near the sunspot minimum year of 1922.

A graphical schedule of these various correlation failures and reversals is given in table 3.6, in which it can be seen that the 1920s decade is the crucial period for most of the meteorological parameters listed. In pondering these results, it is tempting to paraphrase an escape clause from academia: the interpretation of these observations is left as an exercise for the reader.

There appears to be nothing unusual in the cyclical behavior of sunspot number during this period (fig. 2.1); the year 1922 was a cycle minimum marking the end of a positive half of a Hale double cycle. It is, however, near the minimum of a roughly 90-yr cycle, about half-way between the large sunspot maxima in 1871 and 1958. It is apparent that, for interpretation of the significance of the reversals in terms of solar activity, solar parameters other than sunspot

Table 3.6.—Schedule of Reversals (R) or Failure (F) of Correlations Between Sunspot Number and Several Meteorological Parameters

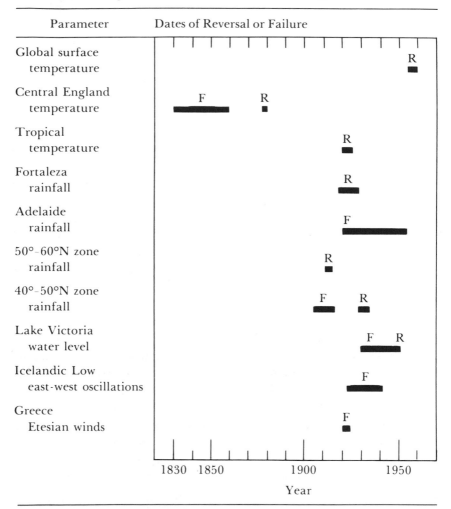

Parameter	Dates of Reversal or Failure
Global surface temperature	R (~1950)
Central England temperature	F (~1835–1855) R (~1880)
Tropical temperature	R (~1915)
Fortaleza rainfall	R (~1915)
Adelaide rainfall	F (~1920–1955)
50°–60°N zone rainfall	R (~1905)
40°–50°N zone rainfall	F (~1910) R (~1925)
Lake Victoria water level	F (~1930) R (~1945)
Icelandic Low east-west oscillations	F (~1920)
Greece Etesian winds	F (~1910)

Year

number must be considered, as well as masking by other effects unrelated to the Sun.

To demonstrate the difficulty in this consideration, let us assume that the atmospheric meteorological system is quasiperiodic. There are to be sure a number of periodicities whose wavelengths are measured in hours, weeks, seasons, and years.

On a simplified approximation, the diurnal temperature variation with a period of 1 day is an example. On an average basis without other contributing factors, the temperature is maximum in early afternoon and minimum before dawn. The driving (forcing) function for this behavior is the relatively steady input of energy from the Sun, which begins cyclically at dawn, maximizes at local noon when the Sun is overhead, and disappears at dusk. The temperature function lags this forcing function by a time that is proportional to the response time of the atmosphere. This response time is related to the heat capacitance and radiative properties of the air.

Superimposed on the diurnal trend of temperature is a seasonal variation, produced by the change in minimum solar zenith angle and fraction of the day that the fixed point observation is exposed to daylight (solar radiation). Here again there is a lag between the occurrence of minimum zenith angle (and concurrent maximum amount of daylight) and maximum temperature in the summer.

Also, one might expect an annual variation in temperature at the equator: maximum following the December solstice when Earth is closest to the Sun in its annual orbit and minimum following the June solstice when the Earth is at apogee in its elliptical orbit around the Sun. The solar constant changes by about 7.2% between perigee and apogee because of the greater Sun-Earth distance at apogee. The corresponding variation in heat input at the equator should affect the temperature.

Longer period variations in temperature show an 11-yr periodicity at some locations apparently related to the solar cycle and 22-yr periodicity at other locations apparently related to the Hale double sunspot cycle. There is some evidence for still longer periods of 40, 80, or 180 yr which may or may not be related to solar variations.

Following a method of analysis elucidated by Yule (1927), let us assume that the atmospheric system has a long natural period. At irregular intervals this system is bombarded with extra bursts of energy which build up an oscillation whose amplitude is limited essentially by damping. By Yule's rule, there is an interval T such that most of the meteorological oscillation at time t will have been damped out by time $t + T$; any oscillation still present at $t + T$ is due to the solar bursts occurring between t and $t + T$. Since we have assumed the extra bursts to occur at random intervals, the meteorological oscillations at times differing by more than T will be practically uncorrelated.

Meteorological parameters other than temperature might be treated in the same way. Thus, even if solar variable energy inputs are identified, it may not be always possible to find a corresponding (or correlative) variation in observed meteorological phenomena.

3.4 Sunspot Cycle and Atmospheric Electric Parameters

Atmospheric electricity plays an important role in the development of some types of weather, most notably thunderstorms. It may also enter into processes leading to "weakly electrified" rain showers with no lightning activity, but just how has not yet been discovered. Chalmers (1967) noted that ". . . the phenomena of atmospheric electricity are very closely bound up with meteorological phenomena and each can contribute to the understanding of the other." In any event, atmospheric electric variations may provide a physical link between solar activity and meteorological phenomena; it is of interest to review reported correlations between the solar cycle and atmospheric electric quantities. This review is prefaced by an orientation discussion of the basic quantities that may be affected by solar activity.

3.4.1 Basic Relations in Atmospheric Electricity

The science of atmospheric electricity is one of the more mature fields of physics, having been pursued continuously for more than two centuries. Its birth is generally recognized to have taken place in 1750, when Franklin discovered the electrical nature of lightning (Gish, 1939; Israel, 1970), and it has progressed through a well-documented historical development (Israel, 1970; 1973, cites well over 2500 references). Israel (1973, p. 354) suggested that solar influences on atmospheric electricity "cannot be established with certainty, and are but weakly, if at all, effective."

Although there is some evidence (Watson, 1928) supporting Israel's conclusion, the results of a number of investigations seem to show a clear correlation between solar activity and atmospheric electric parameters. These are discussed below and in chapter 4, but first it is worthwhile to define the parameters and their interrelationships.

Since the ionosphere and the Earth are both enormously better conductors than the lower atmosphere, they may be considered to be regions of uniform electric potential (Holzer, 1973). Thus they constitute the plates of a spherical capacitor, while the atmosphere may be regarded as a leaky dielectric. Because the plates are electrostatic shields, atmospheric electric phenomena must be produced by generating processes that lie within the atmosphere, although this view may have to be modified later (Park, 1976a). This qualitative model is depicted in figure 3.24. On the fair weather side, the leakage current density, J_c (called the air-Earth current density) flows toward the Earth with a mean density of $3(10^{-12})$ A m^{-2}; the total integrated current is about 1500 A (Holzer, 1973) to 1800 A (Byers, 1954). Its strength at any time is approximately proportional to the total number of thunderstorms in progress. Since the atmosphere has an effective resistance (R) of about 200 ohms (Gish, 1951), the ionospheric potential (V_i) is 300–360 kilovolts (kV).

The potential gradient (E), also referred to as the atmospheric electric field, has an average value of 130 volts per meter (V m^{-1}) at sea level in fair weather, and it decreases with altitude. Its magnitude varies approximately inversely with the conductivity of the air, and the air conductivity (σ) increases with height. The height at which the potential gradient goes to zero, usually near or above 50 km (Hake et al., 1973), is defined as the electrosphere. The magnitude of the potential gradient, like that of the air-Earth current density, is proportional to the number of thunderstorms in progress at any given

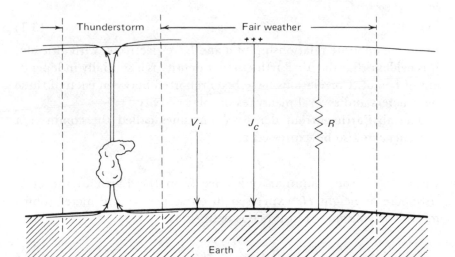

Figure 3.24. Qualitative model of the global electric circuit, illustrating the thunderstorm generator, ionospheric potential (V_i), air-Earth current density (J_c), and total atmospheric resistance (R).

time. The total atmospheric potential between the ground and the atmosphere at height h increases with altitude, and at 10 km it is about 90% of V_i. Above about 50 km, in the electrosphere, it is the same as V_i. This latter quantity, too, is proportional to the number and/or intensity of global thunderstorms in progress.

The air is slightly conductive due to the presence of small ions in the atmosphere, which are produced by natural radioactivity from the solid Earth and by cosmic rays incident from above. The former process is steady, but decreases with altitude, whereas the latter peaks at an altitude of 12–16 km (sec. 2.4). Variations in air ionization and therefore in conductivity are produced by variations in the cosmic ray flux intensity and by solar proton events (sec. 2.3.5).

With no current generator in the system, the air-Earth current would discharge the spherical capacitor in less than 2 hr (Byers, 1954). The necessary generator is generally conceded to be the thunderstorm (Holzer, 1973; Byers, 1954; Gish, 1939), which was first proposed by C.T.R. Wilson in 1921. It has been estimated that, globally, approximately 1800 thunderstorms are in progress at any given time.

The basic relationship between the conductivity, potential gradient, and air-Earth current density at any height is given by Ohm's law:

$$J_c = \sigma E \tag{3.1}$$

From the opposite relationship of σ and E, respectively, with altitude, it is evident that the air-Earth current density is essentially independent of height. Correlations have been reported between each of these parameters and several measures of solar activity.

The air-Earth current density (sometimes called the conduction current) can also be expressed as

$$J_c = V_i/R_H \tag{3.2}$$

where R_H is the columnar resistance from the Earth to the electrosphere at height H, expressed in ohms per square meter (ohms m^{-2}). The columnar resistance is defined as:

$$R_H = \int_0^H (1/\sigma_h)\,dh \tag{3.3}$$

From equation (3.2) it is clear that V_i will be proportional, as is J_c, to the number of global thunderstorms in progress at any given time, provided that R_H is independent of this number.

Consideration of equations (3.1)-(3.3) shows that, if solar activity affects any one atmospheric electric quantity, it should affect them all. That the conductivity should be affected by solar events can be shown in the following way.

The conductivity may be defined as $\sigma = \Sigma_j n_j e \mu_j$, where n_j and μ_j are the number density and mobility of each species (j) of charge carrier, respectively; e is the carrier charge, and the summation includes either positive or negative ions. The mobility, in turn, is $\mu_j = e / m_j \nu_{ij}$, where m_j is the mass of the jth carrier and ν_{ij} is the collisional frequency of the carrier with other constituents (i). Under quasiequilibrium conditions and charge neutrality, the number density of ions with either sign is related to the ion-pair production rate by $n_j = (Q_j / \alpha_j)^{1/2}$, where α_j is the effective recombination rate between the jth ion and all other ions of opposite sign. Thus the conductivity can be derived from

$$\sigma = \sum_i \sum_j \frac{e^2}{m_j \nu_{ij}} \left(\frac{Q_j}{\alpha_j} \right)^{1/2} \tag{3.4}$$

A rigorous calculation of conductivity should include each ionic species with its appropriate number density, mobility, collision frequency, ion mass, and recombination coefficient, all of which are height dependent. Such rigor is not justified for the present argument, nor are the precise values known from present-day measurements. Approximate calculations can be made using average values for m, ν, and α and dropping the summation signs and subscripts in equation (3.4). A specific set of average values for these quantities is given in chapter 6 and applied to calculations of conductivity for specific solar events.

At this point, however, it is sufficient to note that conductivity increases with the square root of the ion-pair production rate. Since Q changes with solar activity through the action of solar protons (sec. 2.3), galactic cosmic rays (sec. 2.4), and precipitating electrons and associated X-rays (sec. 2.3), it is evident that σ should be influenced by solar activity.

3.4.2 Potential Gradient Variations with Solar Cycle

The secular trend of potential gradient measured at stations in the British Isles, France, and Spain over a 20-yr period (1902-1922) was investigated by Bauer (1926). The average potential gradient for all stations combined, expressed in percentage of the 20-yr mean value, was clearly above the mean during sunspot maximum years and below the mean in minimum years (fig. 3.25). For the potential gradient averages, days with local thunderstorms were excluded. The diurnal amplitude and the annual amplitude both show a strong positive correlation with sunspot number over the two solar cycles. No such correlation was found at Potsdam by Kähler (1925), who used data for almost the same period (1904–1923), nor at Munich by Lutz (1939) in the years 1906–1935, although Potsdam and Munich were two of the stations used by Bauer (1926).

There appear to have been few analyses of solar cycle effects on potential gradient in recent years. Precise measurement of this quantity at ground stations is fairly difficult because of the adverse effects

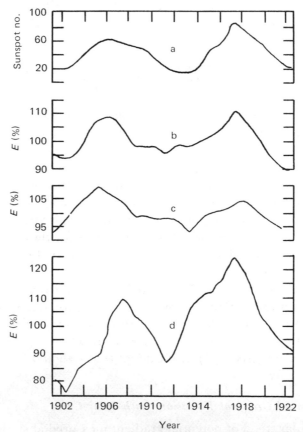

Figure 3.25. Cyclical variations in potential gradient compared to 11-yr sunspot cycle. Curve a, relative sunspot number; b, potential gradient; c, daily amplitude of potential gradient; d, potential gradient annual amplitude. Curves b, c, and d are in percentage of mean value. From Bauer (1926) and Israel (1973).

of humidity, smoke, and other pollutants in the air, and long-term comparisons are risky. Because of this, the use of the total (that is, ionospheric) potential may be advantageous. Thus Mühleisen (1971) and Fischer and Mühleisen (1972) investigated the 11-yr cycle influence in ionospheric potential. Their results indicate a positive correlation with annual mean sunspot number. Since the ionospheric potential is proportional to the number of thunderstorms in progress, it can be expected that the latter should be correlated with sunspot cycle. Evidence for this expectation is given in section 3.4.4.

3.4.3 Air Conductivity

Potential gradient measurements give an indirect indication of air conductivity variations, since these two parameters are clearly inversely correlated (Wait, 1937; Wait and Mauchly, 1937; Israel et al.,

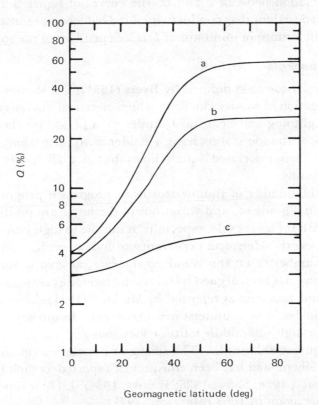

Figure 3.26. Percentage decrease of atmospheric ionization rate (Q) due to cosmic rays between 1954 and 1958 as a function of height (a, 10 mb level; b, 100 mb; c, 1000 mb) and geomagnetic latitude. From Ney (1959).

1951). It has been estimated from cosmic ray data (Dubs et al., 1965) that changes in conductivity of a few tens of percent may be expected at heights above thunderstorm cloud tops over a solar cycle period. At least the ionization rate due to cosmic rays increases from solar maximum to solar minimum by about 30% at an altitude of 10 km and 50% at 15 km. Calculations by Ney (1959) show that the ionization rate due to cosmic rays decreased from solar minimum in 1954 to solar maximum in 1958, with the largest changes occurring at the greatest height (10 mb) and in regions poleward of about 50° geomagnetic latitude, as can be seen in figure 3.26. The percentage decrease is calculated with respect to the ionization rate in 1954. On the basis of this and equation (3.4) it would be expected that the conductivity would be less, on the average, because of the lower rate during solar maximum than solar minimum years. Bearing in mind the inverse relation between σ and E, the curves of figure 3.25 can be interpreted to show that conductivity is indeed lower at sunspot maximum than at sunspot minimum if J_c is independent of the solar cycle.

3.4.4 Thunderstorm Activity

A thunderstorm, as defined by Byers (1951), is a shower cloud or an aggregation of shower clouds in which electrical discharges can be seen as lightning and heard as thunder by a person on the ground. Nontropical thunderstorms have a tendency to form along weather fronts or their associated squall lines, but not all fronts produce thunderstorms.

Since the number of thunderstorms in progress is proportional to the potential gradient, and variations in the latter are positively correlated with the solar cycle, especially at middle to high latitudes, one could expect thunderstorm occurrence to follow secular variations in sunspot number. That this is indeed the case, at least in some localized regions, has been argued by several investigators. Russian work by Likhter and associates as reported by Markson (1971) shows a positive correlation between thunderstorm occurrence frequency and solar activity for high and middle latitude locations and a negative correlation in equatorial latitudes. The strongest correlation (about +.9) is found in Siberia and has been consistently reported as such for many years (Septer, 1926; Shaw, 1928; Brooks, 1934). Likhter reported the same value again in 1968 (Markson, 1971).

The original work on Siberian thunderstorms was apparently done by Septer (1926), who used annual averages of the number of days with thunder at 229 stations between latitudes 71° and 43°N and longitudes 59.5° and 149.5°E, covering almost all of Siberia. The period covered was 1888-1924, including three maxima and four minima of the 11-yr sunspot cycle, all of which are faithfully reproduced by the annual thunderstorm curve. The correlation coefficient is +.88, and the regression equation is

$$N(\mathrm{TS}) = 10.4 + 0.11\, R_z \qquad (3.5)$$

where $N(\mathrm{TS})$ is the average annual number of thunderstorm days. This relationship suggests that about 10 thunderstorm days occur annually in Siberia independent of sunspots, with an additional number (1-9 in the 37-yr period covered) associated with sunspots.

The correlation coefficients between thunderstorms and sunspots found by Brooks (1934) are summarized in table 3.7 for a number of geographic regions including Siberia. For Siberia, Septer's basic data were used, and for the remaining areas annual "thunder heard" reports from a varying number of meteorological stations were averaged together. The "uncorrected data" results in table 3.7 are the correlation coefficients between annual sunspot number and the average annual number of thunderstorms in each region expressed as a percentage of the mean for that region over all years. Noticing that the reporting practices at various stations gradually changed over the years, Brooks "corrected" the data by taking 11-yr means centered on the year of record and subtracting them from the number of thunderstorms in the year of record. The "corrected data" length is thus 10 yr shorter than the uncorrected (table 3.7), since he had no way to correct the first or last 5 yr in the span.

To determine whether the cyclical variation of thunderstorm occurrence was in or out of phase with annual sunspot number variation, Brooks applied a harmonic analysis to each data set. The results, listed in column 5 of table 3.7, are quite varied. In Siberia, where the correlation is highest, thunderstorms and sunspots are nearly in phase, the spot cycle leading thunderstorm occurrence by only 0.1 yr. When the phase difference is several years (e.g., Holland, Australia, New Zealand), the correlation coefficient is very low.

The Russian results of Likhter agree in many respects with those of Brooks, as noted by Markson (1971), and Markson himself found no correlation for thunderstorms in the middle United States, a region for which Brooks' correlation coefficients (table 3.7) are small. Other regions of the world that apparently exhibit a correlation between

Table 3.7.—Correlation Coefficients Between Thunderstorm Occurrence and Annual Sunspot Number (from Brooks, 1934)

Area	Uncorrected Data				Corrected Data			
	1*	2	3	4	2	3	4	5
Siberia	14	37	+ .88	.03	27	+ .91	.02	+ 0.1
Norway	4	66	− .01	.08	56	+ .18	.09	+ 0.8
Sweden (inland)	12	45	+ .22	.09	35	+ .38	.10	+ 0.5
Sweden (coast)	7	35	+ .12	.11	25	+ .21	.13	− 0.2
Scotland	5	57	+ .12	.09	47	+ .20	.09	− 1.8
Ireland	6	60	+ .09	.09	50	+ .13	.09	− 2.8
England and Wales	10	57	+ .03	.09	47	+ .05	.09	− 3.5
Holland	11	47	− .01	.10	37	.00	.12	− 4.4
Germany	21	34	+ .05	.12	24	+ .06	.14	− 1.3
Japan	15	34	+ .12	.11	24	+ .26	.12	− 3.0
USA								
Northeast	26	42	+ .31	.11	32	+ .26	.10	+ 0.3
Lake States	43	42	+ .19	.12	32	+ .19	.10	+ 0.9
Southeast	51	42	+ .15	.12	32	+ .36	.09	+ 1.1
North Central	41	42	+ .11	.12	32	+ .06	.10	− 1.1
South Central	13	42	+ .18	.12	32	+ .09	.10	+ 2.2
Rocky Mountains	28	42	+ .11	.12	32	+ .08	.10	+ 2.5
Pacific Coast	4	42	− .04	.12	32	− .16	.10	− 0.2
West Indies	26	65	+ .41	.07	55	+ .34	.08	+ 0.2
Southern Asia	66	53	+ .26	.08	43	+ .40	.08	+ 0.2
Tropical Pacific	30	31	+ .49	.09	—	—	—	+ 0.5
Australia	36	46	+ .02	.10	36	− .14	.11	− 5.1
New Zealand	8	25	+ .10	.13	—	—	—	+ 4.8

*1, average number of thunderstorm days per year; 2, number of years used in analysis; 3, correlation coefficient; 4, probable error; 5, phase difference in years between sunspot cycle and thunderstorm cycle (plus indicates spot cycle leads thunderstorm cycle).

sunspot number and thunderstorm activity include Japan (Noto, 1932), the West Indies (Brooks and Carruthers, 1953), and England (Stringfellow, 1974).

Stringfellow's (1974) results are illustrated in figure 3.27, in which 5-year running means of both annual mean sunspot numbers and an annual index of lightning incidence are plotted. The lightning index is defined as the square of the mean annual number of thunderstorm days at 40 representative stations in Great Britain. Although there are

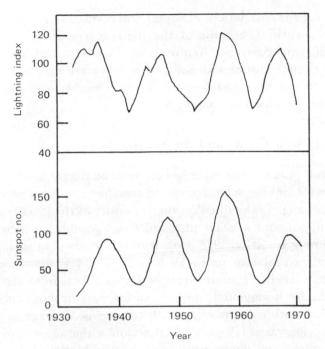

Figure 3.27. Five-year running means of average annual sunspot number (lower curve) and average annual lightning index. From Stringfellow (1974).

year-to-year variations in the index, there is a strong cyclic variation which is in phase with the sunspot cycle and has an amplitude of ±30% of the mean. The correlation coefficient between these two curves is +.8, a result that is statistically significant, according to Stringfellow. However, as so often happens in the Sun-weather litera-ture, Stringfellow's results conflict with those of Brooks for England and Wales (table 3.7). Not only do Brooks' findings suggest that the two phenomena are uncorrelated, but also that they are out of phase by 3.5 yr. The reasons for this discrepancy are far from clear. Brooks used data (annual number of days with thunder heard) for the 57 yr prior to 1934, whereas Stringfellow used the same type of data span-ning the years 1934–1973. Also, the statistical treatment accorded the two sets of data differed. A reanalysis using a common statistical approach might help to resolve the discrepancy if the earlier data set could be retrieved. Otherwise, the prima facie evidence suggests that English thunderstorms are correlated with the sunspot cycle in some years but not in others.

Except for the correlations of Septer and Stringfellow, which themselves are surprising because of the high degree of subjectivity in
establishing the occurrence frequency of thunderstorms, most correlations of thunderstorms with sunspot number are marginal at best;
however, they are suggestive and, if true, might be explained by
mechanisms proposed in chapter 6.

3.5 Atmospheric Ozone and the Sunspot Cycle

The atmospheric ozone layer has come to be regarded as a possible
candidate for linking solar activity to weather responses or climatic
trends. A change in the distribution or density of the layer may serve
to alter the amount of solar ultraviolet (UV) radiation heating the
stratosphere (e.g., Reck, 1976,a,b), with the subsequent variations in
atmospheric circulation (e.g., Dickinson, 1975) and with possible
attendant weather or climate changes. Other effects from ozone variability have been suggested, notably an increase in skin cancer incidence, along with changes in agricultural yields, damage to natural
ecosystems, increased UV germicidal action, enhancement of photochemical smog, and photodegradation of xenobiotic materials. It is
therefore of interest to examine reported correlations between solar
activity and ozone variations and to study the natural variability and
climatology of ozone.

Before addressing the solar aspect, however, it is useful to consider
the characteristic variability of atmospheric ozone with respect to
geographic position and time (sec. 3.5.1) and its basic production
and loss mechanisms (sec. 3.5.2). Reported correlations between the
solar cycle and long-term ozone variations are discussed in section
3.5.3, and the solar dependence of production and loss mechanisms is
treated in section 3.5.4. Ozone responses to short-term solar events
are deferred to chapter 4.

3.5.1 Observed Ozone Variability

For general interest, a large number of papers on the variability of
atmospheric ozone have been collected by Bossolasco (1973). Those
germane to the present discussion are cited directly in the text where
appropriate.

Before discussing the variability, a word about the systems of units
and definitions of terms used for describing ozone concentration is in
order. The total amount of global ozone is sometimes expressed

simply as the total number of molecules obtained by summing up over all latitudes, longitudes, and altitudes. The total number of molecules is on the order of $4(10^{37})$ (Heath, 1974). Commonly used quantities for describing ozone include column density, mass density, number density, partial pressure, mass mixing ratio, and volume mixing ratio. The relationships between these quantities, useful for converting from one to another, are given in table 3.8.

The column density of ozone, usually obtained from optical observations, is often expressed in terms of an equivalent layer thickness in centimeters (at any height), reduced to standard temperature and pressure (STP) per unit vertical distance. The abbreviation is atm-cm/km or cm(STP)/km, and occasionally (especially in older literature) it is expressed as mm O_3(STP)/km or simply cm O_3/km. In terms of mass density, a layer thickness of 0.01 atm-cm/km (or cm(STP)/km) corresponds to $2.14 \ (10^{-7}) \ kg/m^3$.

The ozone number density (molecules per cm^3 or per m^3) is used for ozone height profiles, but because of the wide range of ozone densities, e.g., with height, the mixing ratio is frequently used. The mass mixing ratio is the ratio of ozone density to air density (see table 3.8), whereas the volume mixing ratio is 0.603448 times that ratio. It should be noted that the height of maximum number density is about 15 km lower than the peak height for the mixing ratio. At the peak of the layer, the number density is on the order of $10^{19} \ mol/m^3$, and the mixing ratio by volume is up to 10 parts per million (ppm), depending on location and season.

The term "total ozone," sometimes referred to as the total layer thickness, describes the height integral of the column density and is abbreviated atm-cm or cm (STP). The total layer thickness is on the order of 0.2–0.5 atm-cm. The Dobson unit, derived in the same way and abbreviated m-atm-cm equals 10^{-3} atm-cm.

Seasonal Variation: On a hemispheric basis one of the most pronounced variations in total ozone is a function of season of the year. Data compiled and averaged over the years 1933–1959 by Willett (1962) exhibit a 32% increase from minimum in November to maximum in April (fig. 3.28). Although Willett refers to his data base as average "worldwide" total ozone, in point of fact it is based on observations from 68 northern hemisphere stations and only 4 from the southern hemisphere. The curve in figure 3.28 represents mainly the seasonal variation in northern hemispheric ozone. This is further verified by a similar northern hemisphere distribution found by Heath

Table 3.8.—Relationships Between Quantities Used for Expressing Atmospheric Ozone Concentration (from Krueger and Minzner, 1974)

Derived quantity	Basic quantity	
	Mass density ρ_3	Column density ϵ_3
Number density n_3 (molecules) m^{-3}	$\dfrac{N_A}{M_3} \cdot \rho_3$ $1.25467(10^{25}) \cdot \rho_3$	$10^{-5} \cdot \dfrac{N_A}{V_0} \cdot \epsilon_3$ $2.68684(10^{20}) \cdot \epsilon_3$
Column density ϵ_3 atm-cm km^{-1}	$10^5 \cdot \dfrac{V_0}{M_3} \cdot \rho_3$ $4.66968(10^4) \cdot \rho_3$	ϵ_3
Mass density ρ_3 kg m^{-3}	ρ_3	$10^{-5} \cdot \dfrac{M_3}{V_0} \cdot \epsilon_3$ $2.14148(10^{-5}) \cdot \epsilon_3$
Partial pressure p_3 N m^{-2} ——— mb	$\dfrac{R^*}{M_3} \cdot T_S \cdot \rho_3$ $1.73222(10^2) \cdot T_S \cdot \rho_3$ $1.73222 \cdot T_S \cdot \rho_3$	$10^{-5} \cdot \dfrac{R^*}{V_0} \cdot T_S \cdot \epsilon_3$ $3.70951(10^{-3}) \cdot T_S \cdot \epsilon_3$ $3.70951(10^{-5}) \cdot T_S \cdot \epsilon_3$
Mass mixing ratio r_3 dimensionless	$\dfrac{\rho_3}{\rho_S}$	$10^{-5} \dfrac{M_e \cdot \epsilon_3}{V_0 \cdot \rho_S}$ $2.14148(10^{-5}) \cdot \epsilon_3 / \rho_S$
Volume mixing ratio r_3' dimensionless	$\dfrac{\rho_3 \cdot M}{\rho_S \cdot M_3}$ $6.03448(10^{-1}) \cdot \rho_3 / \rho_S$	$10^{-5} \dfrac{M \cdot \epsilon_3}{V_0 \cdot \rho_S}$ $1.29227(10^{-5}) \cdot \epsilon_3 / \rho_S$

Avogadro's number $N_A = 6.022169(10^{26})$ (molecules) kmol^{-1}
Universal gas constant $R^* = 8.31434(10^3)$ N m K^{-1} kmol^{-1}
Volume of ideal gas at STP $V_0 = 22.4136$ m^3 kmol^{-1}
Molecular weight of O_3 $M_3 = 47.9982$ kg kmol^{-1}
Molecular weight of air $M = 28.9644$ kg kmol^{-1}
Temperature of the U.S. Standard Atmosphere T_S (K at height Z)
Density of the U.S. Standard Atmosphere ρ_S (kg m^{-3} at height Z)
1.0 N m$^{-2} = 0.01$ mb

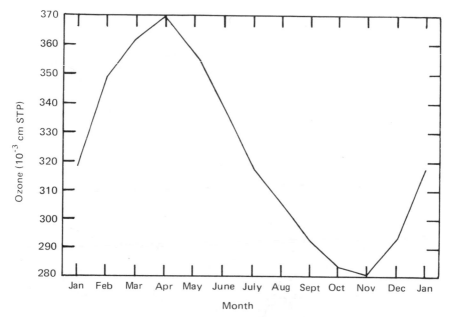

Figure 3.28. Mean annual distribution of total ozone based on measurements at 68 northern hemisphere and 4 southern hemisphere stations over the years 1933–1959. From Willett (1962).

(1974) using Nimbus 4 data from the BUV experiment (fig. 3.29), except that the minimum to maximum range for 1970 was only about 20%.

In the southern hemisphere (fig. 3.29) the hemispheric ozone budget peaks in October and is minimum in February-March. Thus, for both hemispheres total ozone is maximum in the local spring months and minimum in the local autumn months. The maximum amount, however, appears to be much less in the southern than the northern hemisphere. During the summer and winter solstices, the amount of ozone was about the same in both hemispheres and both solstices for the year of measurement.

On a global basis, the mean amount of total ozone (top curves of fig. 3.29) exhibits a much smaller seasonal variation due to the opposite monthly variation in the northern and southern hemispheres. In 1970 the range from minimum to maximum near the June solstice was about 5%, and a smaller maximum occurred near the December solstice. The 1964 curve is discussed further in section 3.5.3, but it should be noted that the global ozone level was lower in all months in

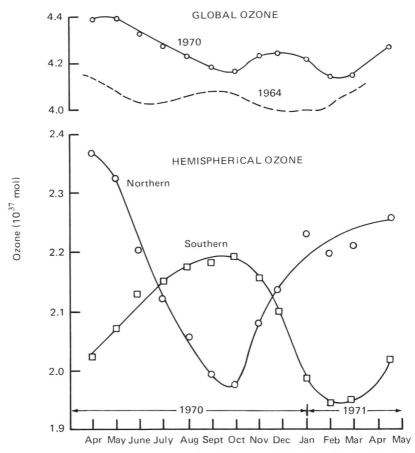

Figure 3.29. Global and hemispherical total ozone as derived by Heath (1974) from monthly means of the zonal means given by the Nimbus 4 BUV experiment. The zonal means are averages of 10° latitude intervals. The 1964 curve of global ozone was derived by Heath from the data of Brewer and Wilson (1968).

1964, a sunspot minimum year, than in 1970, when solar activity was near maximum.

Latitudinal Variations: Large variations in total ozone occur as a function of latitude, the most obvious feature being a deep minimum near the equator. This feature is evident in figure 3.30, based on measurements by the IRIS and BUV instruments on Nimbus 4 for a single pass (Heath et al., 1974). The circles are from an earlier shipboard latitudinal survey (White and Krueger, 1968) as reported by Heath et al. (1974). Differences in measurement techniques account for part of the differences in the plotted values as discussed by Heath

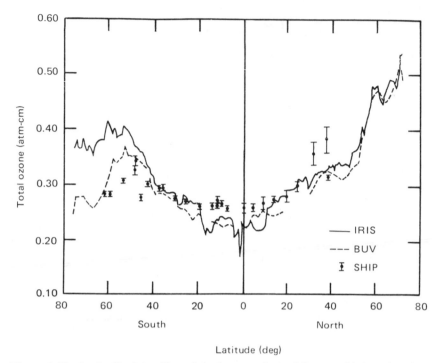

Figure 3.30. Latitudinal profiles of total ozone derived from a shipboard Dobson spectrometer (points with error bars) and from the IRIS and BUV instruments on Nimbus 4 during one orbit. From Heath et al. (1974).

et al., and part is probably due to the different years of measurement between the satellite (1970) and the ship (1965). The main point is to demonstrate the pronounced minimum at the equator. It is also of interest to note the higher maximum near 60°N latitude compared to the southern hemisphere peak, especially in the satellite data which cover a time span of only 54 min.

Similar latitude profiles have been derived by Loewenstein and Savage (1975) from airborne measurements at altitudes of 18.3 and 21.3 km. The similarity is to be expected, since the ozone concentration at about 20 km height, near the layer peak, is a large fraction of the total ozone amount.

Meridional averages of total ozone, in 10° latitude bands, have been established from BUV data by Heath (1974). The annual mean meridional average for April 1970–April 1971 exhibits the same type of latitudinal distribution; this is clear in figure 3.31, in which minimum ozone is again found at the equator, and the northern hemisphere (NH) maximum is significantly higher than the southern

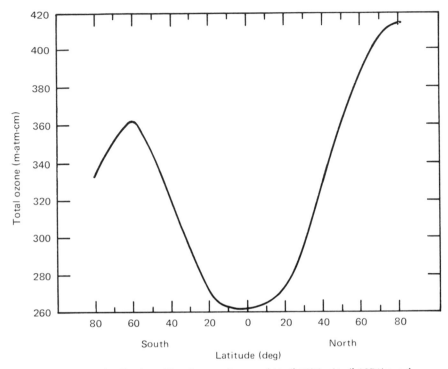

Figure 3.31. Latitudinal profile of annual mean (April 1970–April 1971) total ozone averaged over all longitudes as derived by Heath (1974) from Nimbus 4 data.

hemisphere (SH) maximum. Heath also claimed that on a month-to-month basis, the latitudinal distribution changes somewhat in detail, but the equatorial minimum is always evident, and the NH/SH maximum ratio is greater than 1.0 in all months except August, September, and October. This negative gradient going from pole to equator is typical of total ozone, but is not representative of the latitudinal ozone density profile at all heights.

Dobson (1966) suggested that the relatively greater amount of ozone in the northern hemisphere is due to a substantially greater poleward transport of air from low latitudes in that hemisphere compared to the southern hemisphere; there may also be land mass effects. On the other hand, Willett (1968) suggested that possible differences in auroral activity between the two hemispheres is a more likely explanation. Since auroral activity has been demonstrated to be similar in both hemispheres (Störmer, 1955, p. 18), Willett's suggestion seems untenable.

Although global maps of total ozone (Heath et al., 1974; Komhyr et al., 1973) reflect a latitudinal distribution with maxima near the poles and minimum near the equator, there also appears to be a longitudinal dependence wherein the highest total ozone concentrations tend to be located in two areas, over Siberia and western Greenland. The ozone highs seem to be associated with the semipermanent low-pressure systems of the atmosphere found in the same geographic areas. It may be significant to note that the maximum ozone region over western Greenland and northern Canada, as seen by satellite (Heath et al., 1974) and by Dobson spectrometer measurements from the ground (Komhyr et al., 1973) is centered almost over the magnetic dip pole, where particle precipitation leading to the ionospheric disturbance known as spread F takes place almost all the time (Herman, 1966a,b). According to the analysis of Komhyr et al., the ozone maximum over western Greenland remains roughly stationary all 12 months of the year.

A final note on the latitudinal distribution of ozone has a bearing on production and loss processes to be discussed later. The global distribution of total ozone above the 10- and 2.8-mb levels shows a strong positive gradient going equatorward (see fig. 28 of Heath et al., 1974). Thus the high-altitude latitudinal profile for ozone is opposite to that of total ozone.

Ozone Vertical Structure: The vertical distribution of ozone has been studied for more than half a century, beginning with Fabry and Buisson in 1921 (cf. the review by Goldberg, 1954). The earliest determinations were made using the Umkehr effect to deduce vertical profiles from ground-based observations of the intensity of scattered sunlight at the zenith during sunrise or sunset. Later, more accurate measurements were (and still are being) made by in situ balloon and rocket-borne instruments based on chemical and UV absorption techniques. A typical set of profiles from NRL rocket flights is illustrated in figure 3.32, in which a rather sharp peak can be seen between about 20 and 30 km altitude. Both the peak height and magnitude are different for each flight, demonstrating the long-term temporal vertical structure.

A more recent collection of ozone density profiles demonstrating diurnal and latitudinal effects was given by Heath et al. (1974). The results are reproduced in figure 3.33 and are thought to be typical profiles. In figure 3.33a, rocket and balloon measurements taken at Wallops Island, Virginia (WI, 38°N), in March 1970 are compared

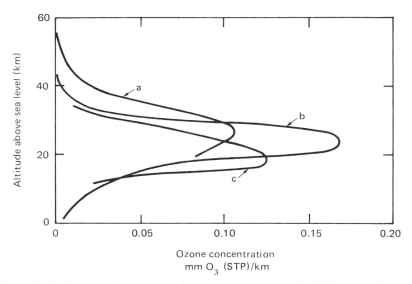

Figure 3.32. Vertical distribution of ozone from three early NRL rocket flights at White Sands, New Mexico. (a) June 14, 1949. (b) October 10, 1946. (c) April 2, 1948. From Goldberg (1954, p. 439).

with those taken about a year later at the Guiana Space Center (CSG, 5°N). Where the measurements overlap (i.e., below about 30 km altitude), there is good agreement between the two techniques. The latitudinal differences most prominent in the height of the maximum are therefore probably real. At 5°N, the ozone peak density is more narrow and of greater magnitude than the somewhat thicker peak at 38°N. There appears to be little difference in the day and night profiles below about 35 km at 5°N and below 55 km at 38°N. The diurnal influence is thus greatest above roughly 60 km altitude. A discussion of the classical and moist models illustrated in the figure to explain diurnal ranges is given by Heath et al. (1974).

In figure 3.33b the results of two rocket shots over Point Barrow, Alaska (71°N) made before and after a stratospheric warming are given. These are winter night profiles. Before the disturbance (January 10) there is marked fine structure near the peak of the layer, and the peak concentration is less than it is after the disturbance (January 30). Above about 45 km altitude, the concentration is less before the disturbance than afterward. According to Hilsenrath (1971), the temperature near 60 km altitude was approximately 50° less on January 30 than on January 10, and the ozone concentration difference could be related to the temperature change.

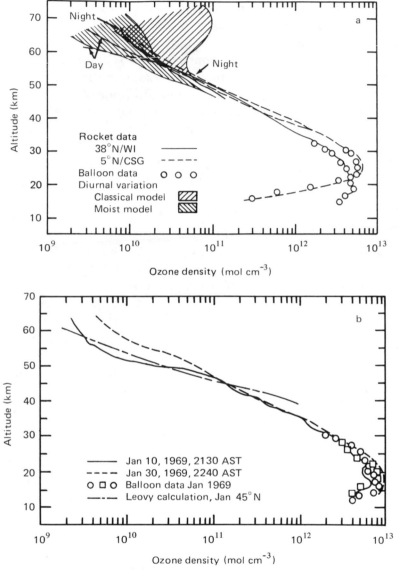

Figure 3.33. Vertical distributions of ozone density. (a) Rocket and balloon measurements at two latitudes for night and day conditions. From Heath et al. (1974). (b) Measurements over Point Barrow, Alaska (71°N) on January 10 and 30, 1969, before and after a stratospheric warming. From Hilsenrath (1971).

In summary, there is a marked variability in atmospheric ozone with respect to season, latitude, and altitude, and lesser variations with respect to time of day and longitude. In assessing the possible effects of solar activity on ozone concentration and distribution, these fluctuations must be kept in mind. For example, both the absolute magnitude and the range of fluctuations with time of total ozone are least at the equator and greatest at high latitudes. Also, the concentration is largest in local spring and least in local autumn. If a portion of the variability with time of ozone is caused by changes in solar activity, there is a greater probability for first detecting those changes in high latitudes and at altitudes above 40 km.

3.5.2 Atmospheric Ozone Chemical Processes

To appreciate the ways in which solar activity may influence atmospheric ozone, it is helpful to review the basic chemical processes involved in its production and loss. The following discussion is exceedingly simplified, but it touches on what appears to be the most important processes.

The production of ozone takes place mainly through the dissociation of oxygen molecules by solar radiation at wavelengths below about 242 nm through a three-body process, followed by rapid attachment of the released oxygen atoms to oxygen molecules. That is (Chapman, 1930):

$$O_2 + h\nu \ (<242 \text{ nm}) \longrightarrow O + O \tag{3.6}$$

$$2(O + O_2 + M) \longrightarrow 2(O_3 + M) \tag{3.7}$$

$$3O_2 + h\nu \longrightarrow 2O_3 \tag{3.8}$$

Based on a model of the average observed global distribution of ozone and temperature, with planar waves of solar radiation incident at all angles (Johnston and Whitten, 1973), the globally integrated rate of formation of O_3 is $5(10^{31})$ mol s^{-1}. In this model, instantaneous local production rates vary from a maximum of $3(10^6)$ mol $cm^{-3} s^{-1}$ at an altitude of about 30 km to a minimum of $10^{-6} cm^{-3} s^{-1}$ at 3 km altitude in the equatorial region. The model predicts similar rates at 40 km altitude (maximum) and 15 km altitude (minimum) at 70°N. The equatorial maximum extends to 20° latitude north and south of the equator, and the principal source region is above about 20 km.

Minor sources of atmospheric ozone include the photolyzation of NO_2, which supplies $NO + O$, and the liberated oxygen atom combines with O_2 to form O_3, as in reaction (3.7). This process is effective for producing ozone at altitudes below 13 km (Johnston and Quitevis, 1974), but, as will be seen shortly, NO_x is the most important destructive agent at higher altitudes.

It is evident from these reactions that the major production of atmospheric ozone depends on UV radiation at wavelengths below 242 nm. Any change in the intensity of this radiation from the Sun, as discussed in section 2.2.2, will alter the amount of ozone produced, that is, the source strength. In this simplified view, there should be a correlation between solar UV variations as they relate to solar activity and ozone production.

The loss of ozone takes place by a number of processes. Ozone that is transported downward into the troposphere is eventually destroyed by contact with the Earth's surface, but it has been estimated that this sink accounts for only about 1% (cf. Brewer and Wilson, 1968). The most important ozone sinks are the chemical and photochemical reactions that take place in the stratosphere. For example, the weak photolysis of ozone by visible light in the wavelength range 450-650 nm and by UV radiation above 310 nm promptly leads to the formation of oxygen atoms in the triplet P state, $O(^3P)$ (Chapman, 1930). Most of these form ozone by reaction (3.7), but some react with the remaining ozone in a destructive way:

$$O_3 + h\nu \longrightarrow O_2 + O \qquad (3.9)$$
$$O(^3P) + O_3 \longrightarrow O_2 + O_2 \qquad (3.10)$$

with the net result:

$$2O_3 + h\nu \longrightarrow 3O_2 \qquad (3.11)$$

Reaction (3.11) is opposite to the formation in (3.8), and its globally integrated rate of destruction amounts to about 17% of the formation rate (Johnston and Whitten, 1973). It takes place mainly above about 25 km altitude.

Strong photolysis of ozone takes place when the wavelength (λ) is less than 310 nm and yields excited singlets, that is $O(^1D)$ atoms on the right side of reaction (3.9). Most of these are first quenched and then combine again with O_2 through reaction (3.7) to reform ozone; thus no destruction takes place. It is by this process that the ozone layer strongly absorbs UV radiation below 310 nm. Some destruction does occur when water vapor is present because a fraction of the $O(^1D)$ atoms initiate a chain of reactions involving the hydroxyl and hydroperoxyl atoms (HO and HO_2, respectively), both of which destroy ozone (Nicolet, 1970). The destructive rate of the HO_x process (globally integrated) amounts to about 11% of the formation rate (Johnston, 1974).

The three processes just discussed account for about 30% of ozone loss, that is, ground effects (1%), oxygen reactions (17%), and the HO_x system (11%). Apart from possible chlorofluorocarbon effects introduced into the stratosphere by human activities, it appears that chlorine (e.g., from the oceans) is not an important sink for ozone (Crutzen, 1974a,b). Also, metallic oxides contributed to the upper atmosphere by meteors are probably unimportant, because no correlation has been found between ozone variations and meteor showers (Johnston, 1968). Atmospheric bromine from marine aerosols may be an important sink for ozone, because it acts as a destructive catalyst similar to NO (Wofsy et al., 1975), but it has not yet been fully evaluated. Oxides of nitrogen have been investigated as the most probable major sink in the stratosphere (cf. McElroy et al., 1974).

The destruction of ozone by the NO_x sink proceeds by a catalytic cycle in the following way (Crutzen, 1970):

$$NO + O_3 \longrightarrow NO_2 + O_2 \tag{3.12}$$

$$NO_2 + O \longrightarrow NO + O_2 \tag{3.13}$$

Thus nitric oxide destroys ozone directly by reaction (3.12), and the byproduct NO_2 removes an oxygen atom (that would otherwise reform ozone) and reforms NO to complete the cycle. However, part of the nitrogen dioxide is photolyzed by radiation of wavelengths less than 400 nm,

$$NO_2 + h\nu(<400 \text{ nm}) \longrightarrow NO + O \tag{3.14}$$

and the liberated oxygen atom can enter into reaction (3.13) or produce ozone through the three-body reaction (3.7) (Crutzen, 1970). In any case, the NO_x system is apparently the largest sink for ozone; its dependence on solar variability and activity is examined in section 3.5.4. The NO enhancements induced by corpuscular sources including cosmic rays will be discussed there also.

The importance of the ozone layer as a linking mechanism for solar activity effects on meteorological phenomena is not yet defined, but seems inevitable, considering the role of ozone as an absorber and shield for solar UV radiation. The absorption of UV radiation as a function of wavelength and ozone layer thickness for a particular model atmosphere is illustrated in figure 3.34. Here it can be seen

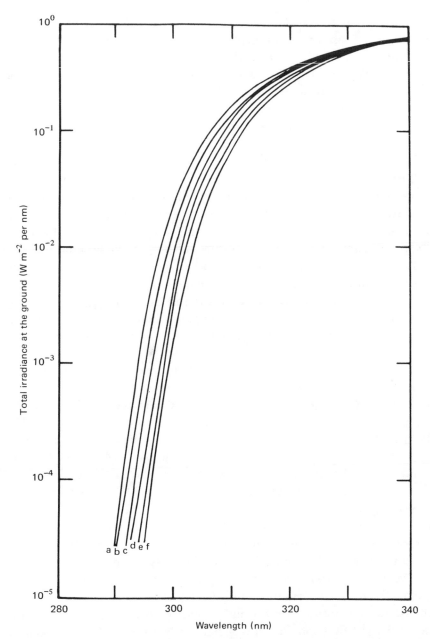

Figure 3.34. Wavelength dependence of solar UV radiation absorption by ozone for solar elevation angle of 60° and a specified model atmosphere. Ozone equivalent layer thicknesses are: (a) 0.20 cm, (b) 0.24 cm, (c) 0.28 cm, (d) 0.32 cm, (e) 0.36 cm, (f) 0.40 cm. From National Academy of Sciences, Environmental Impact of Stratospheric Flight *(Washington, D.C., p. 173, 1975).*

that at and below about 300 nm, if the equivalent layer thickness doubles, the amount of absorption increases by about two orders of magnitude. As has been seen, the total layer thickness can change by at least 36%, and this would have a substantial effect on the release of heat in the stratosphere (Reck, 1976a,b). If the layer thickness is altered by solar activity, it is evident that there would be changes in heat input relatable to that activity.

3.5.3 Ozone and the Solar Cycle

The possibility that atmospheric ozone is correlated with the sunspot cycle has been debated for nearly half a century. Conflicting and confusing results have been presented over the years, but, as will be seen below, the most recent studies have concluded that the solar cycle influence on atmospheric ozone can no longer be ignored.

A high positive correlation (+.94) between annual mean sunspot number and mean total ozone over the stations Harqua Hala, Arizona and Table Mountain, California was found by Fowle (1928, 1929) for the years 1921–1928. When Fowle (1934) extended the data base to 1933, the correlation fell off, implying that the data base used in the earlier analysis was too short.

On a day-to-day basis, Götz (1951) found no correlation between atmospheric ozone values and relative sunspot number, but Ahmed and Halim (1961) computed a significant correlation coefficient of +.50 at Mt. Abu (24.6°N) using springtime data (March 1–June 15, 1955). They found a lower (+.28) but still significant correlation at New Delhi (28.4°N) for data from January 1–April 15, 1955. However, at Quetta (30.2°N), using data for the whole year of 1955, their correlation coefficient was only +.09.

Willett (1962) attempted to relate global total ozone to sunspot number by averaging data from 68 northern hemisphere stations and 4 southern hemisphere stations, without regard to their latitude (or longitude) or relative completeness of data. Using annual averages for the years 1933–1959, Willett computed lag correlations with lags from −16 to +8 yr, where a positive lag means sunspots come after the ozone. His results show a high negative correlation (−.7) with a lag of +2 yr. This conclusion was vigorously attacked by London and Haurwitz (1963), on the basis of bias, both temporal and geographic, which had to be introduced into the data by Willett's statistical treatment. London and Haurwitz showed that the correlation could be reversed by proper treatment of the data, but, on the whole, they concluded that no correlation exists.

Further analysis of the 1933–1959 data base was then made by Willett and Prohaska (1965), broken down into seasonal averages and for individual stations at different longitudes selected for completeness of the data. They still found a negative correlation. Later, Christie (1973) reinvestigated Willett's (1962) original work and showed that weighting by latitude would not change the argument; his results generally supported Willett's conclusions.

In the same year, London and Oltmans (1973) again rebutted Willett's argument and said ". . . actually, a higher, positive correlation was found by him for a lag of three to four years, sunspots coming before ozone." This observation is more in agreement with Fowle's (1929) early finding of a positive correlation.

Careful analyses by Angell and Korshover (1973, 1975) generally support the contention that there exists a positive correlation between sunspot number and total ozone. Using ozone data from North America, Western Europe (principally Arosa, Switzerland and Tromso, Norway), New York, and Washington, D.C., they showed the maximum in total ozone occurring 2–3 yr after sunspot maximum (fig. 3.35). In recent years (from about 1958 on), data from European USSR, Western Europe, and North America indicate that ozone and sunspot maxima have occurred nearly in phase (possibly due to better data in the later years).

Near the pole (Tromso, 70°N), the maximum in total ozone typically lags sunspot maximum by 2–3 yr. The correlation is progressively weaker and has a greater time lag going equatorward. According to Ruderman and Chamberlain (1975), this behavior is characteristic of eddy diffusion away from an oscillating polar source.

Part of the conflict in the various analyses of total ozone based on ground-based (Dobson) measurements arises from the fact that atmospheric ozone below about 25 km altitude has a residence time of about 2 yr, and its distribution and concentration are dominated by transport processes. Since the density is much larger below 30 km than above, the low-altitude component generally dominates the amount of total ozone measured from the ground. The relationship between solar activity (as measured by sunspot number) and total ozone thus tends to be obscured; nevertheless, the analyses of Angell and Korshover (1973, 1975) tend to show a positive relationship.

Above about 25 km altitude, at source region heights where production and loss (other than transport) processes are most important, one should be able to observe more easily the effects of changing solar activity on the ozone concentration.

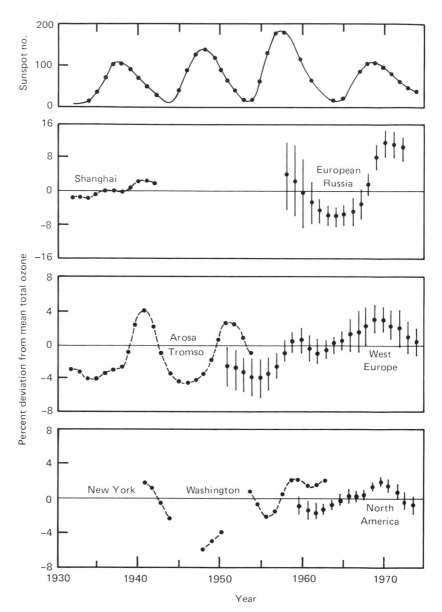

Figure 3.35. Solar cycle variation of total ozone as derived by Angell and Korshover (1975) for regional areas and individual stations. (Note scale change for the Shanghai and European Russia curves.)

This appears to be supported by the measurements of Paetzold (1973), who found from balloon observations a strong positive correlation between sunspot number and ozone content in the altitude interval 20–30 km. As the sunspot number increased from 10 to 180, the ozone content in this altitude range increased from 125 to 170 Dobson units, or about 36%. There was no apparent correlation between O_3 at 15–20 km heights and sunspot number. Earlier, Paetzold (1961) had found that the amount of ozone above 35 km altitude was greater in 1958 (sunspot maximum year) than in 1952, and it exhibited a positive correlation with both sunspot number and the decimeter radio flux.

An ozone budget for the sunspot minimum year of 1964 ($\overline{Rz}$ or annual average $= 6$) as given by Brewer and Wilson (1968) has been compared with global ozone for 1970 ($\overline{Rz} = 105$) by Heath (1974). The results are illustrated in figure 3.29. The 1970 data were derived from Nimbus 4 BUV measurements (Heath, 1974). Notwithstanding the difference in shapes of these two curves, it is evident that the mean monthly number of ozone molecules is greater in each month in 1970 than in 1964. On a yearly average, the BUV measurements give $4.24(10^{37})$ molecules of O_3, equivalent to 0.309 atm-cm if distributed uniformly over the whole Earth in 1970, and the Brewer and Wilson (1968) yearly average for 1964 is equivalent to 0.296 atm-cm. These results imply an increase of 4.4% in total global ozone as $\overline{Rz}$ goes from 6 to 105, if the shipboard and satellite measurements both accurately reflect total ozone.

On a hemispherical basis, Heath's data, reproduced in the lower half of figure 3.29, also exhibit a possible solar influence. That is, the average northern hemispheric ozone in April 1970, when the monthly mean sunspot number was 110, was $2.37(10^{37})$ mol. A year later, when the April 1971 mean sunspot number was 71, the amount of ozone had decreased to $2.25(10^{37})$ mol. This amounts to a 5% reduction. Approximately the same fractional decrease is observed in the southern hemisphere between April 1970 and April 1971.

To resolve the conflict evident in the various results and conclusions summarized above, it is necessary to unravel the competing effects of statistical methods used in the various analyses, different types of measurements, dependence on the sunspot cycle of sources and sinks of ozone, latitudinal and height influences, and transport processes. A total analysis to resolve the conflict is beyond the scope of our effort, but a few of the apparently more important effects should be noted.

The greatest conflict appears in the relationship between the year of occurrence of maximum annual total global ozone and the year of maximum sunspot number. Christie's (1973) work suggests that maximum total global ozone occurs near years of sunspot minimum, whereas Willett's (1962) results, depending on whose analysis is considered (Willett, 1962; London and Haurwitz, 1963; Willett and Prohaska, 1965; London and Oltmans, 1973; Christie, 1973), suggest that the ozone peak occurs 3 or 4 yr before or after sunspot maximum. This school of thought implies a generally negative correlation between total global ozone and sunspot number. On the other hand, Angell and Korshover (1973, 1975), Paetzold (1973), and the results of Heath (1974) show a positive correlation between the two parameters.

The sunspot cycle dependence of ozone sources and sinks and its implications for the above conflict are discussed in sections 3.5.2 and 3.5.4. Depending on the relative dominance of the production or loss process, the amount of ozone could be either greater or less at sunspot maximum. To complicate further the picture of total global ozone, transport processes in the lower stratosphere and troposphere redistribute the ozone latitudinally and obscure any relationship with sunspot cycle.

3.5.4 Influence of Solar Activity on Ozone Sinks

As noted in section 3.5.2, ozone loss proceeds by a number of processes, not all of which depend on solar activity. The major loss process depends on the concentration of the oxides of nitrogen (NO_2 and especially NO). The influence of solar activity on these constituents is examined below. There have been reports of the effects of nuclear explosions on ozone through NO production by the explosions (see review by Bauer and Gilmore, 1975), but, since these are not associated with solar activity, they are omitted.

Cosmic Ray Effects: There is a calculable production of nitric oxide by cosmic rays (Warneck, 1972). Since the cosmic ray intensity exhibits a variability related to solar flare occurrence and shows a 27-day recurrence tendency and a strong solar cycle dependence as well as a response to solar magnetic sector boundary passage, it is to be expected that the nitric oxide production rate would also respond to these short- and long-term solar influences.

No measurements have apparently been made to verify this expectation, but theoretical predictions have been made by Nicolet (1975) and Ruderman and Chamberlain (1975). Also, there have been recent airborne measurements of the columnar content of HNO_3 (Loewenstein and Savage, 1975) which may be used to infer the latitudinal effect of cosmic rays on nitric oxide distributions.

Ruderman and Chamberlain (1975) reported on calculations of ozone density vertical profiles, based on the assumption that destruction by NO is the principal loss process, and compared them with a measured profile over Panama (9°N). The result is given in figure 3.36, in which are assumed mole fractions of NO_x of 3, 10, and 100 parts per billion (1 ppb corresponds to about 10^9 NO_x mol cm^{-3} in the lower stratosphere). The theoretical curve based on 3 ppb of NO_x most closely matches the observed ozone profile, and it is of interest that an increase of about a factor of 3 in NO_x would decrease the ozone density at the peak of the curve by about 30%.

Qualitatively, Ruderman and Chamberlain (1975) showed that their calculations correctly predict the (solar) cyclic variations in total ozone measured for 40 yr at the stations Tromso and Arosa and the phase lag between ozone and the solar cycle. With additional worldwide station data, they demonstrated a latitudinal dependence as well as a time lag and relative amplitude of the effect at different stations, which are in reasonable agreement with their calculations.

Solar cycle variations in the production rate of NO by cosmic rays has been investigated by Nicolet (1975). The calculated variation with latitude for a solar maximum year (1958) and a solar minimum year (1965), based on cosmic ray data by Neher (1961, 1967), is illustrated in figure 3.37 for 20 km altitude, near the height of maximum effect. There is little solar cycle variation in the NO production rate at low geomagnetic latitudes ($<25°$), but poleward of about 50° the rate almost doubled between 1958 and 1965. The latitudinal variation is marked by an increase of a factor of nearly 3 in the sunspot maximum year and a factor of 5 in the sunspot minimum year, when the cosmic ray intensity is maximum. In the cosmic ray minimum year of 1969-1970 (near sunspot maximum) the nitric oxide production rate based on cosmic ray data by Neher (1971) dropped to a value only slightly higher than that in the sunspot maximum year 1958 (Nicolet, 1975).

The height dependence of NO production by cosmic rays as computed by Nicolet (1975) is given in figure 3.38 for high latitude loca-

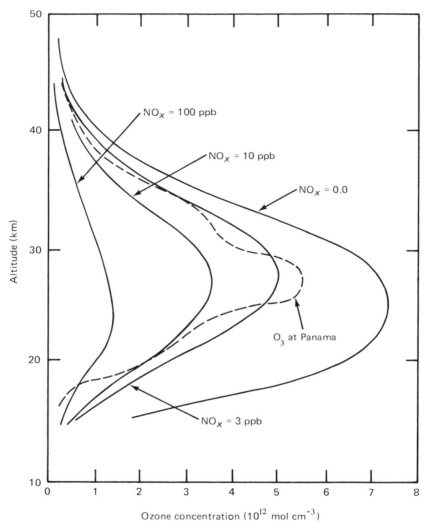

Figure 3.36. Calculated ozone profiles based on NO loss at the equator compared to observed profile at 9°N. NO$_x$ mole fractions assumed are indicated. From Ruderman and Chamberlain (1975).

tions. At the lowest heights there is not much change between solar maximum (1958, 1969) and solar minimum (1954, 1965) years, but near and above the peak height the change is on the order of a 30–80% increase from sunspot maximum to sunspot minimum. During sunspot minimum the production rate at geomagnetic latitude 56°N, based on Neher's (1967) data, is somewhat less than that at Thule (89°N geomagnetic latitude) as derived from Neher's (1971)

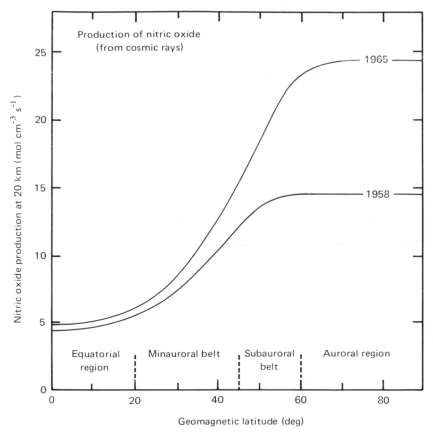

*Figure 3.37. Latitudinal dependence of NO production by cosmic rays at 20 km alti-
tude in a solar maximum year (1958) and a solar minimum year (1965). From
Nicolet (1975).*

data, except at low altitudes. The 1969 curve was extrapolated below
the peak by Nicolet using cosmic ray data at 44°N geomagnetic latitude from George (1970).

The total cosmic ray production of NO down to the base of the
stratosphere is illustrated in figure 3.39. At geomagnetic latitudes
poleward of about 60° during sunspot minimum years, the height-
integrated production of NO amounts to $6(10^7)$ cm^{-2} s^{-1}. The smaller
integrated production in equatorial compared to polar latitudes
comes about because the cosmic ray flux is lower and the height of the
tropopause is greater. In middle latitudes the tropopause height is
quite variable, depending on meteorological conditions; thus a range
of integrated production rates might be expected.

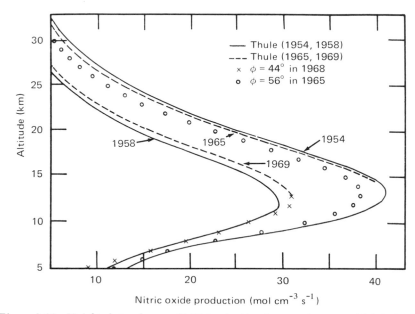

Figure 3.38. Height dependence of NO production by cosmic rays at high latitudes in solar minimum years (1954, 1965) and solar maximum years (1958, 1969). Full and dashed curves are for Thule (89°N geomagnetic latitude) for years indicated; x points are for 44°N, and o points are for 56°N geomagnetic latitude. From Nicolet (1975).

To translate the foregoing production rates into NO concentrations, the various loss processes of NO must be considered. An attempt to do this was made by Rao-Vupputuri (1975), and the governing chemistry has been outlined by Brasseur and Cieslik (1973), among others. Also, there have been some measurements of NO concentrations at specific altitudes (Loewenstein and Savage, 1975), and the results of their series of aircraft flight measurements from 5°–82°N latitude are summarized in figure 3.40.

There is qualitative agreement between the latitudinal behavior of the concentrations at 18.3 and 21.3 km heights and that of the production rates calculated by Nicolet (i.e., figs. 3.37 and 3.39). At 18.3 km altitude, the auroral zone increase begins at about 60°N latitude in the June 1974 flight, but not until about 70°N in the June 1975 flight. (In the longitude sector of the aircraft operation, geographic and geomagnetic latitudes are about the same according to Hakura (1965).) Even though both 1974 and 1975 are regarded as sunspot minimum years, there may be differences in the cosmic ray flux

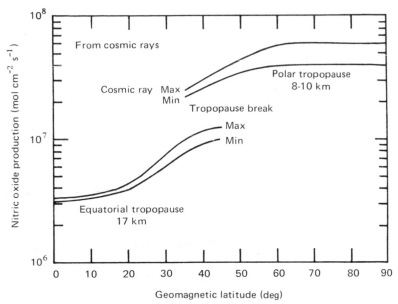

Figure 3.39. Height-integrated production of NO molecules in the stratosphere for cosmic ray maximum and minimum years as a function of latitude. Assumed heights of the equatorial and polar tropopause are indicated. From Nicolet (1975).

intensities or in other solar conditions during the flight periods that might explain part of the differences in the observed NO concentrations; this possibility remains to be investigated. There is closer agreement between the 21.3-km flight results and the production function given in figure 3.37.

Other in situ measurements bearing on the NO_x question have been reported recently by Murcray et al. (1975). Figure 3.41 summarizes their results of a latitudinal survey of the columnar content of HNO_3 measured at altitudes between 12 and 16 km and above 18 km with an aircraft instrumented to measure atmospheric emissions. In both northern and southern hemispheres the column content of HNO_3 increases going poleward, with a deep minimum near the equator. From balloon measurements also incorporated into figure 3.41, it appears that this increase continues to at least 60°N, but there is considerable seasonal and year-to-year variation in the balloon data. The seasonal trends in the northern hemisphere are opposite to those for O_3 presented in figure 3.28, which follows from the concept of ozone loss by NO_x sinks, if NO_x is like HNO_3. From figures 3.40

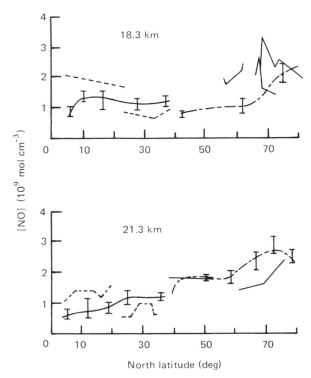

Figure 3.40. Latitudinal profiles of NO concentration measured by aircraft in longitudinal sector 132°–158°W at altitudes 18.3 and 21.3 km. In both panels dashed lines are data from flights in October 1974 (latitudes approximately 5–35°); solid lines are June 1974 flights northward of about 40°; solid lines with error bars south of 35° are July 1975 flights; broken lines with error bars are June 1975. From Loewenstein and Savage (1975).

and 3.41, it appears that the middle to high-latitudinal variations are the same for NO_x and HNO_3.

Solar Protons and Energetic Electrons: We have already seen the ionizing effects of solar protons on the middle atmosphere in chapter 2. There is now emerging evidence that solar proton fluxes of sufficient intensity can also reduce high-latitude stratospheric ozone through the production of NO_x, which reacts to destroy O_3. Weeks et al. (1972) first demonstrated the depletion of mesospheric ozone during a PCA by rocket measurement. More recently, Heath et al. (1977) have verified this earlier result and have shown an equally strong stratospheric reduction, with the Nimbus 4 satellite observation of global ozone above 4 mb during the major PCA event of August 4,

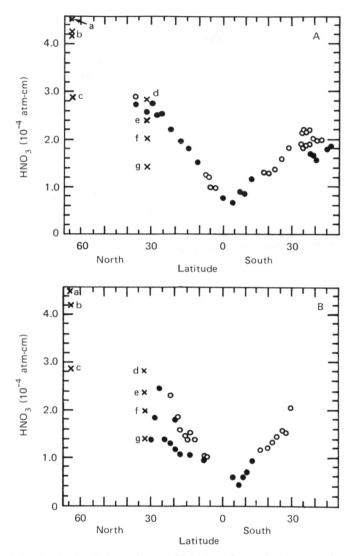

Figure 3.41. Latitudinal dependence of HNO₃ column density. Panel A: x points from balloon flights in (a) September 1972, (b) September 1971, (c) September 1972, (d) September 1970, (e) November 1970, (f) June 1970, (g) May 1970. Filled circles are aircraft flights at 18 km altitude in January 1974; open circles are flights at 12–16 km on same 1974 dates. Panel B: Lower-case letters with x points same as for panel A. Filled circles are flights at 18 km in April 1974; open circles are flights at 15 km on same 1974 dates. From Murcray et al. (1975).

1972. Both Crutzen et al. (1975) and Heath et al. (1977) have demonstrated through models that NO_x production by solar protons is sufficient to explain the observed stratospheric O_3 depletion, although Swider and Keneshea (1973) showed that HO_x chemistry was required to explain mesospheric changes.

Other radiations, including energetic electron precipitation events and their associated X-rays (e.g., Thorne, 1977) are now under consideration as competing sources for ozone depletion, once again through NO_x production in the stratosphere. In this case, a higher frequency of electron events is thought to compensate for their weaker effect per event, when compared to PCAs, to produce a cumulative longer-term modulation of stratospheric ozone.

A discussion of the postulated mechanism caused by solar protons and energetic electrons is reserved for chapter 6. Stratospheric response to intense PCAs is discussed further in section 4.1.3.

4 Short-Term Meteorological Correlations

Climatic change has been defined as the long-term collective effect of changes in the weather. Thus, if there are climatological trends associated with long-period variations in solar activity as discussed in the previous chapter, one should be able to discern weather responses to short-term fluctuations in solar activity. Many correlative studies have been directed toward this end, utilizing solar flares, geomagnetic storms, solar magnetic sector boundary passages, or solar radio noise bursts as the short-term solar activity indicator.

The study of meteorological responses to short-term transient events on the Sun may lead more directly to insights to possible physical linking mechanisms than will the long-term results of the previous chapter. For example, along with the eruption of visible solar flares, as discussed in chapter 2, the Sun emits bursts or streams of energy in the form of electromagnetic radiation (X-rays, ultraviolet), solar wind shock waves, and energetic charged particles which can interact with the atmosphere in a variety of ways. Meteorological phenomena correlated with solar flares may thus have as their root cause one or more of the possible interactions. There is also evidence of greater vertical mixing between the stratosphere and troposphere following flare days, and this process may either affect atmospheric circulation or be a consequence of it. Atmospheric electrical and ozone variations may be particularly fruitful in this regard, but they are considered to be intermediate steps to the ultimate meteorological responses.

This chapter is organized in terms of three main solar activity indicators, with the reported correlations with meteorological phenomena grouped accordingly. Thus section 4.1 deals with meteorological responses to solar flares and includes atmospheric pressure and winds, atmospheric electric quantities (potential gradient, ionospheric potential, air-Earth current density, thunderstorm occurrence), and atmospheric ozone.

In section 4.2, geomagnetic activity is used as an indirect solar indicator. Here we review reported correlations with sea level atmospheric
pressure, upper-level pressure and atmospheric circulation, low-
pressure troughs and vorticity indices, and atmospheric ozone. Little
consideration appears to have been given to atmospheric electrical
variations, except that Märcz (1976) recently reported that the potential gradient measured at a ground station in Poland ($\sim 51°$N) increases by 30–50% in association with geomagnetic storms.

Finally, in section 4.3 we discuss reported responses to solar magnetic sector boundary crossings. There is evidence for sector boundary
effects on surface pressure, upper-level pressure and circulation, low-
pressure troughs and vorticity indices, thunderstorm activity, the
potential gradient, and the ionospheric potential.

4.1 Meteorological Responses to Solar Flares

Several studies have been made using solar flares as the key solar
activity parameter, principally to determine possible meteorological
responses in atmospheric circulation, pressure changes, and atmospheric electrical parameters. The question of short-term solar effects
on rainfall (except for thunderstorm activity as an atmospheric electrical phenomenon) has apparently not been addressed. Temperature
changes may accompany flare-associated atmospheric pressure
changes, as discussed below.

4.1.1 Atmospheric Pressure and Winds

An indication that the mean height of the 500-mb level changes
within 24 hr after the occurrence of a solar flare was found by Schuurmans (1965), who calculated the difference in 500-mb height between
the first 00 UT aerological observation after the flare and that 24 hr
earlier, at 54 grid points in the North Atlantic area. These two observation times were selected to avoid diurnal variations, and, on the
average, the postflare measurement was made about a half day after
the flare in the 53 cases investigated. An extension of this study was
made by Schuurmans and Oort (1969) for 81 flares (importance 2+
or greater) with almost hemispheric coverage provided by 1020 grid
points. They used both 00 UT and 12 UT aerological data; thus the
postflare observation could occur anywhere from 0 to 12 hr after the
flare occurrence. On the average, for the cases investigated, the
observation was made about 6 hr after the flare. In this way they

found that the main pressure response occurred within 6 hr after flare eruption.

The mean of all 81 cases is summarized in the hemispheric 500-mb height difference map in figure 4.1. The differences, with isolines drawn at 1-geopotential decameter (gpdm) or 10-m intervals (full lines) are the height changes between observations spaced 24 hr apart bracketing the flare occurrence. Regions of 500-mb height rise (i.e., increased pressure at a constant height) are seen near the longitudes 5°E, 135°E, 165°E, 150°W, 115°W, and 50°W. Height decreases occur near 85°E, 145°E, 175°W, and 35°W. The more pronounced changes exhibit a preference for ocean and coastal areas, and the most intense (≥ 2 gpdm) centers appear in the middle latitude belt of 40°–60°. Poleward of 70° latitude the height differences are mainly negative, indicating a decrease in pressure following solar flares. The most striking feature is the pronounced cellular structure in pressure

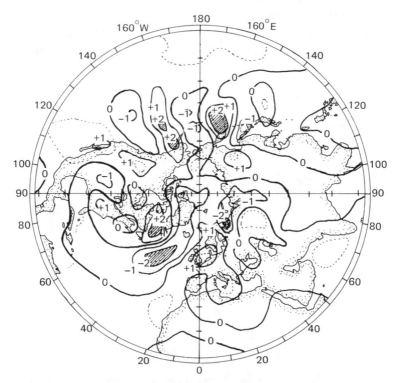

Figure 4.1. Polar plot distribution of 500-mb pressure height difference between first aerological observation after a flare and the observation 24 hr earlier (mean of 81 cases). From Schuurmans and Oort (1969).

175

change. This pattern is also apparent in the surface pressure results of
Duell and Duell (1948) discussed in section 4.2.1. Based on a critical
statistical analysis of these results, Schuurmans and Oort (1969) concluded that "the central values in the main areas of height fall and
height rise in [fig. 4.1] are probably meaningful and thus not due to
pure chance."

In investigating pressure changes in the vertical plane up to the
50-mb level at four stations (A, B, C, D), Schuurmans and Oort
(1969) found that the maximum flare response occurred at the
300-mb level, at least along the 60°N parallel between longitudes of
0°–70°W, as shown in figure 4.2. The greatest mean change, +4.7
gpdm (47 m), was found at the 300-mb level over the North Atlantic
by ship B (56.5°N, 51.0°W); the standard error of the mean attests
to the significance of the response (fig. 4.3). At the higher elevations
maximum response occurred about 6 hr after the flare, and at Earth's
surface ($\sim$ 1000-mb level), flare-associated changes showed up about
2 days after the eruption.

Along with the pressure-height changes observed over the North
Atlantic, significant alteration of the vertical temperature distribution was found, as illustrated in figure 4.4. A maximum change of

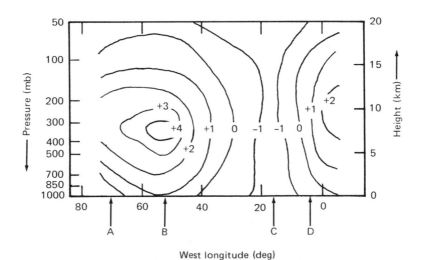

Figure 4.2. Mean height difference of pressure levels up to 50 mb along the approximate parallel of 60°N observed 24 hr apart before and after flares at stations A
(Fort Chimo, 58.1°N, 68.4°W), B (ship at 56.5°N, 51.0°W), C (ship at 59.0°N,
19.0°W), and D (Lerwick, 60.1°N, 1.2°W). From Schuurmans and Oort (1969).

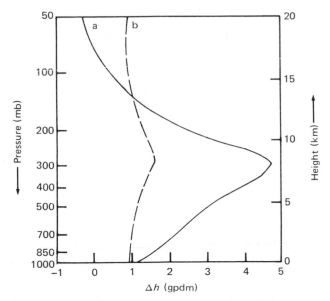

Figure 4.3. Mean height difference of pressure levels up to 50 mb over ship B (56.5°N, 51.0°W) before and after flares (curve a) compared to standard error of the mean (curve b). From Schuurmans and Oort (1969).

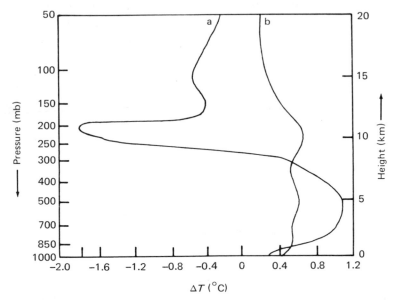

Figure 4.4. Mean temperature difference at pressure levels up to 50 mb over ship B before and after flares (curve a) compared to standard error of the mean (b). From Schuurmans and Oort (1969).

about +1.1°C occurred at the 500-mb level, and a maximum de-crease (−1.8°C) at 200 mb near the tropopause. The strongest gradi-ent in ΔT appeared near the 300-mb level, where the change in pres-sure was greatest.

Geostrophic accelerations calculated from the flare-related height changes by Schuurmans and Oort (1969) show that the zonal mean westerly winds at the 500-mb level in latitudes 55°–75°N were accel-erated by nearly 0.5 m s^{-1} in 24 hr, and near 50°N latitude, a decel-eration of the westerlies amounting to about 0.4 m s^{-1} in 24 hr took place.

On a seasonal basis, the cellular pattern evident in figure 4.1 changed little, but the largest height changes were found in winter (18 cases) and the smallest in summer (25 cases).

The large pressure gradient from about 8 km altitude down to the surface over the North Atlantic, formed after major flares (fig. 4.3), should eventually produce a downward flow of air (Schuurmans and Oort, 1969). It can be seen in figure 4.1 that the location of the Zugspitze observatory at 47.4°N, 11.0°E is within a similar region of flare-produced positive pressure difference; thus one might expect an eventual downward transport of air there, too.

In this connection, Reiter (1973) found greatly increased concen-trations of the tracer elements Be^7 and P^{32} at Zugspitze (elevation 2.96 km) on the second day following the occurrence of major flares of class 2 or greater. According to Reiter, these two radioactive nuclides are formed in the stratosphere by cosmic ray spallation, and their enhanced presence in the troposphere at 3 km altitude is indica-tive of a mass downward transport of stratospheric air about 2 days after a large flare. The possibility that the increased concentration might have arisen from in situ production of the nuclides by enhanced solar cosmic ray fluxes associated with flares was ruled out by Reiter because the production rate would be orders of magnitude too small to explain the observed nuclide concentrations. Reiter observed that the maximum Be^7 and P^{32} enhancements coincide with maximums in solar wind velocity and geomagnetic index Ap following the big flares.

4.1.2 Solar Flare Effects on Atmospheric Electricity

The effects of solar flare occurrence on potential gradient, air-Earth current density, and thunderstorm activity have been investi-gated by Reiter (1969, 1971, 1972), Cobb (1967), Bossolasco et al.

(1972, 1973a), Markson (1971), Holzworth and Mozer (1977), and Herman and Goldberg (1976, 1978).

Reiter's observations were made at the Zugspitze observatory in the Bavarian Alps. The observatory's elevation (2964 m) places it above the exchange layer which commonly extends from sea level up to an altitude of 1-3 km, depending on meteorological conditions. The exchange (or "mixing") layer is characterized by a relatively high ion concentration which usually decreases with altitude and then drops sharply at the top of the layer. Above it, the ion density increases with altitude. Within the layer, the air conductivity (σ) fluctuates considerably with time and location, and at the top it rises sharply (about 50% within 100 m). Above the layer, fluctuations in σ are small and slow, and its magnitude increases rapidly with altitude along with the increase in ion density. For example, at 5 km the conductivity is a factor of 10 higher than at the ground level, and the factor increases to 100 and 500 at 18 and 30 km, respectively.

Above the mixing layer, therefore, potential gradient (E) and air-Earth current density (J_c) measurements have no large, localized fluctuations, so variations in these two parameters should reflect changes in the global ionospheric potential.

For 70 solar flare occurrences in 1956-1959, Reiter (1969) found that both E and J_c increased beginning shortly after the flare, and peaked 3-4 days afterward. In those cases there was a suggestion of an earlier peak about 1 day after the flare eruption. Since the potential gradient is a measure of global thunderstorm activity, Reiter speculated that an increase in that activity should occur a few days after flares. The question of whether increased thunderstorm activity is the cause or the result of an increase in potential gradient remains open, but a few remarks are included in section 6.6.3.

Earlier independent E and J_c measurements made by Cobb (1967) on the mountain of Mauna Loa (3400 m) in Hawaii, which is also normally above the exchange layer and reflective of global changes, anticipated the Zugspitze results. Cobb found both the potential gradient and air-Earth current to rise significantly after a solar flare and remain above normal for several days. Cobb's maximum in E occurred about the same time as that of Reiter, 3-4 days after the flare, but his air-Earth current maximum occurred only 1 day after the solar eruption.

In analyzing the magnitude of the potential gradient response to solar flares, Reiter (1969) found that during the solar minimum years of May 1964–March 1967, the potential gradient at Zugspitze reached 60% above normal about 3 days after flare occurrence and was still 50% greater than normal 1 day later. Further analysis of Zugspitze data for March 1966–July 1968 (Reiter, 1971) revealed that H Lyα flares and proton flares seem to have about the same effect on atmospheric electrical parameters. A standard superposed epoch analysis of proton flares in this 28-month period showed both potential gradient and air-Earth current density to increase beginning about 1 day after the flare and peaking at 30% above normal 2–3 days after flare day.

In a continuing followup, Reiter (1972) analyzed in detail the response of E and J_c to five selected flare events. In addition to the flare eruptions, he considered additional solar activity parameters, i.e., 10.7-cm (2800-MHz) solar radio noise bursts, solar protons recorded by Explorers 34 and 41, solar wind measurements by Pioneer 7, and solar X-ray bursts recorded by Explorers 30 and 34. The net result was that, for these specific events, the best correlation was found with the 10.7-cm radio noise bursts. Flares of importance ≥ 2 are usually, but not always, accompanied by such noise bursts. Along the same line, Sao (1967) has shown that potential gradient variations within the Arctic Circle are positively correlated with solar radio emissions at 1000 and 2000 MHz. He found no correlation with higher or lower frequencies, which may be an indication that only those flares accompanied by Gigahertz radio noise bursts affect the potential gradient; this is in keeping with the association between solar proton bursts and radio noise emission (sec. 2.3.1).

With regard to thunderstorm activity, Reiter (1969) noted a 57% increase in sferics counts (indicative of thunderstorm activity) maximizing about 4 days after flare day during the years 1964–1967. This increase is comparable to that for E found by Reiter for the same years. Also, for low sunspot number years, Flohn (1950) found that the thunderstorm occurrence frequency in Central and Northern Europe rose by about 20% and remained above normal for about 3 days after CM passage of a major active sunspot group.

An analysis of thunderstorm occurrence with solar flares in the United States by Markson (1971) for the sunspot minimum years 1964–1965 indicated a 63% increase in occurrence frequency maximizing about 7 days after flare eruptions. Markson pointed out that his maximum in United States thunderstorm frequency occurred about 3 days after the maximum in potential gradient found by Reiter at Zugspitze. The long lag time of 7 days makes it uncertain whether United States thunderstorm activity is affected by solar flares.

On a global scale, Bossolasco et al. (1972) found that thunderstorm activity increased by 50% (in solar minimum years) to 70% (in solar maximum years) about 4 days after solar flare eruptions. Thunderstorm activity in the Mediterranean area, as deduced from the number of long-range radio direction finding fixes observed in that area by the British thunderstorm detection network, increases markedly about 4 days after solar flare eruptions (Bossolasco et al., 1973a). It is clear in the superposed epoch analysis in figure 4.5 that the increase begins within 1 day after the flare and achieves 50% on the 4th day.

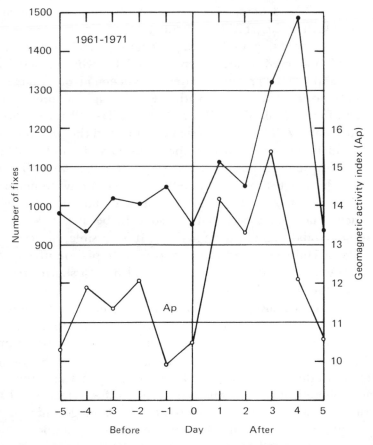

Figure 4.5. Superposed epoch analysis of daily thunderstorm activity and geomagnetic activity index Ap before and after flares of class 2B or greater in years 1961–1971. Day 0 is flare day. From Bossolasco et al. (1973a).

These results are in agreement with the Zugspitze results of Reiter (1969). The data in figure 4.5 span the years 1961–1971, representing a full solar cycle. The flare time history of the magnetic index Ap is included for comparison.

Measurements of the ionospheric potential made at Weissenau, Germany by daily radiosonde ascents, and the product, $E \times J_c$, made at Zugspitze during the major solar events in August 1972 are illustrated in figure 4.6. This product is a measure of the power in the global electric circuit. For comparison, variations in the magnetic activity as indicated by the index Cp and in solar protons detected by the satellite ATS-1 in synchronous orbit are included. Class 3B flares occurred on August 4 and 7, preceding the two major increases in V_i and $E \times J_c$ by 2½–3 days. The results of this specific event are in agreement with earlier statistical results.

For this particular period in early August 1972, Holzworth and Mozer (1977) showed a large increase in VLF whistler activity on August 4 and a smaller but broader enhancement on August 7–8. These enhancements coincided with the peaks in solar proton fluxes evident in figure 2.20, about 12 hr after the class 3B flare eruptions on August 4 and 7. The ionospheric potential and the product $E \times J_c$, both of which are correlated with the intensity and number of thunderstorms in progress, peaked 2½–3 days after the flares (fig. 4.6), and one can expect statistically a delay of about 4 days to maximum thunderstorm response (fig. 4.5). It appears that the whistler enhancement maximums occurred too soon to be attributable to an increase in global thunderstorm activity. It is possible, however, that the index of Holzworth and Mozer was more representative of nontropical thunderstorm activity, which could have a shorter response time to proton-induced effects.

Although it is known that whistlers are generated by lightning flashes (Storey, 1962), an increase in whistler occurrence rate observed at a ground station can reflect an increase in either the number of lightning flashes within a certain range of the station's conjugate location or in the number of available propagation paths through the magnetosphere from one hemisphere to the other (Helliwell, 1965). Whistlers follow ducts, that is, field-aligned inhomogeneities in electron density, through the magnetosphere, and the number of ducts increases during magnetospheric disturbances associated with solar events. Since the maximum whistler rate observed by Holzworth and Mozer occurred at the same time as the proton peak fluxes, an alter-

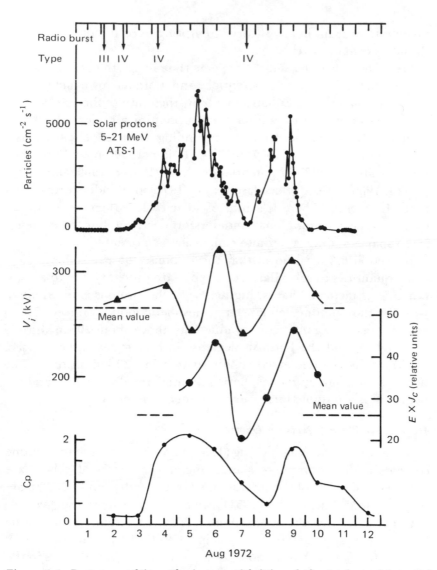

Figure 4.6. *Responses of ionospheric potential (V_i) and the product of potential gradient (E) and air-Earth current density (J_c) to large flare events in August 1972. Solar protons measured by ATS 1, geomagnetic activity index Cp, and times of solar radio noise bursts are shown for comparison. From Mühleisen and Reiter (1973).*

native possibility is that the enhancements were partially due to im-proved propagation conditions rather than increased lightning activ-ity at that time. In any case, the lag in thunderstorm response, which is also observed to be similar for cosmic ray decrease events, must be

183

taken into account in any theory attempting to relate solar activity to thunderstorm occurrence.

From these diverse results it appears that air-Earth current, potential gradient, ionospheric potential, and thunderstorm activity respond to solar flares. Enhancements in these atmospheric electrical quantities occur 1–4 days after the eruption of a major solar flare, with thunderstorm occurrence responding slowest. The increases range from 12% (Cobb, 1967) to 50% (Reiter, 1969) in air-Earth current density, 30–60% in potential gradient (Reiter, 1969), and 20% (Flohn, 1950) to 70% (Bossolasco et al., 1972) in thunderstorm occurrence frequency. There is a hint of solar cycle influence on the responses, especially for global thunderstorm activity, but the evidence is too sparse to draw a definite conclusion at present.

In section 6.6 it is shown that the responses of atmospheric electrical quantities to solar flare occurrence are probably due to a combination of factors. That is, high-energy solar protons emitted along with the flare produce enhanced atmospheric ionization (sec. 2.3.5) and accompanying increased conductivity above about 20 km altitude (sec. 3.4.1), and the Forbush decrease in cosmic ray intensity (sec. 2.4.5) results in a decreased conductivity below 20 km altitude. The potential gradient and ionospheric potential are also altered, and the net result is a possible increase in thunderstorm activity.

4.1.3 Solar Flare Effects on Ozone

About two decades ago, Craig (1951) suggested that the total ozone content of the atmosphere should increase at times of solar flare occurrence because of the intense burst of UV radiation known to accompany large flares. Fritz (1951) attempted to verify the suggestion, but could find no obvious response. A rather strange result came from an analysis of 220 flare events in 1959–1961 by Steblova (1968); her conclusion was that in most cases ". . . a disturbance arises in the ozonosphere long [½ hour] before the optical phase of chromospheric flares." From Steblova's statements in the cited paper, it appears that her ozone "disturbance" is an increase in total ozone. Insufficient data were given in the paper for a verification of this apparent effect. One can only speculate that it meant either that undetected UV radiation enhancements might begin prior to the optical phase and produce ozone increases, or that the total ozone was higher before the flare than afterward because of a decrease in total ozone after the flare occurrence.

The latter speculation appears to be more reasonable, since it is supported by the rocket observations of Weeks et al. (1972). Their results showed that a strong reduction of ozone accompanied an intense solar proton flare event on November 2, 1969. Also, Angell and Korshover (1975) have shown that the seasonal average total ozone over the United States, Great Britain, Mauna Loa, and Huancayo was significantly depressed for several months following the great solar outbursts of August 1972 (fig. 4.7). This has been further verified and explained for the same proton event using the Nimbus 4 satellite data from the BUV instrument (Heath et al., 1977).

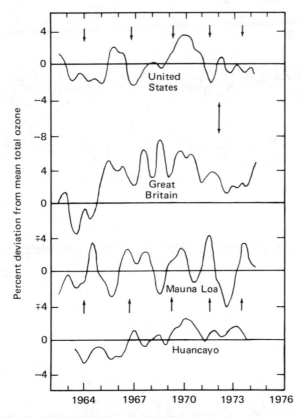

Figure 4.7. Smoothed total ozone deviations demonstrating the effect of a strong solar flare (double-headed arrow). U.S. curve based on five stations, Great Britain on three. Single-headed arrows denote time of quasi-biennial west wind maximum at 50 mb in the tropics. Smoothing is by 1-2-1 running mean of successive seasonal averages; each of the four seasonal values was computed as a deviation from the mean of total length of record. From Angell and Korshover (1975).

This result is shown in figure 4.8, wherein we observe a marked and substantial depletion in total O_3 above 4 mb, most pronounced at the higher latitudes. That there may be a connection between the two phenomena, rather than chance occurrence in an isolated event, is

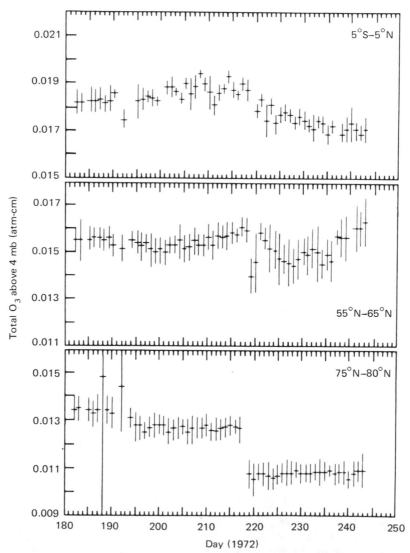

Figure 4.8. Daily zonally averaged total ozone above 4 mb pressure level (about 38 km) for equatorial (top panel), middle (middle), and high (bottom) latitudes during July and August 1972. From Heath et al. (1977).

suggested by additional observations reported by Angell and Kor-shover (1975). Following an intense solar flare outburst in September 1966, total ozone was again depressed for several months over the same stations (fig. 4.7) and additionally over stations at Leningrad (60°N, 30°E) and Alma Ata (43°N, 77°E). Another intense flare occurring in November 1960 was followed by ozone decreases over Alma Ata, Leningrad, West Europe, Canada, and Japan (ozone data for this event were not given by Angell and Korshover for the stations included in fig. 4.7). Finally, the averaged data from Angell and Kor-shover show some indication of an ozone decrease at all the afore-mentioned locations except Huancayo and Alma Ata in the months following the November 1969 flare studied by Weeks et al. (1972).

In summary, there is experimental evidence that the total ozone content over widely separated locations decreased following strong solar flares occurring in November 1960, September 1966, November 1969, and August 1972. Based on these few observational results, it is probable that other solar events not yet investigated would exhibit a similar ozone response. Possible reasons for a decrease, rather than an increase as predicted by Craig (1951), are discussed in section 3.5.4.

4.2 Meteorological Correlations with Magnetic Activity and Solar Corpuscular Emission

The general philosophy underlying the use of magnetic activity indices for Sun-weather investigations is that a sharp increase in mag-netic index is indicative of enhanced solar corpuscular emissions arriv-ing at the Earth. Past definitions of what constitutes a "sharp rise in geomagnetic indices" vary from one worker to another and sometimes from period to period by the same worker (Roberts and Olson, 1973a). Analysis and comparison of past investigations is therefore difficult, but an attempt is made below in spite of the past subjectiveness in the selection of magnetic disturbances. Another pitfall is that there has not always been a clear distinction between geomagnetic storms asso-ciated with active, flare-emitting sunspot regions and those associated with solar M regions or coronal holes. Also, in the flare-associated storms, no separation of gradual and sudden commencement storm types has been made. Further, there is the untenable question as to the importance of tropospheric influence on geomagnetic phenom-ena, which is discussed in greater detail in chapter 5. In spite of these drawbacks, the bulk of the evidence presented below suggests a link between magnetic disturbances and meteorological phenomena with a common, or at least associated, cause rooted in the Sun.

4.2.1 Sea Level Atmospheric Pressure

Pioneer work by Duell and Duell (1948) showed that within 2–3 days after "geomagnetically disturbed days" in winter months (November through February), surface pressures at European stations fell by an average of 2 mb, coincident with a rise of equal or greater amount in the Greenland-Iceland area. Because of this change, the pressure difference from Greenland to northwestern Europe was increased by about 5 mb, with an attendant increase in cyclogenesis.

These results have been verified and extended by Mustel (1972), based on data for December through February in the years 1890–1967. Note in figure 4.9 the pressure rise following geomagnetic storms in southern Greenland (filled circles) and the pressure fall in northwestern Europe (area V with open circles). The magnitude of these changes is indicated in the curves below the map in figure 4.9; it averages about 2 mb for pressure increases in areas II, III, and IV and about 4 mb for decreases in areas I, V, and VI, in agreement with Duell and Duell (1948). The lag time from key geomagnetic storm day to maximum pressure change is 2–3 days, also in accord with the Duell results. A widespread decrease occurs over the eastern USSR (area I), and an even greater area of increase covers all of middle-latitude Europe.

Another Russian study of surface pressure changes following geomagnetic disturbances was based on 14 geomagnetic disturbances occurring during winter months of the years 1950–1970 (Sidorenkov, 1974). The results, expressed as the average difference in pressure (mb) between the day of onset of a geomagnetic disturbance and 3 days later, are given in the map in figure 4.10. The pressure falls (negative-valued contours) are observed in the regions of the North Atlantic and eastern USSR, and increases are observed over Europe, the center of the Arctic Ocean, and western Canada.

A comparison of the major features of the pressure-change distribution maps of Schuurmans and Oort (1969), figure 4.1, Mustel (1972), figure 4.9, and Sidorenkov (1974), figure 4.10, is given in table 4.1. The agreement is remarkably good considering that Schuurmans and Oort dealt with upper-level (500 mb) pressure changes following solar flares in the years 1957–1959, Mustel treated

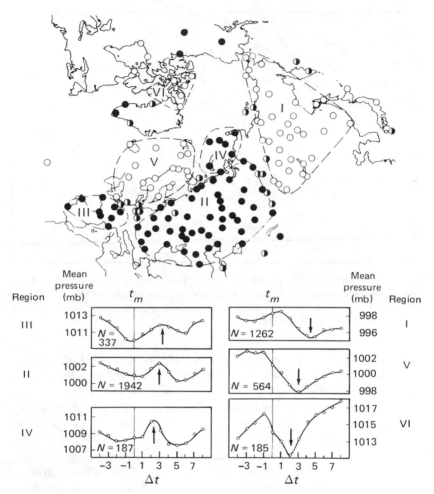

Figure 4.9. Distribution of surface pressure variations in the northern hemisphere 2–4 days after geomagnetic disturbances in the months December through February for 1890–1967. Filled circles are mean pressure increases; open circles are decreases. Mean statistical curves for regional pressure from 3 days before beginning of disturbance to 8 days afterward are given at bottom of figure; N = number of cases used for each region. From Mustel (1972).

surface pressure winter data associated with magnetic disturbances in the years 1890–1967, and Sidorenkov also used winter surface pressure data, but for the years 1950–1970.

The magnitudes of the pressure changes found in these as well as the Duell and Duell (1948) investigations are small, a few millibars, but the consistency of results between several completely independent

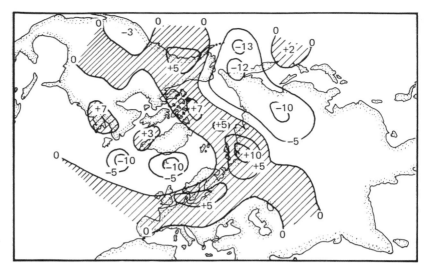

Figure 4.10. Distribution of average surface pressure changes 3 days after 14 magnetic storm commencements in the northern hemisphere during 1950–1970 winter months. Contours are differences in millibars, and regions of pressure increase are shaded. From Sidorenkov (1974).

Table 4.1.—Comparison of Major Features in Pressure-Difference Distribution Maps Following Solar Flares and Geomagnetic Disturbances

Area (demographic)	Approximate Center (geographic coordinates)	Pressure Responses I*	II	III
Germany	55°N, 5°E	Rise	Rise	Rise
Eastern USSR	60°N, 135°E	Rise	Rise	Rise
South of Kamchatka	50°N, 165°E	Rise	Fall	Fall
Gulf of Alaska	55°N, 150°W	Rise	Rise	Rise
Western Canada	55°N, 115°W	Rise	Rise	No data
Kara Sea	70°N, 85°E	Fall	Fall	Fall
South Japan	45°N, 145°E	Fall	Fall	Fall
South of Aleutians	50°N, 175°W	Fall	Fall	No data
South of Iceland	45°N, 35°W	Fall	Fall	Fall

*I. Schuurmans and Oort (1969). Flare response. 500-mb level. Figure 4.1.
 II. Sidorenkov (1974). Magnetic activity response. Surface. Figure 4.10.
III. Mustel (1972). Magnetic activity response. Surface. Figure 4.9.
Data Base
  I. 1957–1959; 81 flare events $\geq 2^+$, 1 day after flare.
 II. 1950–1970; 14 geomagnetic disturbances, 3 days after start of disturbance.
III. 1890–1967; 834 geomagnetic disturbances, 2–4 days after start of disturbance.

studies is promising evidence of a link between solar activity and atmospheric pressure.

A number of other Russian investigators have also found surface pressure responses to geomagnetic disturbances (Mustel et al. 1966; Mustel, 1966; Kubyshkin, 1966a,b). In contrast, Stolov and Spar (1968) and Stolov and Shapiro (1969) could find no evidence of such in their own data. In the meantime, Shapiro (1956, 1959, 1972), who had been working with surface pressure data, found a significantly "higher persistence" of pressure over North America and Europe during the first week after a geomagnetic storm along with an increase in the north-south pressure gradient, which lent support to the Russian results.

Neglecting any fuzziness in definitions of time lags, further suggestion for a cause/effect relationship between solar activity and surface pressure can be gained by considering the time sequences involved in the results presented in this and the earlier section (4.1.1) on solar flares. Schuurmans and Oort (1969) showed that, although upper-level pressures changed within 6 hr after a flare occurrence, the surface pressure did not respond until about 2 days later. In association with most solar flares, a geomagnetic storm develops within 24 hr (Smith and Smith, 1963, p. 234); thus the surface pressure change of Schuurmans and Oort would follow the geomagnetic storm by about 1 day, as found by Mustel (1972). These phase relationships favor arguments that the tropospheric disturbances are somehow induced by magnetic-related effects and not vice versa.

4.2.2 Upper-Level Pressure and Circulation

Soviet studies (Sarukhanyan and Smirnov, 1970; Mustel, 1970) have shown that the zonal character of the atmospheric circulation is disrupted and meridional processes are enhanced during geomagnetically disturbed periods, but at one time, Stolov and Shapiro (1971) rebutted the claim. The positive results of Shapiro (1956, 1959, 1972) coupled with those of Roberts and Olson (1973a) for low-pressure trough developments related to magnetic storms (sec. 4.2.3) encouraged Stolov and Shapiro (1974) to reanalyze their 700-mb data.

The data used were 700-mb contour heights between latitudes 20° and 70°N for the years 1947–1970, along with 272 "key days" in this period in which the magnetic index Ci (sec. 2.6.1) equaled or exceeded 1.0. Applying the superposed epoch method from -33 to

+66 days relative to the key day for several zonal and meridional meteorological indices, Stolov and Shapiro (1974) found that the 700-mb height difference between 20° and 55°N increases significantly in winter months about 4 days after a geomagnetic disturbance (Ci ≥ 1.0). The height difference is normally 304 m; after an enhancement of Ci, it increases to 325 m. This change corresponds to an increase of 0.6 m s^{-1} in the mean geostrophic wind flow. It comes about through a combination of the growth and development of large pressure falls in the latitude belt 40°–60°N and smaller pressure rises at lower latitudes. In summer months a less prominent but still significant increase in this zonal index occurs only 2 days after a key day; the associated increase in zonal flow appears to be uniformly distributed around the globe. The increased zonal flow of about 7% in winter appears to be limited mainly to the half-hemisphere 90°–265°W and is most pronounced in the longitude band 90°–175°W.

In a study of wind profiles, Kasimirovskii and Loginov (1973) considered the magnetic activity index Ap and 10.7-cm radio flux measurements as solar activity indicators. High solar activity was defined as $F_{10.7} \geq 140$ units, Ap ≥ 20, and low activity by F ≤ 85 and Ap ≤ 5. Rocketsonde measurements of winds in the stratosphere and lower mesosphere over Fort Churchill, Fort Greeley, White Sands, and Cape Kennedy in the years 1964–1969 were utilized.

The maximum difference in wind profiles between "high" and "low" solar activity occurred 2 days after a solar radio flux enhancement and 2–3 days after Ap increased. These delay times are shorter than the 4-day lag at the lowest altitudes observed by others, implying that delay times decrease with increasing height.

The westerly zonal winds exhibited the greatest variability in late winter and spring over Fort Greeley, Alaska (64°N, 146°W) in the height range 20–40 km (approximately 80–5 mb) (Kasimirovskii and Loginov, 1973). From September through April, strengthened westerly flow occurred in conjunction with increased Ap index, and in winter only, 10.7-cm flux enhancements produced a similar response. In the warm half of the year there was a tendency for decreased westerly flow and increased easterly flow following flux enhancements.

At the high latitude stations (Greeley and Churchill) the wind change correlation was better with Ap than with $F_{10.7}$, implying that corpuscular effects are more important than electromagnetic effects in high latitudes. At the middle latitude stations (White Sands and Cape Kennedy) the corpuscular effect (that is, the correlation of Ap and wind change) was less pronounced.

4.2.3 Low-Pressure Troughs and Vorticity Indices

Based on an analysis of low-pressure trough development at the 300-mb level in the North Pacific and North America areas for the years 1956–1959, Macdonald and Roberts (1960) concluded that, in wintertime, 300-mb troughs entering or forming in the Gulf of Alaska area 2–4 days after a major geomagnetic index rise are likely to undergo much greater deepening than those entering at other times. These troughs may be regarded as cyclonic waves in the zonal westerly winds, and they move in a generally eastward direction. They are also manifest at the 500-mb level (Macdonald and Roberts, 1961; Twitchell, 1963).

To extend these earlier analyses, Roberts and Olson (1973b) utilized a vorticity area index (VAI), defined as the area of a trough wherein the absolute vorticity is $\geq 20(10^{-5})$ s^{-1} summed with the area where it is $\geq 24(10^{-5})$ s^{-1}. This index, derived by computer, removes the subjectiveness from the assessment of the intensity and importance of troughs, and the minimum (threshold) vorticities for the definition were so chosen because most wintertime 300-mb troughs exceed a vorticity of $20(10^{-5})$ s^{-1}, and large ones have a substantial region exceeding the largest vorticity value.

Before proceeding to the analysis itself, it may be illuminating to consider the basic concept of vorticity. One may define vorticity as the circulation per unit area, where circulation in turn is defined as the line integral of the velocity of a stream traveling along a closed path in a fluid (Svalgaard, 1973). The absolute vorticity as used by Roberts and Olson (1973a,b), Svalgaard (1973), and Wilcox et al. (1973a,b) is the sum of the relative vorticity of the atmospheric airflow relative to the Earth's surface, and the vorticity of the Earth itself. The magnitude of the latter term is simply twice the angular velocity of the Earth's component of rotation about an axis normal to the surface.

Now, it can be shown (Svalgaard, 1973) that for a rotating air column in the atmosphere the absolute vorticity is conserved for that volume of air. The distribution of absolute vorticity over the Earth's surface is very irregular, with numerous centers of high separated by areas of low absolute vorticity. The highs move across the Earth's surface with weather systems (e.g., circumpolar jet streams) while conserving their value of absolute vorticity. When the pressure decreases in one of these centers, its area increases to conserve the volume, and the area covered by the high vorticity expands accordingly.

The high vorticity centers are seen in connection with low-pressure troughs associated with increased storminess and precipitation. A deepening of these troughs leads to an increase in the area having high absolute vorticity; thus one can define a vorticity area index (VAI), as Roberts and Olson did, to indicate the overall severity of the low-pressure system. This area index is the total area over which the absolute vorticity exceeds a given threshold value.

For the Roberts and Olson (1973b) analysis, the trough "lifetime" is defined to begin on day 0, that is, when a trough is formed or when an existing one crosses 180° longitude moving eastward. A "key trough" is one that forms or crosses 180° after a sharp rise in geomagnetic activity, and a "key day" is the day on which the geomagnetic event occurs. Here, a trough is identified by its vorticity area index. It generally persists for 1–2 weeks until it either dissipates or moves into western Europe and out of the Roberts and Olson (1973b) frame of study. It would be interesting to follow the troughs beyond western Europe and around the globe to determine whether they again cross 180° longitude into the North Pacific.

Results using winter data for 1964–1971 (Roberts and Olson, 1973b) confirmed the earlier finding of Macdonald and Roberts (1961). Further, during the travel of troughs across the North Pacific/North America areas, there are two statistically significant periods of time when key troughs undergo a sharp rise in vorticity area index. The first occurs during the first 3 days of trough lifetime, as is evident in figure 4.11; on the average this occurs 3–5 days after a geomagnetic key day. It is important to note that 2–4 days must elapse between the key day and trough start in order for the effect to be observed. On occasions when less than 2 days elapsed, no VAI intensification took place (Olson et al., 1975). The second enhancement of VAI occurs 9 days after zero day (fig. 4.11), by which time the key trough has usually moved to the North Atlantic coastal region of the United States. This second enhancement may be related to the observations of significant pressure falls and increased cyclogenesis over northeastern coastal North America about 10 days after geomagnetic storms, as reported by Asakura and Katayama (1958). If so, Roberts

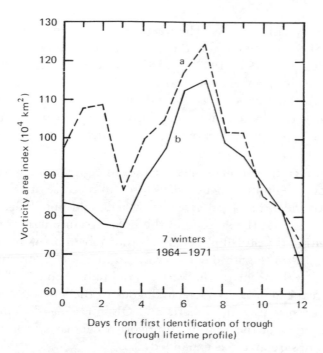

*Figure 4.11. Mean vorticity area index for troughs preceded by a sharp rise in geo-
magnetic activity (curve a) and for troughs preceded by a 10-day period of geomagnetic quiet (curve b). For curve a, add 3 days to the days shown to correct for
lag time after geomagnetic storm event on zero key day (see text). From Roberts
and Olson (1973a).*

and Olson (1973a) would regard it as "an indirect, or second-stage effect" of solar activity on weather.

The early results of Clayton (1923) showing a wintertime decrease
in pressure at about 55° latitude (fig. 3.12) during solar maximum
years suggests the likelihood of a greater trough intensification in
solar maximum than in solar minimum years. The Roberts and Olson
(1973a,b) analysis spanning years from solar minimum in 1964
through maximum in 1969 unfortunately cannot be used to test this
speculation.

Over the 20-yr period 1951–1970, Reitan (1974) has shown that the
distribution of cyclonic event occurrence in January (northern hemisphere winter) exhibits maxima in the areas of the Gulf of Alaska and
the northeastern coastal region of the United States. These are the
areas where Roberts and Olson found increases in vorticity area index
following geomagnetic storms. As discussed in section 3.1.7, the number of events is negatively correlated with the 11-yr solar cycle;

another correlation analysis, between SSC geomagnetic storm occurrences (Mayaud, 1973) and the number of cyclonic events in the United States for 1951–1967, yielded a statistically significant (94% confidence level) correlation coefficient of −.46. These results, combined with those of Roberts and Olson (1973a,b), suggest that, although fewer cyclonic centers may form in sunspot maximum years, they are larger and more intense than the more numerous ones that form in solar minimum years.

An indirect indication of pressure falls in high latitudes even at the 10-mb level beginning about 3 days after an increase of 15 or greater in the Ap index has been given by Macdonald and Reiter (1975). They showed that the latitude of the polar stratospheric vortex contained within the 30 640-m height contour moves poleward about 3° from the 3rd to the 8th day following an increase in Ap, indicating that the areal extent of the vortex gradually shrinks. This polarvortex areal extent is inversely analogous to the vorticity area index for low pressure used by Roberts and Olson (1973a,b). Thus, when the area index for the high-pressure vortex decreases, it implies that the low-pressure area has expanded.

4.2.4 Geomagnetic Activity, Ozone, and Temperature

The earliest suggestions for a correlative relationship between magnetic activity and total ozone were apparently made by Dobson et al. (1927, 1929), who concluded that total ozone was enhanced during magnetically disturbed conditions. Ahmed and Halim (1961) correlated daily departures of ozone value from monthly means against Kp for the same day at several individual stations over a range of latitudes from Mt. Abu (24°N, 73°E; 15°N geomagnetic latitude) to Tromso (70°N, 19°E; 67°N geomagnetic latitude). They found a small but persistent correlation which was positive at low latitudes and negative at high latitudes. In correlating the daily departure with Kp of the following day, they found the same trend, and the correlation coefficients were a bit higher.

Malurkar (1954) found a close relationship between the diurnal range of total ozone and magnetic activity; the range was greatest during magnetically disturbed periods, and the amount of variability decreased with decreasing latitude. To the extent that anomalous D-region absorption of radiowaves is correlated with magnetic activity (i.e., high absorption in auroral latitudes accompany magnetic disturbances), the recent results of Grasnick and Entzian (1973) are appropriate in this discussion. They performed power spectrum analyses of total ozone, D-region absorption, and 10.7-cm solar radio emissions. Typical periodicities of 4–8 days were found, but, more important, the correlation coefficient between total ozone and absorption periods was +.95, significant at the 1% level (99% confidence level). The amount of variability in both ozone and D-region absorption decreased toward the equator. These findings are consistent with Malurkar's (1954) earlier results and suggest that the causative agent(s) for associated fluctuations in ozone, absorption, and magnetic activity decreases in effectiveness going equatorward.

Stratospheric and mesospheric temperatures (which can be related to ozone), measured by rocket datasondes, have been investigated by Ramakrishna and Seshamani (1976). Their preliminary findings, claimed to be statistically significant, seem to show a temperature enhancement between 61- and 90-km heights at high latitudes following geomagnetic activity. The effect is found to be nonexistent in the tropics, and delay times for temperature enhancement range from several days at middle latitude to less than 1 day in the auroral zone (Ramakrishna, private communication, 1977). Ramakrishna and Heath (1977) have now reported a more detailed analysis of 125 soundings at lower altitudes from Wallops Island, Virginia in 1975. They found as much as a 10° enhancement in temperature between 35- and 65-km heights following geomagnetic storms. A physical mechanism to explain these results has not been found.

4.3 Responses to Solar Magnetic Sector Structure

The discovery of well-defined, sharply bounded sectors in the solar magnetic field direction (sec. 2.5) has opened a new way to study Sun-weather relationships. Since the sector structure is closely related to other solar activity indicators, as well as to terrestrial magnetic activity indices, statistically significant correlations between sector crossings and meteorological phenomena support the results of solar-weather studies that have used the more traditional indicators. More important, the magnetic sector structure is a purely solar parameter, uncontaminated by any possibility of meteorological influences (cf. ch. 5). The results reviewed in this section suggest that there are definite correlations between sector boundary crossings and meteorological parameters such as atmospheric pressure, vorticity, and atmospheric electrical phenomena.

4.3.1 Surface Pressure

Investigators in the Soviet Union seem to have been first to attempt to relate meteorological parameters to the structure of the interplanetary magnetic field (IMF). Kuliyeva (1975a,b) investigated effects on zonal circulation indexes, and Mansurov et al. (1975) reported on their studies (published originally in Russian in 1972) of surface pressure at the magnetically conjugate stations of Mould Bay (80.8°N; 264.0°E) in the Arctic and Dumond-D'Urville (80.1°S, 228.7°E) in the Antarctic.

Rather than sector boundary passage across the Earth, Mansurov and colleagues utilized the predominant polarity of the IMF as inferred from polar geomagnetic measurements (Svalgaard, 1968; Mansurov, 1969; Wilcox, 1972) to correlate with atmospheric pressure during 1964. They showed statistically that when the IMF was directed toward the Sun (negative polarity) the average surface pressure in the northern hemisphere at Mould Bay was about 5 mb higher than at times of positive IMF polarity. At the southern conjugate station (Dumond-D'Urville) the pressure was about 4 mb higher with a positive IMF direction, just opposite to the northern hemisphere result.

Interestingly, the magnitude of the characteristic disturbance of the geomagnetic field at high latitudes that enables determination of the interplanetary field direction with ground-based magnetometer data (see Wilcox, 1972) exhibits precisely the same relationship with the IMF as does the atmospheric pressure. That is, when the IMF is toward the Sun the magnitude of the geomagnetic signature observed at Thule in the northern hemisphere is about 100 gammas compared to almost 0 gammas at Vostok in the southern hemisphere, and when the IMF is away from the Sun, the Vostok signature magnitude is about 100 gammas greater than that for Thule. The reason for the magnetic perturbation is that the IMF direction determines whether coupling to the geomagnetic field takes place in the northern or the southern polar hemisphere. The reason that the surface atmospheric pressure at polar stations follows the same pattern is not clear, but its correlation with the IMF is not incompatible with the observed correlations discussed in section 4.2.1.

4.3.2 Upper-Level Pressure and Circulation

Changes in atmospheric pressure in relation to magnetic sector boundary (MSB) crossings have been studied by Svalgaard (1973).

With MSB crossing defined as the zero (key) day, the quantity investigated was the average height of given pressure levels (850–30 mb) over a latitude belt 10° wide.

Significant systematic variations were found in response to MSB crossings. For example, at high latitudes the pressure-level heights increased a few days after boundary passage, and at middle latitudes they decreased. This is the same as saying that the pressure at a constant height increases in high latitudes and decreases in middle latitudes after a MSB passage.

To illustrate these variations, Svalgaard (1973) used the height difference Δh between levels of constant pressure in the 40°–50° belt (middle latitude) and 60°–70° belt (high latitude) averaged over all longitudes in the northern hemisphere. The results, based on a superposed epoch analysis of 54 MSB crossings during the winters of 1964–1970, are given in figure 4.12. Several features in this figure are noteworthy. For example, at all levels investigated the height difference decreased from about day 0 to a minimum approximately 4 days later, then increased again over the next day or two. Also, there was a consistent increase in Δh from 4 or 5 days prior to day 0 to a maximum reached on day 0 at the 30-mb level, but 1 to 2 days earlier at successively lower altitudes. The decrease in Δh thus began on day 0 at 30 mb, but 1 to 2 days *before* MSB crossing at the greater pressure levels, and minimum Δh was reached soonest at the lowest altitude (850-mb level).

It has recently been shown that a minimum in the Kp index occurs about 1 day before a sector boundary passage, and Shapiro (1974) argued that this minimum is more important than the subsequent rise in Kp after the passage. One might speculate that the maximum height difference prior to sector crossing is most closely associated with the minimum Kp and represents the meteorological equivalent of very quiet conditions.

The subsequent rise in Kp and concomitant decrease in pressure-height difference would thus represent a departure from quiet conditions after a MSB passage. At any rate, the height rise of all the investigated pressure surfaces (850–30 mb) at high latitude implies anticyclogenesis following a crossing, and the height decrease at middle latitudes leads to cyclogenesis with its consequent increase in storminess and precipitation.

The results of this analysis will be seen to be quite consistent with the vorticity analysis discussed in section 4.3.3, which shows increased

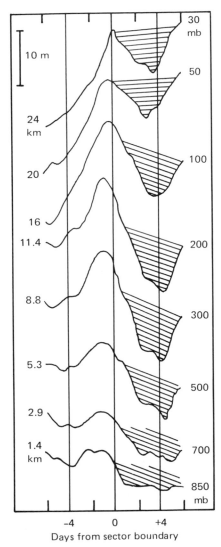

Figure 4.12. Variation of height difference of pressure surfaces between 40–50°N and 60–70°N latitudes before and after a solar magnetic sector boundary passage on day 0, based on superposed epoch analysis of 54 crossings during 1964–1970 winters. Approximate heights (km) of pressure surfaces (mb) are indicated. From Svalgaard (1973).

vorticity index (lower pressure and more storminess) about 3–4 days after a MSB crossing, since most vorticity centers causing the high index are located in middle latitudes (~40°-60°).

4.3.3 Low-Pressure Troughs and Vorticity Index

The trough analysis of Roberts and Olson (1973; see sec. 4.2.3) was extended by Wilcox et al. (1973a,b, 1974) using the total vorticity area index summed over the northern hemisphere from the latitudes of 20°N and poleward. Sector boundary crossings listed by Wilcox and Colburn (1972) were used for key days in lieu of the Ap magnetic index.

The response of the vorticity area index at the 300-mb level to sector boundary crossings is illustrated in figure 4.13, based on 54 crossings in November–March 1964–1970. The index from 6 days before

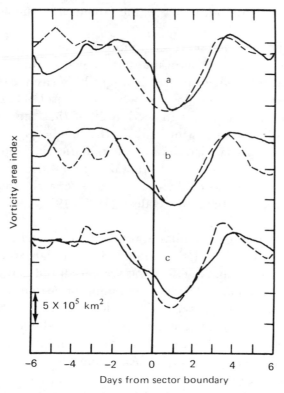

Figure 4.13. Average response of vorticity area index for magnetic sector boundary passage on day 0. Curve a: dashed, 30 boundaries separating positive to negative sectors; full, 24 boundaries separating negative to positive sectors. Curve b: dashed, 22 boundaries in second half of winter; full, 32 boundaries in first half of winter. Curve c: dashed, 28 boundaries in the interval 1967–1970; full, 26 boundaries in the interval 1964–1966. Total of 54 boundaries. Ordinate axis in units of $5(10^5)$ km². From Wilcox et al. (1973a).

to 6 days after MSB passage (day 0) was averaged for each day, and the data sample was broken into two parts, three different ways:

1) boundaries separating adjacent positive to negative sectors and boundaries separating adjacent negative to positive sectors;

2) first half of winter (November 1–January 15) and second half of winter (January 16–March 31);

3) years 1964–1966 and years 1967–1970.

As can be seen in figure 4.13, the response pattern is quite similar in all six cases. On the average, the VAI decreases from about 2 days before to 1 day after day 0, and then increases to a maximum or recovers to its predisturbance value about 3½ days after MSB crossing.

Little or no such response was found for the summer months, in keeping with the conclusion of many investigators that the influence of solar activity (in whatever way it might be measured) on weather tends to be strongest in local winter when solar insolation is least. This follows from the arguments in section 2.2.4 that the relative solar energy input by the solar wind and Earth's magnetosphere is significant compared to solar electromagnetic radiation in winter. A superposed epoch analysis of 81 additional cases (Wilcox et al., 1975) substantiates the results of the first 54 cases, and rigorous statistical tests conducted by Hines and Halevy (1975, 1977) also support the results.

To see if the trend was similar at other pressure levels, Wilcox et al. (1973a,b; 1974) repeated the analysis for standard pressure levels from 850 up to 10 mb. No effect was seen at altitudes above the 100-mb level, but the index decrease beginning prior to day 0 starts earliest at the maximum pressure levels, closest to Earth's surface. The magnitude of index change is least at 850 mb (about 10^6 km^2) and gradually increases to about $9(10^6)$ km^2 at 300 mb. There appears to be no longitudinal effect on index change at any pressure level (Wilcox et al., 1974).

It should be noted that the VAI hits a minimum 1 day after sector boundary passage (fig. 4.13). In figure 2.40, however, it can be seen that the Kp index maximizes at this time, implying an inverse relationship between VAI and Kp when the two are ordered according to sector boundary passage. This negative correlation is also strong on the basis of annual average values of daily hemispheric VAIs and annual average values of Ap (Zerefos et al., 1975). On a seasonal average basis, the negative correlation is significant in winter, spring, and fall.

Because the VAI begins to decrease prior to day 0 (fig. 4.13), it is evident that if there is a solar influence on atmospheric vorticity, it has already started by the time a magnetic sector boundary sweeps past the Earth. It is therefore of interest to note that Olson et al. (1975) studied these data from the viewpoint of solar flare association. Defining the day of large solar flare occurrence as day 0, they found that by day 1 or 2 the northern hemisphere VAI increased sharply by 5-10% above its background value. The VAI then decreased to 5-10% below its preflare level by day 3 or 4, and by day 5 or 6 it recovered to its predisturbance level. A search for physical causes for a solar influence could thus conceivably begin with consideration of the energetics associated with solar flare eruptions.

4.3.4 MSB Passage and Thunderstorm Activity

At least two attempts have been made to relate thunderstorm occurrence with MSB passage. Markson (1971) used the occurrence of thunderstorms in the United States during the solar minimum period of November 1963 through December 1964 for a total of 15 solar rotations, and Bossolasco et al. (1973b) used 10 yr of data on the occurrence frequency of daytime lightning in the Mediterranean area in all seasons.

Although the analysis technique was not described very clearly in the Markson paper, there appears to be a definite preference for United States thunderstorms to occur from about 1 day before to 1 day after a boundary crossing from a positive into a negative sector. No discernible change in activity occurred in crossing from a negative to a positive sector. The maximum in thunderstorm occurrence near the positive to negative boundary was slightly above the 2σ statistical level, making it marginally significant statistically. The Bossolasco results, on the other hand, indicate an approximate 15% reduction in lightning frequency with the Earth near positive to negative boundaries. No correlation was found by Bossolasco near a negative to positive boundary, in agreement with the Markson results.

The lack of change across a negative to positive boundary might be related to the difference in magnetic activity behavior at such times compared to times of positive to negative crossings. Shapiro (1974) has shown that the day before a positive to negative crossing, the Kp index reaches an absolute minimum, whereas the day before a crossing from negative to positive the minimum is scarcely less than minima occurring at other times. In a search for mechanisms relating thunderstorm occurrence to solar activity, this peculiarity may be significant.

The opposite behavior of Mediterranean lightning frequency and United States thunderstorm occurrence is strange. It might be explained by diurnal effects (assuming that Markson used nighttime as well as daytime thunderstorms in his data sample) or seasonal effects. According to Park (1976b), the inconsistency may have arisen because regional data were used in both cases; what is needed is a study of global thunderstorm activity with respect to sector boundary crossings, preferably in periods when high-latitude atmospheric electric field and air-Earth current density measurements are also being made (see sec. 4.3.5).

4.3.5 MSB and the Atmospheric Electric Field

A recent study by Park (1976b) shows that the vertical electrical field measured at Vostok, Antarctica (78°S, 107°E) responds to sector boundary crossings whether the direction change from the Sun is negative to positive or positive to negative. The data covered the months March–November 1974, a period near solar minimum in which only two sectors per solar rotation were evident. Seventeen boundary crossings occurred, but even with such a small data sample, Park obtained statistically significant results. His superposed epoch analysis showed that the electric field magnitude sharply increased beginning about 3 days after MSB passage (fig. 4.14), and the effect was more pronounced in austral winter than during the equinoxes. Since the electrical field at Vostok is essentially free of localized perturbations due to local thunderstorms, air pollution, and magnetospheric field effects, it should be representative of global thunderstorm activity. Park's (1976b) results would thus seem to indicate that global thunderstorm activity begins to increase about 3 days after the passage of a solar magnetic sector boundary. This increase begins about the same time as the minimum in cosmic ray intensity following sector boundary crossing (see fig. 2.38).

A somewhat shorter time response of the atmospheric electrical field at Zugspitze to sector boundary crossings was found by Reiter

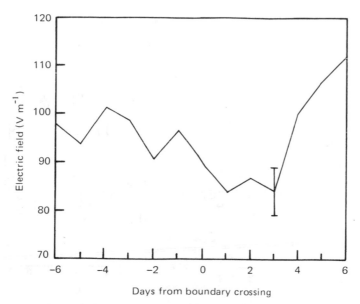

Figure 4.14. Average behavior of Vostok vertical atmospheric electrical field for 17 solar magnetic sector boundary crossings. The standard error is indicated by vertical bar at day 3. From Park (1976b).

(1976, 1977). The maximum field strength, as well as maximum air-Earth current density, peak 1–2 days after passage of a negative to positive boundary and just on the crossing day for a positive to negative boundary (fig. 4.15). Reiter's superposed epoch analysis utilized Zugspitze atmospheric electrical data for one full solar cycle (May 1964–February 1975), along with the same sector boundary listing by Svalgaard (1975) that was used by Park in his analysis. In figure 4.15 it is evident that the response to negative to positive crossings is more dramatic in years of high solar activity (1967–1971) than in all years of the cycle combined, but for positive to negative crossings the response was similar for both time spans.

The reason for the difference in response time between the results of Reiter and Park is not clear. Some speculative possibilities are (1) it may be due to the small data sample representing only one winter in a year near sunspot minimum as used by Park compared to the 11-yr sample including all seasons of the year used by Reiter; (2) it may be a latitude effect; (3) with Vostok and Zugspitze being in opposite polar hemispheres the response lag may be a function of a difference in

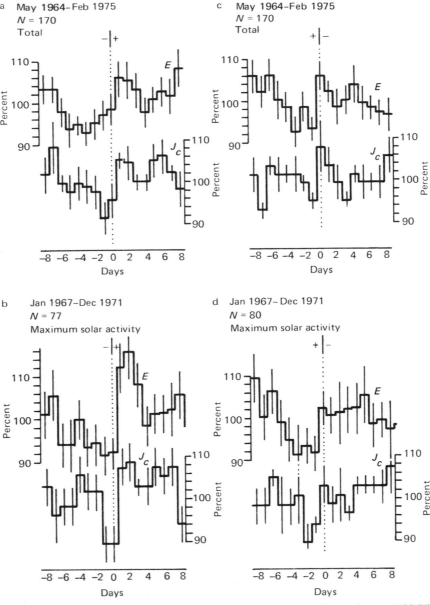

Figure 4.15. Superposed epoch analysis of fair-weather atmospheric electric field (E) and air-Earth current density (J_c) recorded at Zugspitze on days surrounding solar sector boundary crossings on day 0. (a) Data for total solar cycle with negative to positive boundary crossings. (b) Negative to positive crossings for maximum solar years only. (c) Positive to negative, all years. (d) Positive to negative, maximum years only. From Reiter (1977).

coupling of the IMF to the geomagnetic field during different dominant solar field direction periods, although this seems unlikely; (4) it may not be any of these.

In conclusion, it may be remembered that the product $E \times J_c$ is proportional to V_i, which is itself proportional to the number and intensity of thunderstorms globally active at a given time (sec. 3.4.1 and 4.1.2). The results in figure 4.15 can therefore be read as an increase in global thunderstorm activity following MSB passage.

5 Miscellaneous Obscuring Influences

Before addressing the question of physical mechanisms to link solar variability to meteorological phenomena in the next chapter, it is appropriate to pause here to examine arguments that would create only the illusion of a link. One argument is that the energy contained in meteorological disturbances propagates upward to ionospheric heights, where it induces fluctuations in the geomagnetic field to produce an observable correlation between magnetic activity and weather. In this process solar variability would be unnecessary.

Another argument, however ill founded it might be, is that the Moon influences the weather, and if there are lunar effects on geomagnetic activity, ergo there would be a correlation between weather and magnetic activity.

In considering the long-term correlations between meteorological phenomena and the solar cycle, it is difficult to imagine why upward propagation of energy from the troposphere would be any different during sunspot minimum, say, compared to sunspot maximum, unless the wave propagation properties of the atmosphere were somehow altered by solar influences. This then would still be a solar-related perturbation; therefore it is discussed in section 6.7. In section 5.1, we concentrate only on the argument that it is tropospheric effects which influence the geomagnetic field. The possibly obscuring influence of the Moon on the geomagnetic field is briefly addressed in section 5.2.

5.1 Upward Energy Transport

Arguments for a solar influence on weather that rely on correlations between meteorological parameters and geomagnetic activity (sec. 4.2) have been subject to criticism on the basis that the energy generated in the troposphere could propagate upward to ionospheric heights and perturb the geomagnetic field. Although there is a strong association between solar activity and geomagnetic perturbations, there is also this meteorologically induced component which casts "serious doubts" on the so-called Sun-weather correlations (Hines, 1973). The criticisms have persisted in spite of the fact that most of the reported correlations indicate a lag of 2–4 days between the time that the geomagnetic storm begins and the onset of a following tropospheric event, such as an increase in vorticity index or changes in atmospheric pressure over wide geographic areas. The results discussed in section 4.3, showing that at least one meteorological parameter (the vorticity index) responds to changes in a purely solar parameter (the magnetic sector structure), have quieted some of the opposition to arguments for a Sun-weather relationship (Hines, 1974; Hines and Halevy, 1975, 1977). Nonetheless, there is observational evidence for a coupling between causative meteorological phenomena and responses in the ionosphere, which could complicate studies attempting to analyze coupling processes in the reverse direction. This evidence is summarized below (sec. 5.1.2) after a few introductory words on the vertical propagation of atmospheric waves (sec. 5.1.1). The possibility of a consequent ionospheric effect on geomagnetic activity is then assessed in section 5.1.3. A mechanism whereby solar activity may impose alterations on the wave reflection properties of the upper atmosphere and induce an apparent meteorological response is discussed in section 6.7.

5.1.1 Vertical Propagation of Atmospheric Waves

The general topic of vertical propagation of atmospheric waves in their various forms has been treated mathematically in books by Gossard and Hooke (1975) and Holton (1975). The effects of acoustic gravity waves in the upper atmosphere have been reviewed by Yeh and Liu (1974), and the vertical propagation of stationary planetary waves in the winter northern hemisphere has been examined by Matsuno (1970). Vertically propagating planetary waves have been utilized by Matsuno (1971) to explain sudden stratospheric warmings, which affect stratospheric circulation (Holton, 1975).

Although the subject of waves in the atmosphere and oceans is one of the oldest aspects of fluid dynamics, its study is difficult, partly because the terminology is either confusing or ambiguous as used by various authors (Gossard and Hooke, 1975). Rather than add to the confusion by an inadequate treatment of the topic here, we refer the reader to the aforementioned books and papers for details.

For the purpose of this discussion (and for application to sec. 6.1.1), we merely show the dispersion diagram of hydrodynamic waves in the atmosphere in figure 5.1. The diagram, applicable to middle and high latitudes (Matsuno, 1977), illustrates the wavelengths, frequencies, and periods of acoustic waves, internal gravity waves, cyclones, and internal Rossby (or planetary) waves. The domains in which vertical propagation is possible are indicated in the figure, along with a scale of vertical velocities.

The vertical distribution of kinetic energy of various atmospheric waves is given in figure 5.2 in terms of the vertical velocities. Here it is evident that the velocities have a tendency to increase with increasing height, with some exceptions, but the kinetic energy carried by the waves is a decreasing function of height. The gravity wave curve is

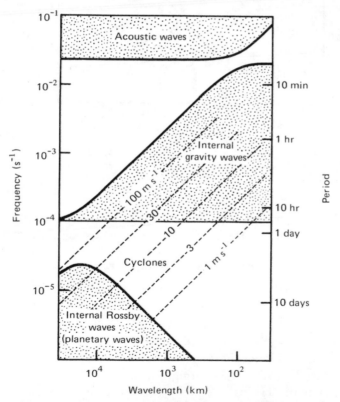

Figure 5.1. Dispersion diagram for hydrodynamic waves in the atmosphere. Applicable to middle and high latitudes. Shaded areas show domains in which vertical propagation is possible. From original diagram by T. Matsuno (1977).

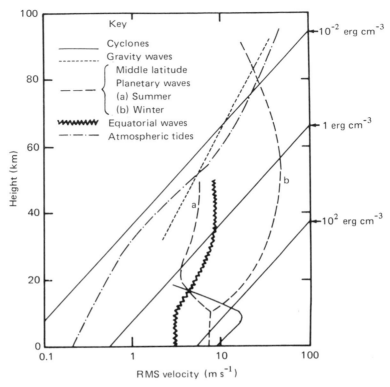

Figure 5.2. Vertical distribution of kinetic energy of atmospheric waves (gravity wave curve is order of magnitude only). From original graph by T. Matsuno (private communication).

based on meager and scattered data and is meant to give only an order of magnitude estimate (Matsuno, private communication).

5.1.2 Meteorological Effects on the Ionosphere

One of the earliest correlations between weather and a subsequent ionospheric response was reported by Gherzi (1950), who suggested that the reflection height of the ionosphere decreases about 320 km in advance of the direction of movement of a hurricane. Bauer (1958a) analyzed ionospheric perturbations associated with four hurricanes passing close to Washington, D.C. in 1954 and 1955 and showed that the critical frequency of the F layer (f_oF2) clearly increased as the hurricanes approached, and reached a maximum at about the time of closest approach of the hurricane to the station (when atmospheric pressure reached minimum). According to Bauer, the reflection height of the layer decreased as the hurricane approached, in agreement with Gherzi's (1950) observation.

Bauer (1958a) explained the apparent association between the critical frequency increase (which implies an increase in electron density at the peak of the F layer) and the hurricane passage as arising from convergence and subsidence in the ionosphere which is related to divergence in the lower atmosphere. This explanation was supported by a study of the divergent outflow on one of the hurricanes by Mook (1958). However, in connection with the hurricanes' passages, there was no significant rise in the level of geomagnetic activity as recorded at Cheltenham, Maryland, near Washington.

Apparent ionospheric responses to the passage of cold fronts have been noted by Gherzi (1950), Bauer (1957), and Arendt and Frisby (1968). Gherzi used vertical incidence radio reflections to show that echoes were received from the lower part of the F layer when polar air was present and from the upper part when tropical air was present. With a superposed epoch analysis, Bauer (1957) found that the virtual height decreased on the day of cold front passage; 44 cases covering a 9-month interval were utilized, and the results are significant with better than 95% confidence. Gherzi's observations were made in China, Bauer's in Washington, D.C. The great majority of Bauer's 44 cases occurred on geomagnetically quiet days.

To explain the observational results, Bauer (1957) hypothesized a dynamic coupling between the troposphere and ionosphere that would take place because the wavelength of tropospheric circulation (about 1000 km) is much longer than the thickness (about 100 km) of the barrier between the troposphere and the ionosphere. With such a large ratio, no barrier is completely effective. Also, the real atmosphere has a temperature gradient that varies with height and would act as a wave duct wherein the energy propagates between two boundaries; the Earth serves as the lower boundary, and the upper boundary is at the appropriate level in the upper atmosphere. For the simple case of a compressional wave where the energy flow is proportional to ϱv^2 (ϱ is atmospheric density and v is the velocity of the wave), the velocity increases with increasing height (fig. 5.2) because ϱ decreases exponentially to conserve energy flow. This would predict an amplification of 10^3–10^4 in the ionosphere for a wave originating in the troposphere. Bauer's analytical results support this simple hypothesis. It appears that conditions in the lower atmosphere would be more favorable for strong coupling in winter and spring than in

other seasons. In support of this, Bauer (1958b) showed that the correlations between surface pressure and the ionosphere were significant only during (1) hurricanes, (2) the breakdown of the circumpolar vortex (winter/spring transition period), and (3) the beginning
and ending of the monsoon season.

Under Bauer's hypothesis, an eastward moving cold front would
have an associated eastward drift in the F-region. This drift would set
up irregularities in the electron density distribution that would appear
as spread F on an ionosonde recording (cf. Herman, 1966a) and also
produce scintillations on radio signals passing through the ionosphere
from a satellite transmitter to the ground. An observational verification of this extension to Bauer's hypothesis has been given by scintil-
lation measurements of satellite S-66 signals on 41, 40, and 20 MHz
received at Fort Monmouth by Arendt and Frisby (1968). Further
verification is found in the measurements at Tsumeb, South West
Africa, by Schödel et al. (1973).

Acoustic waves generated by severe local storms have been detected
in the F-region by Georges (1968), Baker and Davies (1969), Hung et
al. (1975), and Davies and Jones (1971). The waves, whose periods in
the ionosphere are in the range 2–5 minutes, are detected by CW
doppler techniques on an oblique radio path whose ionospheric
reflection point is located directly above the tropospheric phenomenon generating the waves. The disturbances last from less than 1 hr to
as long as 9 hr, but most events observed by Baker and Davies (1969)
typically lasted 2–4 hr in association with the storm. The characteristic ionospheric signature (oscillating reflection height of CW signal)
was never seen in the absence of severe weather; i.e., a storm was
always present when the signature was observed. In some cases a
severe storm was unaccompanied by an ionospheric response, leading
Baker and Davies to speculate that atmospheric conditions above the
storms would sometimes be such as to produce damping of the acoustic wave before it reached ionospheric heights.

Apart from acoustic waves generated by thunderstorms, the rf
radiated energy associated with lightning flashes has been investigated as a possible source of ionospheric modification by severe
weather. Calculations by Healey (1938) indicate that the rf energy
would be sufficient to create extra ionization at E layer heights (~ 100
km) and produce a localized sporadic E layer. In an unpublished
manuscript, Herman (1970) showed that a power flux density of up to
50 μW m^{-2}, sufficient to produce localized heating of a magnitude
similar to that produced by the Platteville, Colorado "ionosphere

modification transmitter facility" (Utlaut, 1970a,b), could be delivered to the F-region by the lightning activity of a severe thunderstorm. The comparable power fluxes of severe storm lightning and the Platteville facility are sufficient to raise the F-region temperature by about 35%. Other less common but severe tropospheric disturbances (e.g., tornadoes) have also caused measurable effects on the ionosphere (Hung et al., 1975).

5.1.3 Ionospheric Effects on the Geomagnetic Field

According to Hines (1965), winds in the ionosphere may induce magnetic fluctuations of 3–6 gamma in amplitude. The winds themselves may be produced by acoustic or gravity waves propagating up from the troposphere during meteorological disturbances (Davies and Jones, 1971). Thus one could expect to see a degree of correlation between localized tropospheric disturbances and magnetic activity. However, it must be noted that the Hines (1965) mechanism produces very low-amplitude magnetic fluctuations, whereas the magnetic storms that precede increases in vorticity index, for example, are characterized by fluctuations of several hundred gamma (1 gamma = 10^{-5} gauss). The ionospheric responses to specific meteorological disturbances as discussed above have no obvious relation to magnetic activity measured by the standard indices such as Kp, Ap, and C, because these indices are too coarse to reflect such small changes in magnetic field strength.

The often-stated argument that correlations between magnetic activity and meteorological phenomena merely reflect an upward transport of energy from the troposphere thus appears to be without merit. A further effective rebuttal against that argument has already been mentioned; it is difficult to imagine a tropospheric disturbance powerful enough to reverse the direction of the solar magnetic field and create a sector boundary, especially if that boundary has swept past the Earth 2 or 3 days before the meteorological disturbance began (see Wilcox et al. 1973a,b; 1974.)

5.2 Lunar Influences on Geomagnetic Activity

In the search for mechanisms linking solar activity to weather, other possibly obscuring influences with periodicities of lengths similar to those of solar periodicities should be considered. The lunar sidereal period of 27.3 days, for example, is almost the same length as the average solar rotation period of 27 days. As a matter of fact, there have been reports of a lunar influence on weather (cf. Markson, 1971 and references therein) and on atmospheric ozone (Adderley, 1963), but it would seem that the lunar synodic period (29.5 days from new Moon to the next new Moon) would be a more appropriate periodicity to study than the sidereal period measured with reference to the stars.

Since several meteorological phenomena are probably related to geomagnetic activity (sec. 4.2), there could be an apparent lunar influence on weather if the Moon were in some way related to geomagnetic activity. In this section the possibility of such a relationship is examined.

The idea that the phase of the Moon might have an effect on geomagnetic activity seems to have been introduced by Wulf and Nicholson (1948), who found that recurrent magnetic storms might be related to lunar declination. Several years later Sucksdorff (1956) showed that geomagnetic activity was apparently 12% lower than average at new Moon and 7% lower at full Moon. During first quarter the activity appeared to be 7% higher than normal. Bigg (1963a) independently found evidence for a lunar influence on geomagnetic disturbances; using storm data from the catalog by Jones (1955), he determined that there was a minimum number of storms at new Moon, 20% lower than any other minimum, and a broad maximum a few days after full Moon. Moreover, Bigg (1963a,b) showed that storms seemed to occur preferentially near first and third quarters, but Bartels (1963) illustrated that the same results are obtained from random data.

Triggered by Bigg's results and Bartels' rebuttal, searches for a lunar influence were undertaken independently by Davidson and Martyn (1964) and Michel et al. (1964), and both groups failed to find a statistically significant relationship. At about the same time, Bartels (1964) issued a rousing criticism of research directed toward finding a lunar influence and spelled out the statistical techniques that should be used in such investigations.

Stolov and Cameron (1964), acting on Bartels' advice, used good statistical techniques to show that in the previous 31 yr a general decrease in Kp of about 4% could be consistently found for the 7 days preceding full Moon, and a general increase of about 4% began at about full Moon phase and continued for another 7 days. Concurrently, Bell and Defouw (1964) utilized the superposed epoch approach and found a small but statistically significant enhancement of geomagnetic activity (Kp) for several days following full Moon. It seems that Sucksdorff and Bigg had the right idea but the wrong results.

Within a short time Stolov (1965) was able to show that the lunar modulation of geomagnetic activity takes place when the Moon is within 4° or less of the ecliptic plane and within the tail of the magnetosphere. There was no apparent effect with the Moon on the day side (after last quarter and before first quarter). This led Stolov to postulate a physical mechanism for the lunar modulation effect, recently reiterated by Markson (1971), that when the Moon is close to the ecliptic at full phase, it will be in the (then) newly discovered (Ness, 1965) neutral sheet of the magnetotail. The neutral sheet, being inherently unstable, might be perturbed by the Moon in such a way that magnetic field annihilation would accelerate particles toward the Earth. These particles, entering the ionosphere, could produce currents that would in turn perturb the Earth's magnetic field.

Support for this postulation and an amplification of it have been given by Bell and Defouw (1966a). The principal results of their superposed epoch analysis of daily Kp sums for the 30-yr period 1932–1962 are given in figure 5.3. First, with the Moon more than 4°

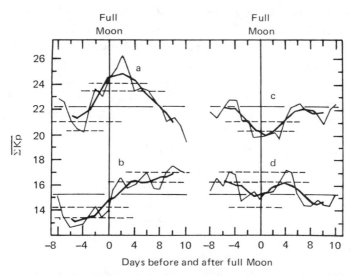

Figure 5.3. *Average value of daily Kp sum associated with full Moon. (a) Elevation of Moon less than 4° from ecliptic in disturbed periods ($\overline{\Sigma Kp} > 18.7$). (b) Elevation less than 4° in quiet periods ($\overline{\Sigma Kp} < 18.7$). (c) Elevation greater than 4°, disturbed periods. (d) Elevation greater than 4°, quiet periods. Thin curve, daily values; thick curve, 5-day running averages. Levels of 2σ are indicated by dashed lines. From Bell and Defouw (1966a).*

out of the ecliptic plane on the night side in the tail (i.e., full Moon phase), no statistically significant variations in $\overline{\Sigma Kp}$ are discernible; the daily and 5-day running mean values vary by less than 2σ in both quiet and disturbed periods (curves c and d). Second, the largest statistically significant increases in $\overline{\Sigma Kp}$ are seen in disturbed periods beginning at full Moon and continuing for 7 or 8 days when the Moon is within 4° of the ecliptic (curve a); even during quiet periods, there is a discernible increase in geomagnetic activity following full Moon (curve b). Even larger disturbed-period increases (not shown) were found when the full Moon was within 1° of the ecliptic plane.

Dodson and Hedeman (1964) found a 29.5-day periodicity in PCA events and Forbush decreases, with a peak in the number of days the two types of event are in progress occurring broadly around 5–8 days after new Moon. The length of the periodicity (29.5 days) is equal to the synodic month, and the time of their peak number of days occurs near the first quarter lunar phase. What connection these results have with the foregoing analyses of lunar modulation of magnetic activity is not yet clear.

Another result is also unclear at present. When Bell and Defouw (1966b) attempted to extend their analysis back to 1884 using the index Ci, they obtained the disconcerting result that no lunar modulation was evident under the expected (or any other) conditions in the years 1890–1933. They suggested the possibility of an effect from the 80-yr solar cycle (sec. 2.1), wherein the average maximum annual sunspot number was somewhat low between 1890 and 1933 (fig. 2.1). This lack of activity might in turn produce a shorter magnetotail which would be less affected by lunar transit through the neutral sheet.

An elaboration of the lunar-perturbation-of-the-magnetotail hypothesis was made by Markson (1971). He offered the rather interesting suggestion that the magnetohydrodynamic wake of the Moon (analogous to Earth's magnetotail) produced by the solar wind interacts with the Earth's magnetotail, as sketched in figure 5.4, or perhaps modulates the flow of solar particles to the tail.

It is difficult to see from Markson's (fig. 5.4) geometry just why the lunar wake modulation would be effective only after full Moon, yet the Stolov (1965) and Bell and Defouw (1966a) results imply that this would indeed be the case. Without going into detail, it should be noted that in proceeding from full Moon to last quarter the Moon is moving toward the morning side of Earth, where there is a greater

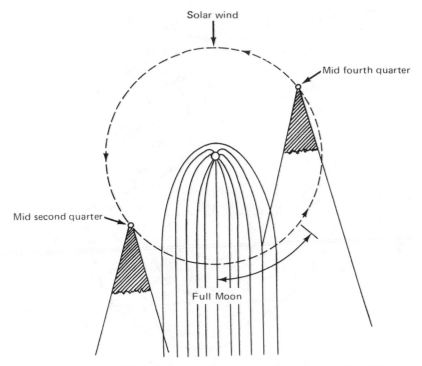

Figure 5.4. Geometry of Moon's wake relative to magnetospheric tail used by Markson (1971) to explain mechanism for lunar modulation of geomagnetic activity. Heavy line with arrows indicates region of maximum effect.

preference for particle precipitation from the magnetosphere (cf. Paulikas, 1971). This preference can be seen in figure 5.5, which illustrates a diurnal pattern of electron precipitation (after Paulikas, 1971). Note that in the magnetic local time (MLT) hours of 00–06, corresponding to the Moon's position denoted by the heavy line in figure 5.4, soft electron (~ 0.5 keV) precipitation maximizes, and the latitudinal zone covered by >40 keV electrons is greatest.

From Markson's geometry (fig. 5.4) it appears that geomagnetic field lines in the magnetotail, which are connected to the Earth at high latitudes, would be perturbed more than would the total geomagnetic field. It would be interesting to conduct an analysis similar to that of Bell and Defouw (1966a), but using the AE magnetic index (sec. 2.6.1) rather than Kp. If such an analysis revealed a stronger lunar influence on AE than Kp, Markson's hypothesis would be on firmer ground.

219

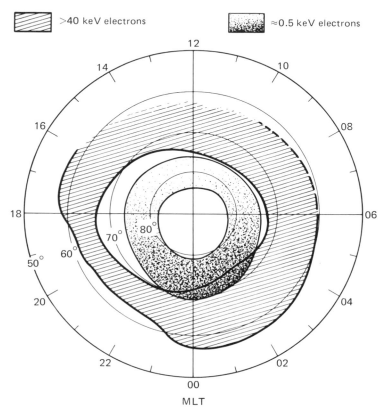

Figure 5.5. Electron precipitation pattern over the polar caps. No significance is attached to the gaps between the 40- and 0.5-keV zones, as it is assumed that intermediate energies would fill them in during a precipitation event. From Paulikas (1971).

In summary, on a statistical basis there does appear to be a lunar modulation effect on geomagnetic activity when the Moon is within 4° of the ecliptic plane on the morning side of the Earth (i.e., between full Moon and last quarter positions). A possible explanation is that the magnetohydrodynamic wake of the Moon interacts with the Earth's magnetotail to promote energetic particle precipitation into the ionosphere, thereby setting up electric currents that perturb the magnetic field.

Additional investigation is required to determine the quantitative extent of any lunar modulation on the solar wind and Earth's magnetotail that might ultimately affect meteorological phenomena, including atmospheric ozone.

In the practical case of relatively long-range forecasting of geomagnetic storms, it appears harmless at worst and statistically significant at best (in spite of the late Bartels' viewpoint) to predict a geomagnetic storm occurrence simply using an appropriate lunar ephemeris to determine when the Moon will be at full phase within 4° of the ecliptic plane. This would not, of course, anticipate the great storms associated with major solar proton flares, but it could forecast the moderately large disturbances apparently associated with lunar phase.

6 Physical Processes and Mechanisms

In the foregoing chapters we assembled and presented various statistical findings and facts concerning Sun-weather relationships as they have been reported by numerous investigators. The sum of evidence strongly indicates a relationship between solar activity, both short- and long-term, and meteorological phenomena. None of the correlations is perfect, which suggests that fluctuations in weather parameters such as atmospheric pressure, temperature, rainfall amounts, winds, cyclogenesis, anticyclogenesis, and so on, take place whether or not there is any fluctuation in solar activity. However, since there is a statistically significant correlation in many cases, it appears that solar activity, when it does occur, can produce changes or perturbations in the weather and climate.

The central question centers on what physical processes or mechanisms might act to couple the variable solar energy into the atmospheric system and produce the observed correlations. A number of possible linking mechanisms have been suggested, but none has been proved. The content of this chapter is largely speculatory and, in spots, admittedly naive; it is included nevertheless partly to demonstrate the status of contemporary thinking regarding mechanisms, but, more important, to serve as a guide for experimental planning. A mix of mechanisms for short-term meteorological changes up to long-term climatological trends is discussed. It must be emphasized that all the physical mechanisms discussed below are speculations that must be verified or rejected by experiment and analysis. In searching for links, it may be best to follow an admonition attributed to William of Occam (1300–1349):

> "Neither more, nor more onerous, causes are to be assumed
> than are necessary to account for the phenomena."

6.1 Atmospheric Effects of a Variable Solar Constant

As discussed in section 2.2.1, in the early part of the twentieth century it was believed that the solar constant, that is, the electromag-

223

netic radiation from the Sun at the top of the atmosphere integrated over all wavelengths, is not really a constant. Rather, it was believed to vary with time, and variations of only a few tenths of a percent would be sufficient to cause profound climatological changes through direct heating effects at the Earth's surface and the base of the atmosphere.

Apparent correlations were found between the magnitude of the solar constant as measured at the Earth's surface and sunspot number (cf. Abbott, 1958), and this would seem to supply the needed mechanism to explain many of the historical correlations between solar activity and the weather. This mechanism did not gain widespread acceptance because it was argued that the solar constant is actually invariant, and apparent changes in its magnitude at the surface were believed instead to be caused by changes in the transmissivity of the atmosphere. The criticism could not be rebutted at the time because of a lack of precise knowledge of the atmosphere's density, composition, and radiation transmission characteristics, and measurements of the solar constant at the top of the atmosphere were impossible.

With the introduction of rockets and satellites as a means to make measurements at the top of the atmosphere, it has been discovered that at least the short wavelength portion of solar radiation varies in intensity with time, and those variations are related to changes in solar activity as measured by sunspots on the long term and solar flare eruption on the short term (cf. sec. 2.2.2). Since the short wavelengths vary, should it not be suspected that the longer-wave (visible and infrared) radiation also varies, perhaps in relation to the degree of solar activity?

If the solar constant does vary, as suggested by Abbott (1958), Clayton (1923), Bigelow (1915), and recently by Eddy (1976), Volland (1977a,b), Albrecht et al. (1969), Foukal et al. (1977), Fröhlich (1977), and Lockwood (1975), it would provide a very powerful physical mechanism to explain Sun-weather correlations. The fundamental importance of this possibility and the necessity for spacecraft experiments to investigate it was suggested by Mitchell (1965) a decade ago. Recently, Thekaekara (1975) gave a more detailed argument for solar constant measurements, with special emphasis on the Solar Energy Monitor in Space (SEMIS) experiment. It is evident that this type of measurement should be given a high priority in planning experimental investigations of Sun-weather relationships, especially those concerning long-term changes in the solar constant and climate.

The possibility of short-term variations on a scale of days as envisioned by the early researchers may be no less important, especially in light of an intriguing new causal mechanism suggested by Volland (1977a,b). Volland's hypothesis is of sufficient interest to warrant further elaboration here (sec. 6.1.1), particularly in light of the results of a contemporary analysis of atmospheric pressure by King et al. (1977).

Also, there has been a revival of interest in the so-called Milankovitch effect, due chiefly to the recent work of Hays et al. (1976). Although the Milankovitch (1930) theory does not depend on a variable Sun, it does predict long-term variations in the amount of insolation incident at the top of the atmosphere as a function of latitude due to changes in the Earth's orbital characteristics. Because these variations may explain climatic changes on a geologic scale related to the ice ages, the consequences of this theory and recent work related to it are outlined in section 6.1.2.

6.1.1 Atmospheric Pressure and the Solar Constant

The important new results of King et al. (1977) are an integral background to Volland's hypothesis and are therefore reviewed first. The King analysis indicates that both longitudinal and latitudinal standing planetary waves (which oscillate but do not propagate) exist in atmospheric pressure at the surface and at the 500-mb level. The oscillations of the wave amplitudes are attuned to both the 11-yr solar cycle and the 27-day rotation period of the Sun.

It was found from a superposed epoch analysis of winter data (1963–1972) that the height of the 500-mb level at 70°N shows a significant 27.5-day recurrence pattern in the deviations from the climatic mean height. Maximum deviations of about +5 decameters (dm) and −3 dm occurred at longitudes of 140° and 340°E on day 8 and day 22, respectively, following a key date defined so that day 8 of the solar rotation was close to the epoch at which most solar emission occurred during the years studied. Day 22, a half solar rotation later, turned out to be near the epochal main minimum. From the results of this phase of the analysis, King and associates went on to plot, as a function of longitude, the 500-mb pressure height deviations along 70°N on day 8 and day 22 (fig. 6.1). The pattern that emerged has the form of a standing wave describable as a predominately wavenumber 2 type, but with a wavenumber 1 component, because the antinode amplitudes are not equal. The "nodes" are at about 60° and

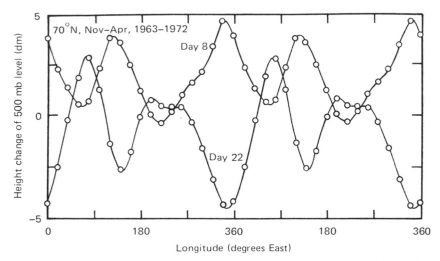

Figure 6.1. Longitudinal variations relative to the climatic mean over a solar cycle of the height (dm) of the 500-mb pressure level at 70°N on days 8 and 22 of the solar rotations during winter months. Note that the standing wave pattern is duplicated and plotted over two global circuits (720° longitude). From King et al. (1977).

240°E, and the "antinodes" are at 140° and 340°E. The largest oscillation, with a maximum range of about 9 dm, occurs over the eastern Atlantic Ocean (320°–360°E). The corresponding standard error is approximately 1.8 dm; thus the 9-dm excursion is statistically significant.

The oscillatory range of the height deviations over a solar rotation, obtained by subtracting the value on day 22 from that on day 8, varies with longitude at 70°N in the manner shown in figure 6.2. Also in the figure is the longitudinal variation of the change in average January surface pressure at 70°N relative to the 11-yr solar cycle; the change was obtained by subtracting the sunspot minimum value from that for sunspot maximum. King displaced the 500-mb curve 90° eastward in figure 6.2 to compensate for the fact that in the northern hemisphere stationary wave patterns are tilted in such a way that their fronts at the 500-mb height are 90° west of the corresponding front at the surface. Plotted in this way, the curves are similar, and they show that longitudinal standing waves in atmospheric pressure can be produced by both 27.5-day solar rotations and 11-yr sunspot cycles. The positive maximums (greater surface pressure at sunspot maximum than at sunspot minimum) occur near the longitudes of 45° and 235°E, and the negative maximums are centered near 175° and

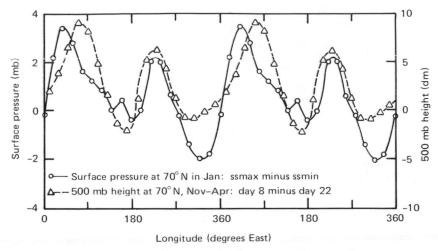

Figure 6.2. Longitudinal variation at 70°N of the difference in surface pressure between sunspot maximum and sunspot minimum in January (solid line) and 500-mb height difference at 70°N between days 8 and 22 of the solar rotations in winter months (dashed line). Note that the 500-mb height-difference curve has been shifted 90° eastward. From King et al. (1977) (see text).

320°E. The range of pressure oscillation is about 3.4 mb at 45°E and −2.4 mb at 320°E.

The latitudinal variations in surface pressure associated with the 11-yr and 27.5-day cycles as deduced by King and associates are illustrated in figure 6.3. Here it can be seen that the pattern of the $(m,4)$ standing wave type is the same for both the 27.5-day rotation and the 11-yr cycle; the pressure change is negative southward of about 45°N and positive northward of it. The maximum changes are at about 30°–40°N (negative) and 70°N (positive). For the solar rotation, the latitudinal effect is larger in the 0°–40°W longitude sector than it is for the pressure averaged over all longitudes.

These results help to explain the apparent contradictions in earlier studies that found correlations between sunspot cycle and atmospheric pressure to be positive in some areas, negative in others, and uncorrelated (zero) in still others (sec. 3.1.5).

Further, with power spectrum analysis, King et al. (1977) showed a significant 27.5-day variability in sunspot number and in 2.8-GHz (10.7-cm) solar radio emission over the last 11-yr cycle, indicating that the sunspots tended to appear on preferred solar longitudes (fig. 6.4). The same periodicity was found by Toman (1967) using daily sunspot numbers for the previous two cycles (1940–1964), and it also showed

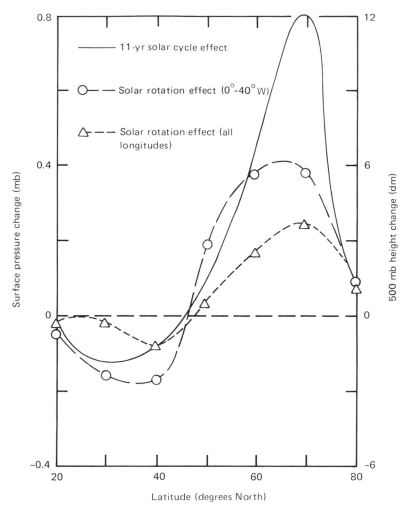

Figure 6.3. Latitudinal variations of the change in surface pressure between ssmax and ssmin for winters 1899–1939, averaged for all longitudes (solid line). Dashed curves show the change in 500 mb height between times of minimum and maximum solar flux during the 27.5-day solar rotations (Nov–Apr 1963–1972). From King et al. (1977).

up in a spectral analysis of daily Ci (geomagnetic activity) values covering the years 1888–1959 (Shapiro and Ward, 1966). A spectrum analysis by King's group of the 500-mb height variations in the auroral zone revealed a peak corresponding to the 27.5-day rotation period. There are other peaks in the 500-mb height spectrum corresponding to smaller peaks in sunspot number and 2.8-GHz radio flux

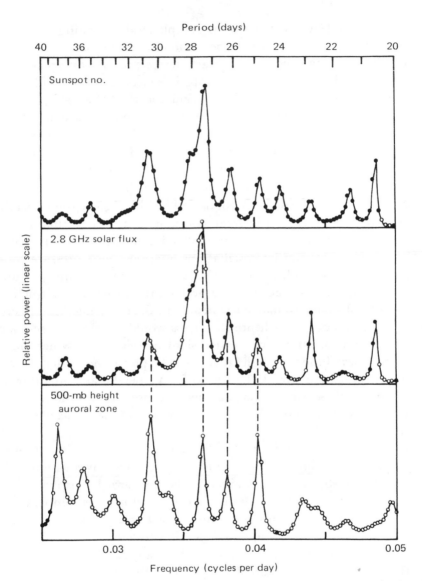

Figure 6.4. Power spectra of the daily values of sunspot number, 2.8-GHz (10.7-cm) solar radio emission, and the average height of the 500-mb level around the auroral zone for the 10-yr period January 1, 1963–December 31, 1972. From King et al. (1977).

(fig. 6.4), leading King to suspect that some of the atmospheric variability other than that associated with solar rotation might also have a solar origin. Overall, the results make the similarity between the

229

27.5-day and 11-yr cycle patterns for planetary standing waves in atmospheric pressure appear to be something more than accidental.

Finally, since the climatic average surface pressure difference between 50° and 70°N is less than 4 mb, it is clear that the oscillations associated with the solar rotation period and the Schwabe cycle can have a profound effect on the pressure gradients and consequent atmospheric circulation in middle latitudes. These oscillations may also explain the apparent tendencies of the major "centers of action" to shift their positions over 11 yr or longer (sec. 3.1.6) and possibly influence the course of storm tracks (sec. 3.1.7).

Noting the King results, Volland (1977a,b) argued theoretically that a 27.5-day variation in solar constant of not more than 0.3% associated with long-lived corotating active longitudes on the Sun might produce appropriate oscillations in atmospheric pressure consistent with those results. Briefly, the solar constant variability would induce a change in surface heating preferentially over the continents, and the land would exchange the heat with the overlying atmosphere by eddy transport. This heating process would generate large-scale planetary waves, mainly of the Rossby-Haurwitz type, which have maximum amplitudes at high latitudes. The prevailing westerly wind in the troposphere would then modify the height and meridional structures of these waves in such a way as to produce a standing wave pattern of zonal wavenumber $m = 2$ at the 500-mb level, as observed by King.

By nature of the land-ocean distribution over the globe, the heat input to the atmosphere would generate planetary waves with $m = 0$, 1, and 2 (Rossby-Haurwitz waves) in the northern hemisphere, because the large heat capacity of the oceans suppresses temperature variations on time scales up to 1 month. The $m = 2$ waves, with meridional wavenumbers $n = 5$, 6, and 7, are illustrated in figure 6.5; here it is evident that the theoretical waves have a great deal of similarity to the waves deduced by King from pressure measurements (fig. 6.3). Waves with $n \leq 3$ possess long vertical wavelengths and would not be strongly influenced by an irregular solar signal (Volland, 1977b).

The planetary waves propagate upward (cf. Matsuno, 1970; 1971), and lunar tidal theory shows that in the presence of a constant prevailing wind of the order of 10 m s^{-1} only those waves with $m = 2$ are significant (Volland, 1977a). They are of the Rossby-Haurwitz type propagating eastward and westward with an amplitude and

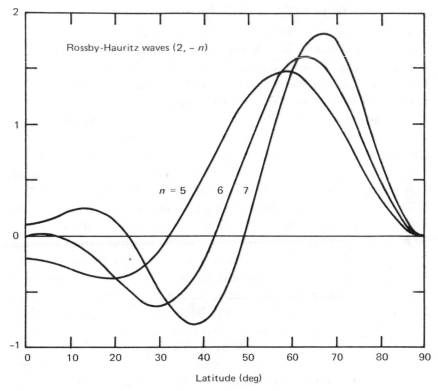

Figure 6.5. Latitudinal variation of theoretical Rossby-Haurwitz normalized pressure waves with zonal wavenumber m = 2 and meridional wavenumbers −5, −6, and −7. From Volland (1977b).

phase relationship that produces standing longitudinal planetary waves of the type King deduced from observations (fig. 6.1).

In summary, it appears that Volland's theoretical argument satisfactorily explains King's analytical results, provided that the solar constant varies slightly ($\sim 0.1\%$) over a 27-day solar rotation. Volland (1977a) concluded that "If short-lived meteorological phenomena such as those associated with solar flares or sector boundary crossings are generated by active longitudes on the Sun, the 11-yr solar-cycle effects may be the result of an 11-yr variation of the amplitude of the 27-day forcing function." The King and Volland results, along with those of Ebel and Bätz (1977), who showed that stratospheric circulation at the 10-mb level is responsive to solar rotation effects, reinforce the necessity for precise solar constant measurements to be carried out over a reasonably long period of time.

6.1.2 *Earth's Orbital Changes and the Solar Constant*

The idea that variations in the Earth's orbital parameters will influence the continental ice sheets and therefore the climate during periods of glaciation has been with us since at least 1842 (see the review by Broecker and Van Donk, 1970). However, it was Milankovitch (1930, 1938) who showed rigorously that the orbital changes lead to variations in the amount of insolation received by the Earth as a function of latitude and season. It appears that during periods of strong seasonal contrast in heating (hot summers and cold winters) the ice sheets will diminish, and in those periods with little contrast they will grow, with a consequent impact on global climate.

There are three major long-term variations in the orbital elements that modulate the seasonal contrasts at any point on the Earth's surface. These are illustrated in figure 6.6. The shortest period variation is known as the precession of the equinoxes, wherein the season in which perehelion occurs advances through the year in a period of 21 000 yr. At present the Earth and Sun are closest together in January (southern hemisphere summer), but 10 000 yr from now this will happen in July. Circa 8500 BC the Earth was at apehelion during the northern hemisphere winter. When it is at the long end of the elliptical orbit, the Earth as a whole receives less than average radiation, and at the short end it receives more. Thus the days are warmer during periods when local summer occurs at the short end than at the long end, and the winter days are colder. In these periods there will be greater contrast between summer and winter, as there is today in the southern hemisphere. It should be noted that this effect is exactly out of phase in the northern and southern hemispheres, and it does not show a marked latitudinal dependence.

Because of gravitational effects from other bodies in the solar system, the angle the Earth's rotational axis makes with the orbital plane varies from a minimum of 21.8° to a maximum of 24.4°. One cycle from minimum tilt to maximum and back again was calculated by Milankovitch (1930) to be 40 400 yr, but the period is somewhat irregular, with an average length of 41 000 yr (fig. 6.6). As is well known, the present tilt (or "obliquity of the ecliptic") is 23.5°; the last maximum tilt occurred around 8000 BC, and the next minimum is expected about 10 000 yr from now. It is evident that at minimum tilt the contrast in seasons will be least, and at maximum tilt the difference between the amount of heat received in summer and winter is greatest. Unlike the precessional effect, this tilt effect is synchronous

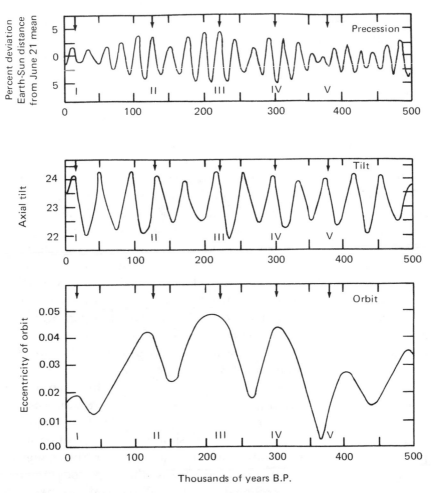

Figure 6.6. Variation of the precession of the equinoxes expressed as percentage deviation from the mean June 21 Sun-Earth distance (top curve), the obliquity of the ecliptic in degrees (middle), and the orbital eccentricity (bottom) over the past half-million years. The Roman numerals and arrows mark the timing of sudden terminations seen in the O^{18} record from deep-sea cores. From Broecker and Van Donk (1970).

in the northern and southern hemispheres. Also, it is clear that the tilt effect is strongly latitude dependent; it is negligible at the equator and maximum at the poles (Milankovitch, 1938). For example, the mean summer insolation at 45° latitude changes by 1.2% for each degree change in tilt, but at 65° the corresponding change is 2.5%. From this it appears that not only will the growth and recession of ice

233

sheets be affected over the 41 000-yr period, but also in light of Vol-land's (1977b) analysis, the atmospheric pressure gradients and consequent circulation patterns should be influenced. That is, in a period of maximum tilt (with its great seasonal contrast and ice sheet recession) there will be greatly increased circulation, manifested especially by severe winter storms.

Finally, the third orbital parameter affecting the amount of insolation received by the Earth is the eccentricity of the orbit. Over an irregular period of 90 000–100 000 yr the Earth's orbit goes from more nearly circular to more elliptical and back again. The ellipticity has varied from 0.00 to about 0.07 over the past million years. In an elliptical orbit, the hemisphere with winter in perehelion (as the northern hemisphere is now) would have short, mild winters and long cool summers if ellipticity effects were the only controlling factor, and the opposite hemisphere, being in winter at apehelion, would have short hot summers and long cold winters. The seasonal contrast would be greatest in periods of maximum ellipticity, as was the case about 20 000 yr ago, when a minor maximum occurred (see fig. 6.6). We are now proceeding slowly toward a period of less ellipticity wherein the seasonal contrast will be less; this fact forms part of the basis for current projections of an impending ice age.

If the precession of the equinoxes were the only orbital parameter to change and if the Earth's orbit were circular, there would be no effect on the amount of insolation and hence climatic change. It would mean simply that northern hemisphere winter would occur in July instead of January at some point in time. However, the change in ellipticity modulates the precessional effect so that in periods of maximum ellipticity the precessional effect (and the contrast between northern and southern hemisphere seasons) would be greatest.

From the foregoing it can be seen that variations in seasonal contrast are dominated by the precessional and obliquity effects, but modulated by the longer-term change in ellipticity. Furthermore, because of the differing phases of the two effects with respect to hemisphere, the resultant time variation of the solar constant is different in the northern and southern hemispheres. There are also differences in detail as a function of latitude due to the latitudinal dependence of the tilt effect. The combined effect of all three orbital-parameter changes on summer insolation at three northern hemisphere latitudes over the past 500 000 yr has been derived by Broecker and Van Donk

(1970), as illustrated in figure 6.7. The maximum variations are about ±5% around the mean summer insolation value. Since a variation of 0.1% in solar constant is sufficient to cause profound changes in climate (cf. sec. 6.1.1), the relatively huge change of 5% noted here would be catastrophic.

Early attempts to explain the geologic and historical changes in climate in terms of the Milankovitch theory have been reviewed by Brooks (1951). The explanations lacked credibility, in retrospect largely because of a lack of sufficient or appropriate data, leading Brooks to conclude in 1951 that "the trend of modern thought is against the astronomical theory."

With the advent of deep-sea core analysis beginning about 4 yr later (Emiliani, 1955), appropriate and sufficient data have gradually accumulated; the Milankovitch theory is now believed to have been positively verified (Hays et al., 1976; Mason, 1976b). Progress in this type of analysis to 1970 has been reviewed by Broecker and Van Donk

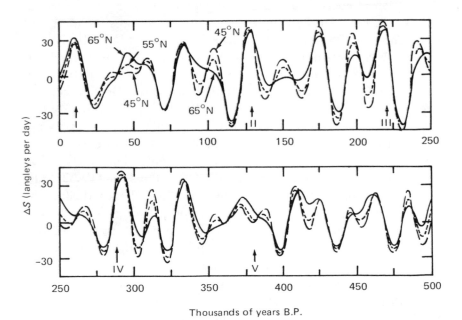

Figure 6.7. Summer insolation curves for latitudes of 45°N, 55°N, and 65°N, taking into account combined effects of orbital tilt, eccentricity, and precession of equinoxes. The variation ΔS is the departure from the mean caloric summer radiation at each latitude. The Roman numerals and arrows mark sudden terminations in O^{18} deep-sea core records. From Broecker and Van Donk (1970).

(1970) and further discussed by Budyko (1972) in connection with other causes of climate change. On the basis of O^{18}/O^{16} ratios measured in deep-sea cores, Broecker and Van Donk showed that the primary glacial cycle over the past 400000 yr is sawtoothed, characterized by gradual glacial buildups for about 90000 yr, followed by relatively abrupt deglaciations taking less than 9000 yr. Secondary oscillations modulating the primary cycle produce recognizable glacial growth phases averaging 20000 yr in length, terminated by retreats over the next 1000 yr. Comparison of their O^{18}/O^{16} curve with the insolation curve given in figure 6.7 indicates that the rapid deglaciations occur during times of unusually great seasonal contrast (Roman numerals in the figure), whereas the secondary oscillations in glacial buildups closely follow the insolation variations. Broecker and Van Donk (1970) concluded that the Milankovitch theory satisfactorily accounts for the glaciation terminations, but the sawtoothed character of the curve was left unexplained.

The latest continuous record of climate change over the past 450000 yr, provided by Hays et al. (1976), is perhaps the most satisfactory to date. The Hays group utilized analysis of both the O^{18}/O^{16} ratio and the distribution of plankta concentrations in two selected deep-sea cores from the floor of a relatively undisturbed portion of the Indian Ocean. The first type of analysis was based on the fact that, because the O^{16} molecules are lighter than O^{18}, they evaporate from the ocean surface faster than the heavier isotope, and during ice ages a greater portion of them are presumably trapped in the continental ice sheets to leave a relatively greater concentration of O^{18} in the ocean to become bound up in the sediment. Thus the O^{18}/O^{16} ratio reflects this process. The second type of analysis relies on the fact that the reproductivity of radiolaria (a type of protozoa) is particularly sensitive to temperature changes; thus the concentration of their skeletal remains in deep-sea cores gives a record of the ocean temperature variation over geologic time scales.

The resultant temperature profile is compared in figure 6.8 to the temperature variations expected from changes in insolation imposed by the orbital eccentricity effect. The observed temperature profile using the radiolaria data was deconvolved to obtain the precessional and obliquity components shown at the top and bottom of the figure, respectively. It is evident that the variations in these two deconvolved components are agreeably close to those derived strictly from orbital

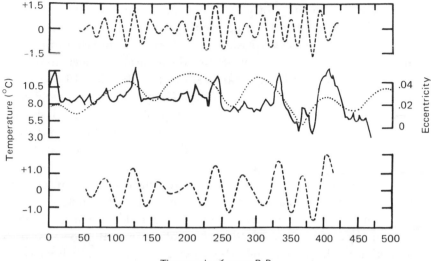

Figure 6.8. Variations in climatic temperature for the past half-million years (solid curve) derived from radiolaria concentrations in two deep-sea cores from the Indian Ocean. The dotted line in the middle is the corresponding change in orbital eccentricity. The dashed curves at the top and bottom of the figure are, respectively, the precessional and tilt components of the orbital changes as deconvolved from the temperature record. From Hays et al. (1976).

elements in figure 6.6. Furthermore, the observed temperature maximums (both large and small in fig. 6.8) correspond to maxima in insolation as plotted in figure 6.7. However, a strict comparison cannot be made between all aspects of figures 6.7 and 6.8, because the first is for northern hemisphere insolation and the second is for southern hemisphere temperatures.

Spectral analysis of the temperature record shows that, over the frequency range 10^{-4}-10^{-5} cycles per year, the variance is concentrated in three discrete peaks corresponding to 23 000, 42 000, and approximately 100 000 yr and containing respectively 10, 25, and 50% of the total variance. The 23 000-yr portion of the variance is actually two periods of 23 000 and 19 000 yr, in accordance with the quasiperiodic precession index.

Prompted by a prepublication view of the results of Hays et al., Mason (1976b), used Milankovitch's theory to estimate the variations in heating north of 45° latitude and found good agreement between times of minimum solar heating and ice sheet advances over the past 150 000 yr. His calculations of heat deficit during glaciation periods and heat excess in times of glacial retreat accounted for the energy absorbed by the ice sheets during melting and that lost during formation. Mason's results are surprisingly good, considering that imperfect knowledge of the actual extent of the continental ice sheets may lead to large errors in heat budget calculations (cf. Budyko, 1972).

In summary, it appears that the Milankovitch theory has now been reasonably well verified. It explains the geologic climate past adequately and probably can be utilized to predict the long-term future if anthropogenic factors do not override the effects of variations in insolation due to orbital changes. Within the context of this book, it seems reasonable to suppose that, since dramatic changes in climate occur because of insolation changes from the Milankovitch effect, lesser semiperiodic variations in climate could be expected on a shorter time scale because of changes in solar constant associated with solar activity. The discussion in the previous section (6.1.1) is a case in point.

6.2 Atmospheric Ozone Shielding

As intimated earlier (sec. 3.5), we consider the major role for the stratospheric ozone layer to be that of a buffer zone, where energy inputs from external (including tropospheric) sources are modulated, filtered, transmitted, and/or reflected into the troposphere. Furthermore, observable effects from this type of process would more than likely be cumulative and would affect long-term climatological changes rather than induce sudden changes in tropospheric weather. Chamberlain (1977) has suggested that screening of cosmic rays by solar and terrestrial magnetic fields may induce climatic variations through long-term modulation processes in the stratosphere.

On an 11-yr-cycle, global basis, ozone production by solar UV radiation should be greatest in sunspot maximum years, because the UV irradiance is most intense then, and least in sunspot minimum years, because of a comparatively low intensity of solar UV radiation. At the same time, ozone loss by cosmic ray-produced NO should be least at sunspot maximum and greatest at sunspot minimum, because of the inverse relationship of cosmic ray intensity with the 11-yr sunspot cycle. Thus, with maximum production and minimum loss of ozone occurring in sunspot maximum years, the total ozone amount should be greatest then. By the same reasoning, one would expect minimum total ozone in sunspot minimum years. To a first approximation this is what has been observed, but ozone transport and other loss processes due to NO production by solar proton events in sunspot maximum years or REP events would tend to reduce the magnitude of the 11-yr peak to valley ratio in total O_3 and shift the phasing between maximum ozone and sunspot maximum.

Meteorological correlations with the sunspot cycle indicate that the annual average global surface temperature is lower at sunspot maximum, when the total ozone budget is greatest. This suggests that shielding of the Earth's surface from UV radiation by the ozone layer is more efficient in sunspot maximum years, and the lower temperature would result from a smaller energy input to the lower atmosphere in those years. In other words, the ozone layer would produce an 11-yr period modulation on the amount of solar UV radiation reaching the lower atmosphere, which in turn would induce a similar period modulation on the global annual average temperature.

To continue this discussion, it is helpful to keep in mind the dual role of atmospheric ozone concentration as a barometer of stratospheric changes on one hand and a possible driver of atmospheric and climate changes on the other. In the first case, a depletion of ozone concentration may be indicative of an enhanced loss rate due to a stronger sink produced by external processes or to a decrease in production rate. Alternately, such a depletion could be associated with a rise in stratospheric temperature produced by an enhanced energy input from external sources. Above about 50-km altitude, the reaction rates for ozone chemistry increase with increasing temperature (e.g., Hilsenrath, 1971). In these cases ozone concentrations would reflect the other processes but would not be the cause of them.

The role of the ozone layer as a possible driver of atmospheric changes is of principal concern in this section. As noted above, it appears that variations in the ozone layer density modulate the amount of solar UV radiation reaching the lower atmosphere, with a consequent variation in heating that would lead to temperature changes and attendant changes in atmospheric circulation patterns. Let us examine this mechanism of solar modulation by O_3 further.

From the known inverse relationship between the intensity of galactic radiation measured at the Earth and solar activity as measured by sunspot number (sec. 2.4.1), it could be expected that the Maunder minimum in sunspot sightings during the period 1645–1715 (Eddy, 1976) would have been accompanied by greater than normal cosmic ray intensities. This expectation has been borne out by C^{14} analysis of tree rings. The higher cosmic ray intensities would produce enhanced NO concentrations below 20 km, and this important ozone sink would tend to deplete the O_3 concentration or alter its vertical distribution. Then, with reduced or redistributed O_3, a greater amount of solar UV radiation could penetrate to the lower atmosphere and produce a warming trend.

However, the Maunder sunspot minimum coincides in time with the "Little Ice Age" of the late seventeenth century (Eddy, 1976) wherein colder temperatures were experienced in the northern hemisphere. This would indicate that less, not more, UV radiation penetrated to the lower atmosphere if in fact surface temperatures are measurably affected by variable solar UV radiation. In such a case, it appears that the Sun radiated so much less UV radiation during the Maunder minimum that even with a more transparent ozone layer, insufficient solar UV radiation reached the lower levels to produce a warming trend. Contemporary analyses of the 11-yr cycle behavior of solar UV radiation up to wavelengths of 175 nm indicate that the intensity is actually somewhat less during sunspot minimum than maximum years (sec. 2.2.2); this might have been the situation during the Maunder minimum.

Hemispheric average surface temperatures may be a better indicator of UV heating variations than individual stations, since temperature fluctuations due to atmospheric circulation effects would presumably be averaged out. For the period 1880–1958, northern hemisphere annual average temperatures were negatively correlated with the 11-yr sunspot cycle; the lower temperatures in sunspot maximum years thus occurred contemporaneously with a relatively higher hemispheric ozone budget, if the results of Heath (1974) for the years 1964 and 1970 can be extrapolated backward in time. The greater UV irradiance at 175 nm during sunspot maximum, coupled with a minimum in cosmic ray intensity (and therefore in the NO ozone sink), would result in a more abundant ozone supply, in agreement with the above. This line of argument suggests that, even though the UV irradiance available to penetrate to the Earth's lower atmosphere is greater at sunspot maximum than sunspot minimum, the larger ozone budget at sunspot maximum prevents this from happening, with a resultant cooler average temperature in sunspot maximum years. On this basis, the ozone-shielding mechanism makes sense qualitatively.

In sunspot minimum years, the hemisphere average temperature is relatively high at a time when the ozone budget is less. This happens in a period when the cosmic ray intensity is maximum with an attendant maximum loss of ozone due to the NO sink; at the same time, production of ozone is least because of the relatively lower intensity of UV radiation from the Sun. In this case, even though the UV radiation available for penetration to the lower atmosphere is less than it was in sunspot maximum years, the more transparent ozone layer allows a sufficient UV flux to penetrate and produce a warming trend. Thus, under these conditions, the ozone-shielding mechanism would be qualitatively correct for both sunspot maximum and minimum years. It applies to years prior to 1958, but since then an apparent reversal of the global temperature relation with sunspot number complicates the question.

In projecting back to historic times, however, we find the opposite behavior during the Maunder minimum. As noted above, the prolonged period of no (or very few) sunspots and a presumably depleted ozone layer was accompanied by cold temperatures. From this it would appear that the UV output (or perhaps the total radiation) of the Sun was much less in the seventeenth and early eighteenth centuries than it has been in recent years, or that solar UV radiation is not an important control of tropospheric temperature.

To further complicate the problem, it should be noted that two recent suggestions may have a bearing on the preceding arguments. The recent results of Heath et al. (1977) have demonstrated sustained periods of up to 1 month for total ozone depletion above 4 mb following a major solar proton event. Furthermore, Thorne (1977) has now argued that relativistic electron precipitation (REP) events occur with much higher frequency than proton events; thus, although their single-event contribution does not compete with that of a PCA, the cumulative effects of REPs may actually exceed those of PCAs. This issue is complicated even more by the different height ranges in which each of these processes operates to create an NO_x sink. In particular, at the higher altitudes, where solar radiation produces a diurnally variable source, the net effects introduced by isolated particle events may be canceled by solar UV production of ozone.

6.3 Cirrus Cloud Shielding

A different type of shielding mechanism that will modulate the intensity of visible radiation reaching the lower atmosphere and surface has been postulated by Roberts and Olson (1973a,b). They suggest that highly energetic solar corpuscles can deposit their energy at

241

and near the 300-mb level either directly or through secondary electromagnetic (bremsstrahlung) radiation and produce ionization. The atmospheric ions would serve as condensation nuclei to form cirrus clouds. According to Roberts and Olson, a cirrus cloud deck could cause heating of up to 1°C per day in the upper troposphere in winter at high latitude over a relatively warm ocean surface. Radiational heat energy from the surface would be blocked by the cloud deck to produce this heating. A strong temperature gradient through the cirrus level would thereby be created, leading to changes in atmospheric circulation.

Johnson and Imhof (1975) criticized this theory on the grounds that the ion-pair production rate due to cosmic rays at 28 km altitude is a factor of 10 higher than the rate due to bremsstrahlung associated with precipitating 100-keV electrons during a typical geomagnetic storm, except that they did not consider REP events (Thorne, 1977). However, Roberts (1975) cited evidence that cirrus clouds often appear following auroral displays (which are now firmly believed to be produced by precipitating electrons). Since the clouds do appear, and calculations of Johnson and Imhof seem to rule out their formation by bremsstrahlung-produced ionization associated with auroral precipitation, it would appear that direct solar proton deposition is required to support the suggestion of Roberts and Olson. Problems concerning transport of proton-produced ions to tropospheric altitudes (cf. sec. 6.6.2), and the low frequency of occurrence for proton events, still exist, however. That this might be possible can be shown on the basis of calculations derived from the discussion in section 2.3.5. A solar proton flux ($E \geq 60$ MeV) of a magnitude comparable to that from the great August 1972 events would increase the ion density at 40 km altitude by a factor of about 500 over its normal value of about $5(10^3)$ cm^{-3} as produced by cosmic ray ionization. The higher proton energies ($E > 60$ MeV) would produce enhanced ionization at altitudes below 40 km. If the atmospheric ions do in fact serve as condensation nuclei, the mechanism proposed by Roberts and Olson may be real. It has been argued that small atmospheric ions are unlikely to be condensation nuclei (Dickinson, 1975), but atmospheric aerosols produced by incoming protons would be a good candidate. This argument is examined in section 6.6.3.

In support of their theory, Roberts and Olson (1973) showed that low-pressure troughs develop over the Gulf of Alaska presumably as a consequence of the temperature instability following geomagnetic storms. It would be of interest to measure atmospheric temperature profiles directly over the Gulf of Alaska along with cloud observations and atmospheric pressure profile measurements during solar proton events to critically test the theory of Roberts and Olson.

Schuurmans and Oort (1969) speculated that the corpuscular particles would penetrate down to stratospheric heights and below the 200-mb level and somehow react with the atmospheric constituents (possibly ozone) on their way down. A change in vertical distribution would disturb the heat balance of the atmospheric layers near the tropopause, as indicated by the large temperature drop at 200 mb in figure 4.4. Vertical and horizontal air motions imposed by the temperature imbalance would eventually result in pressure changes. Some support for this hypothesis is given by the observation of Reiter (1972) that air moves down from the stratosphere after solar flares.

6.4 Shielding by Nacreous or Noctilucent Clouds?

If cirrus clouds produced directly or indirectly by incoming protons act to shield the lower atmosphere and surface from the Sun's rays, it seems reasonable to suppose that other water-vapor cloud types possibly triggered by proton influxes could do the same.

Consider, for example, nacreous (mother of pearl) clouds. This type of cloud has been observed only rarely, but almost always in the stratosphere at a height of 30 km. It is sighted most often in northern latitudes (Norway, Iceland, Canada, and Alaska) in local winter. Nacreous clouds can be observed visually only near sunrise and sunset by reflected sunlight, which may account partially for the rarity of sightings. Meteorologists consider nacreous clouds to be purely orographic, but, if so, it seems unusual they would be seen only at high latitudes and not at low or middle latitudes in the vicinity of mountains or other orographic surface features leading to their development.

It is quite possible that ionization or aerosols produced by solar protons at altitudes near 30 km could serve as condensation nuclei for nacreous clouds in the manner suggested by Roberts and Olson for the lower-altitude (~ 6 km) cirrus clouds. Since the (scanty) observational knowledge of nacreous clouds is based on reflected sunlight, it is clear that they are good reflectors. Under favorable geometry, then, they would reflect the sunlight away from the surface and serve as a shielding mechanism. Whether they occur often enough to produce any discernible changes in the lower atmosphere will have to be determined by experimental observations. A detection method independent of twilight visual sighting would have to be developed to gain reliable statistics. The fact that nacreous clouds are almost exclusively a high-latitude phenomenon makes them a good candidate for investigation as a possible shielding mechanism that would be responsive to magnetic control.

Noctilucent clouds (NLC) might also be considered. These are found at about 80 km altitude and apparently consist of ice crystals formed when the mesospheric temperature is around 135 K (Fogle and Haurwitz, 1966). Recent satellite evidence (Donahue et al., 1972) shows NLC to be continuous over the polar cap ($>80°$ latitude) for several weeks during polar summer. This is in contrast to ground-based measurements, which have historically indicated temporally varying and spatially discontinuous structure, especially at lower latitudes within the auroral zone. Hummel and Olivero (1976) have now calculated radiative temperature changes at the Earth's polar surface on the basis of the satellite observations and conclude that changes of up to 1°C are possible, depending on particulate size, shape, and concentration. This is a major temperature change, if correct.

It is not clear what, if any, relationship NLC might have to solar activity, although some connections have been suggested. For example, there is experimental evidence that NLC suffer a large reduction in intensity and sometimes disappear altogether within an hour after the onset of an aurora. This behavior suggests aurorally induced heating, and D'Angelo and Ungstrup (1976) postulated that it may be due to Joule dissipation of large ionospheric electrical fields. They support this contention by showing statistically that the occurrence frequency of NLC decreases with increasing Kp and tends to zero on moderately disturbed days (Kp sum ≥ 20), that is, periods when ionospheric electrical fields in the vicinity of aurorae are large.

Additional recent experimental evidence (Goldberg and Witt, 1977) also suggests that metallic species of meteoric origin (especially Fe^+) may be nucleation agents for NLC formation. Since the production of Fe^+ ions is enhanced by precipitating particles, this may have some bearing on NLC formation when other meteorological conditions are satisfied.

The minor atmospheric constituents other than ozone and water vapor appear to offer little prospect as possible direct shielding mechanisms. Although the nitrogen compounds (e.g., HNO_3, NO_x) absorb certain wavelengths, their concentrations are roughly three orders of magnitude less than O_3 and H_2O (Shimazaki and Whitten, 1976). In spite of this, they may play an indirect role through atmospheric chemistry. Atmospheric aerosols, especially nucleated sulfuric acid (Dickinson, 1975), may serve as efficient condensation nuclei leading to cloud development. The manner in which the production of this aerosol (H_2SO_4) may be associated with solar proton influxes is examined in section 6.6.3.

6.5 Circulation Changes and Storm Tracks

Surface and lower atmosphere temperature changes may stem from the shielding modulation processes described above or from mass transport of air by atmospheric circulation. With the latter, in middle latitudes warmer temperatures result when warm southerly air is transported northward, and cooler temperatures result when polar air is transported equatorward by meridional circulation. Atmospheric circulation changes result from a spatial redistribution of atmospheric pressure, and, since the latter has been observed to correlate with solar activity, especially in terms of stationary planetary wave oscillations in the surface and 500-mb pressures, one might conclude that some circulation changes may be indirectly responsive to solar influence.

But what is the physical mechanism that would alter the pressure in response to a solar trigger? A possibly significant clue to the answer to this question rests in the observed penchant for low-pressure troughs to develop or intensify over the Gulf of Alaska following a solar magnetic sector boundary passage (sec. 4.3.3). Also, the observed 27.5-day rotation and 11-yr cycle oscillations in the standing planetary waves in surface pressure and 500-mb height (as discussed in sec. 6.1.1) may lead to circulation changes. A third clue may reside in the behavior of the main ionospheric trough (Muldrew, 1965) during periods of geomagnetic disturbance.

The main trough of the ionosphere is so called because, in proceeding from the equator toward the pole at a fixed altitude, the ionospheric electron density gradually decreases, then drops suddenly (within a degree or two of latitude) by a factor of 4 or more near a geomagnetic latitude of roughly 60°, and then increases again toward the pole. The width of this depression or trough is about 10° in latitude, and it is centered on a magnetic L shell of about 4 near the midnight meridian. It develops in the local afternoon and persists through the night to early morning, is most pronounced near local midnight,

and is present on nearly 100% of the nights in winter and 60% in summer. An important feature of the trough is that it intensifies (the electron density decreases) and moves equatorward by about 3.5° latitude
per unit increase in Kp. The electron density depression is manifest
from the D-region ($\sim$65–100 km altitude) through the F-region
($\sim$300 km peak) and beyond, and its equatorward wall coincides
with the foot of the plasmapause; these characteristics make it unlikely that tropospheric dynamics cause the electron trough.

During geomagnetic disturbances, the trough's southward movement places it over the Gulf of Alaska during the evening and night
hours, and it may therefore be associated with the meteorological
depressions leading to increases in vorticity area index. Research has
shown that the vorticity area index increases a few days after an increase in the magnetic activity index Kp (sec. 4.2.3) and also that
it increases a few days after the passage of a solar magnetic sector
boundary (sec. 4.3.3). The tie-in between these two findings is that
the Kp index maximizes about 2 days after a sector boundary passage
(Wilcox and Ness, 1965). When one considers that the main ionospheric trough moves southward with increasing geomagnetic activity
(Muldrew, 1965), it is evident that the trough should move southward
a few days after the crossing of a solar magnetic sector boundary.

It is noteworthy that the latitudinal position of the trough places it
in the vicinity of the polar vortex that is so well known to meteorologists. A southward movement of polar vortex in association with the
geomagnetic storm time behavior of the main trough would tend to
force the cold polar air equatorward and produce a cold front bring-
ing colder temperatures to middle latitude locations. Southward
movement of the polar vortex would tend to force low-pressure storm
tracks associated with the jet stream toward lower latitudes and
thereby alter the circulation pattern of the atmosphere. During solar
maximum years when geomagnetic storms occur often, there would
be frequent southward movement of the trough, polar vortex, and
the jet stream, with a resultant greater occurrence of stormy weather
over the contiguous United States and central Europe. Known correlations between geomagnetic activity and weather and between sunspots and weather tend to support both the short- and long-term
aspects of this speculation.

There is some indirect evidence that precipitating particles influence atmospheric pressure patterns and therefore the general circulation. King (1973), drawing on the results of Bradley (1973), showed
that contours of the average height of the 850-mb surface in July

(1964–1972) are almost parallel to lines of constant invariant latitude (INL). The height decreased with increasing INL, which means that the pressure at constant height decreased going toward the invariant pole. The pattern departs from this parallelism near geographic longitudes of 75°–80°W and exhibits a ridge of high pressure between 76°–79°INL, peaking at 78°INL. King (1973) pointed out that this is an area in which cusp particle precipitation takes place (Heikkila and Winningham, 1971; Frank, 1971). On disturbed days, cusp particle precipitation extends equatorward to at least 75°N, placing it in the center of southern Greenland where Duell and Duell (1948) observed pressure increases associated with geomagnetic disturbances. According to the studies of Berko and Hoffman (1974), the most intense particle precipitation takes place in local winter, and this is the season in which the most pronounced meteorological responses to solar activity occur. It would be interesting to calculate the amount of heat input provided by integrating this mechanism over a period of several days. As noted in section 2.2.4, within the auroral zone in winter nighttime the amount of energy could be on the order of 20% of the amount that would be provided by insolation *if it were present*. Since Volland's hypothesis (sec. 6.1.1) requires only a 0.1% change in solar constant to influence the planetary standing waves in pressure distribution, it appears plausible that a 20% difference introduced by particles would be even more influential.

This additional heat input at high latitudes should also alter the average latitudinal gradient in atmospheric temperature. It is evident that the gradient going poleward would be decreased, but to what extent is unknown. A consequence would be a shift in the position of the jet stream, since this phenomenon is found at the latitude at which the average temperature gradient divided by the Coriolis force parameter is a maximum (Holton, 1972, p. 96).

A graph of the zonal averages of the height change of the 500-mb level, observed 24 hr apart with a major flare ($\geq 2+$) occurring between observations, is given in figure 6.9. This solar-flare response pattern contrasts distinctly with that for solar rotations and the 11-yr cycle (fig. 6.3). However, the important point in the present context is the difference in geographic latitude where the height difference changes from positive to negative in the northern and southern hemispheres. Note that in the north, the geographic latitude of sign change at about 65°N is some 8 or 9 degrees lower than in the southern hemisphere. Schuurmans' measurements were made on ships and at observatories in the western hemisphere, where the geomagnetic equator is

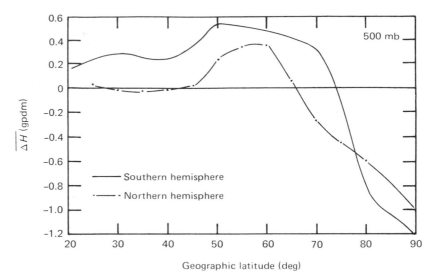

Figure 6.9. Zonal averages of the height change (ΔH) of the 500-mb level based on observations 24 hr apart bracketing major solar flares. Geographic latitudes are for northern hemisphere (81 cases) and southern hemisphere (56 cases). From Schuurmans (1969).

displaced southward from the geographic equator. The significance of this is that, recast in geomagnetic coordinates, the two height-difference curves of figure 6.9 would more nearly coincide, with $\overline{\Delta H} = 0$ falling at about 60° geomagnetic latitude. Particle precipitation is geomagnetically controlled and, during moderate disturbances, can extend equatorward to about the same latitude. Thus the better agreement in the pressure data when expressed in geomagnetic coordinates implies a connection with magnetically controlled phenomena.

A final speculative point is that the relatively greater height difference in the southern compared to northern hemisphere poleward of 60° geomagnetic latitude may be a consequence of the difference in IMF polarity in the two hemispheres, as discussed by Mansurov et al. (1975). Also, atmospheric circulation may respond to solar magnetic sector boundary crossings (Kuliyeva, 1975a,b).

6.6 A Triggering Mechanism for Thunderstorm Occurrence

There is a growing belief that atmospheric electrical processes might in some manner form a basis for linking mechanisms between solar activity and the weather (Markson, 1975; Dickinson, 1975; Park, 1976b). In this section a mechanism is postulated that might explain the suggestive correlations between thunderstorm occurrence frequency and solar activity discussed in sections 3.4.4, 4.1.2, and 4.3.4. This section, based on work by Herman and Goldberg (1976, 1978) and Herman et al. (1977), is purposely long to demonstrate in detail the subtleties involved and the multiplicity of disciplines that must be addressed in seeking viable physical mechanisms. Since thunderstorm occurrence is intimately involved with atmospheric electrification, the postulated mechanism emphasizes this process rather than the meteorological properties of thunderstorms.

Noting that the intensity of galactic cosmic rays varies inversely with the solar cycle with increasingly greater amplitudes at higher latitudes and that they are the prime cause of ionization in the lower atmosphere, Ney (1959) suggested that cosmic ray variations rather than a direct solar influence might explain the previously reported correlations. Additional support for a strong solar-related cosmic ray influence on short-term thunderstorm correlations is given by the fact that the galactic cosmic ray intensity decreases dramatically following solar flares (the Forbush decrease), and it decreases following the passage of a solar magnetic sector boundary past the Earth (Wilcox and Ness, 1965). It would appear, then, that the previously reported results could just as well be interpreted as negative correlations between thunderstorm activity and cosmic ray intensity rather than positive ones with solar activity (Ney, 1959; Markson, 1971).

On the other hand, strong solar flare eruptions are accompanied by the emission of high-energy solar protons, the proton events occur more often in solar maximum than solar minimum years, and there is indirect evidence for solar proton emission near solar magnetic sector boundaries. The high-energy protons ($E \geq 300$ MeV) penetrate to altitudes at and below about 20 km and produce ionization (Reid, 1974). Thus the previously reported statistics could also be interpreted as being positive correlations between thunderstorm occurrence and solar proton enhancements.

These two interpretations suggest that it is the combination of proton enhancements and cosmic ray decreases that is important in triggering conditions conducive to thunderstorm formation, or at least electrification. In the next sections the question of how the atmospheric electrical parameters are altered by these two agents is addressed, and the results are used to postulate an initiation mechanism

249

leading to thundercloud development. The mechanism differs from that proposed by Markson (1975) and Holzworth and Mozer (1977), who suggested that the regulation of the electrical resistance between cloud tops and the ionosphere by solar influences might be the key.

6.6.1 Atmospheric Electric Effects

Energetic protons emitted by the Sun during large solar flares penetrate the Earth's atmosphere to various depths depending on energy spectrum, atmospheric density, and terrestrial magnetic field shielding. For most strong events, the magnetic field effect is small for geomagnetic latitudes poleward of about 45°. The following discussion neglects magnetic field influence and therefore applies principally to high-latitude regions. Any atmospheric electric effects that may be produced by the incoming protons and cosmic rays can be considered to occur through alteration of the ionization and conductivity distributions in the atmosphere. The ionization processes due to solar protons and cosmic rays were discussed in sections 2.3.5 and 2.4, and ion-pair production rates (Q) due to several solar proton events are illustrated in figure 2.22. It should be noted that the decrease in Q due to the reduction of cosmic ray intensities from sunspot minimum to maximum years is comparable to the magnitude of reduction expected in connection with Forbush decreases. The basic relationships in atmospheric electricity required for the following discussion were developed in section 3.4.1.

To convert Q to atmospheric conductivity (σ) we require the use of an approximation to equation (3.4), i.e.,

$$\sigma = \frac{e^2}{m\nu}\left(\frac{Q}{\alpha}\right)^{\frac{1}{2}} \tag{6.1}$$

where it is understood that m, ν, and α represent average values for ionic mass, ion neutral collision frequency, and recombination coefficient, respectively, all of which are height dependent, and Q is the total production rate for ions of all species, also dependent on height, as shown in figure 2.22.

What are thought to be reasonable averages of m^+, ν, and α for positive ions are illustrated in figure 6.10. They could not be selected rigorously but are considered to be within acceptable limits. For example, the collision frequency profile is within 20% of that established by Nicolet (1953) and is still an acceptable value. For the ion-ion recombination coefficient, the "selected values" of Cole and Pierce

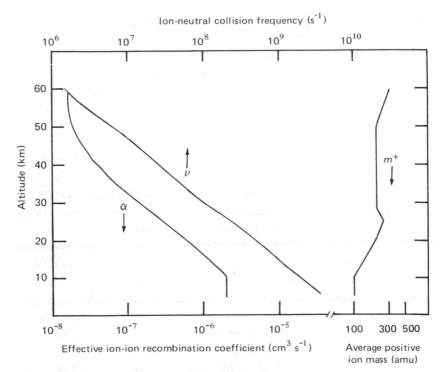

Ion-neutral collision frequency (s^{-1})

Figure 6.10. Height-profile models of the ion-ion recombination coefficient (α), ion-neutral collision frequency (v), and average positive ion mass (m^+).

(1965) for altitudes below 30 km, along with a slight modification of results from Hale et al. (1972) above 30 km, form the profile in figure 6.10; the arithmetic average of the Cole and Pierce and Hale values at 30 km joins the two sets of data in a smooth transition.

Perhaps the most difficult selection was that of the ion mass as a function of height. There appears to be no widely accepted model for an ion-mass profile, and there have been relatively few measurements, especially below 30 km. It is generally agreed, however, that atmospheric conductivity is due principally to the motion of small ions, each ion consisting of a single ionized molecule with other molecules clustered around it and held together by the charge (Chalmers, 1967, p. 86). The clustering molecules are probably H_2O, and their number per small ion may cover a wide range. Investigators (e.g., Mohnen, 1971) now postulate an abundant supply of hydronium ions, $H^+ \cdot (H_2O)_n$, with an optimum n of 7–5 from 5 to 30 km for the positive ions. The most abundant negative ion would be NO_3^- with a

251

similar value of clustered water molecules attached. These clusters would lead to ion masses up to about 200 amu. Near the Junge layer (~ 20 km altitude) the ions might consist of hydrated sulfates with 10 or 12 H_2O molecules; the mass could then exceed 300 amu.

Since there are large uncertainties in the ion chemical processes and in the terminal ion identifications for this part of the atmosphere, it seems best to follow a corollary of Hoppel's (1969) advice, namely, determine ionic masses indirectly from experimental measurements of other quantities. The positive ion-mass profile of figure 6.10 was therefore derived from equation (6.1) using balloon conductivity measurements up to 20 km altitude by Paltridge (1965) on November 20, 1964 (a sunspot minimum year on a geomagnetically quiet day) over Melbourne, Australia (geomagnetic latitude $\sim 46°S$), and from 30 to 60 km by Hale (1974) on October 13, 1971 (near sunspot maximum) over Wallops Island, Virginia (geomagnetic latitude $\sim 51°N$). The average positive ion mass was then derived from equation (6.1) by using the α and ν profiles of figure 6.10 with the ion-pair production curves for cosmic rays from figure 2.22. The resulting ion-mass profile ranges from 100 amu below 10 km to 300 amu at 60 km. The bulge at 25 km was shaped by Paltridge's (1965) conductivity estimates from 20 to 28 km in the aforementioned 1964 flight, but there were telemetry problems in this altitude range, and the result may not be reliable; it was left in the curve as a possible influence from the Junge layer.

Theoretical conductivity curves for sunspot maximum (i.e., cosmic ray intensity minimum) and sunspot minimum have also been calculated from equation (6.1) with the α, ν, and m^+ data of figure 6.10 and the Q curves 7 and 6 from figure 2.22, respectively. These are illustrated in figure 6.11 for comparison with the Paltridge and Hale quiet period measurements. The curves and experimental points should agree, of course, since the data in figure 6.10 were considerably influenced by the experimental results. However, further verification was obtained when the same profiles for α, ν, and m^+ were used along with an ion-pair production rate profile derived from the proton flux data at 0300 UT for the November 3, 1969 event (fig. 2.18). The resulting disturbed-period profile is agreeably close to the blunt-probe conductivity measurements made about an hour earlier by Hale et al. (1972) at Fort Churchill, Canada (geomagnetic latitude $\sim 69°$) over most of the height range covered. This good agreement suggests that our simple approximation to determine conductivity is

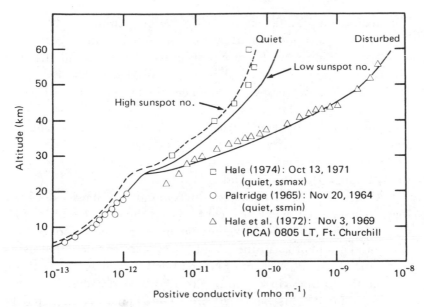

Figure 6.11. Comparison of theoretical and measured positive conductivities due to cosmic rays during geomagnetically quiet periods in sunspot maximum and minimum years, and due to solar protons during a PCA event on November 3, 1969.

adequate and consistent above about 25–30 km for conditions following a solar flare.

At and below 25 km the theoretical curve greatly underestimates the actual conductivity during the solar proton event. Since quiet-period data provide closer agreement down to at least 5 km height, it may be that the disturbed-period ion-pair production rates below about 30 km were seriously underestimated. Hence it is possible that the higher-energy component of the solar proton flux during this phase of the event was actually larger than previously suspected, or that the ion mass was smaller.

It seems certain that the conductivity would be enhanced above about 20 km in every solar proton event, judging from the ion-pair production profiles of figure 2.22 and those given by others (e.g., Zmuda and Potemra, 1972). We also note that a similar enhancement of smaller magnitude would be associated with proton bursts from recurrent solar storms occurring near the feet of solar magnetic sector boundaries and in the regions of coronal holes or M-regions. The conductivity below 20 km, however, would once again be decreased because of the associated reduction in cosmic ray flux.

The decrease in cosmic ray intensity, ranging from roughly 40 to 70% near 10 km altitude, would produce a corresponding decrease in ion-pair production rate. From equation (6.1) it is evident that the conductivity, being proportional to $Q^{1/2}$, would decrease by about 23–45%. Smaller decreases would occur in association with solar magnetic sector boundary crossings.

The potential gradient or vertical electric field, E_h, at height h is related to the conductivity at h by $E_h = J/\sigma_h$, where J is the air-Earth conduction current density. It is generally accepted that J is essentially constant with altitude, and its value is in the range $1\text{-}4(10^{-12})$ A m^{-2} (Chalmers, 1967). If the conduction current density does not change during a solar event, it is evident that the height profile of E_h would change in concert with the change in conductivity. To see this, the potential gradient as a function of height can be calculated using the σ profile for the PCA event of November 3, 1969 (fig. 6.11) above 20 km and the σ values corresponding to a Forbush decrease in cosmic ray intensity for heights below 20 km. The results are depicted in figure 6.12, compared to a quiet time profile of the potential gradient calculated with the σ profile for quiet conditions in sunspot minimum

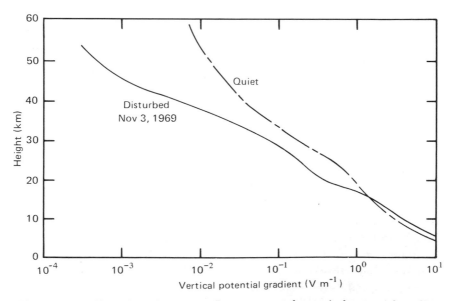

Figure 6.12. Effect of a solar proton flare event on the vertical potential gradient height profile ("disturbed" curve) compared to background profile due to cosmic ray-produced conductivity ("quiet" curve).

years (fig. 6.11). A constant value of 10^{-12} A m^{-2} was used for J in these calculations, derived at 5 km height with $\sigma = 10^{-13}$ mho m^{-1} (fig. 6.11) combined with $E_h = 10$ V m^{-1} (Hake et al., 1973). The validity of the assumption of a constant current density is examined later.

As expected, the disturbed electrical field is decreased above roughly 15 km and enhanced at lower altitudes. The possible reality of this behavior is demonstrated by in situ aircraft and balloon measurements. At a constant altitude of 19.5 km, Hoffman and Hopper (1969) measured a mean field of 0.7 V m^{-1} that showed fluctuations of about 5% on a time scale of roughly 10 minutes. Then, over a period of about 20 minutes, the field decreased to 0.2 V m^{-1}, in association with a solar flare (Hake et al., 1973). The observed decrease of a factor of 3.5 lends credence to the hypothetical decrease computed by the present simplified methods. Further, balloon measurements at 30 km height during the August 1972 proton event by Holzworth and Mozer (1977) showed a decrease in field strength by a factor of 10, indicating that even larger changes than those estimated here are possible.

In the 4–15-km height range, the potential gradient would increase by 23–45% or more because of the Forbush decrease. This increase would be manifest over a much larger region of the globe than that due to solar protons, because of geomagnetic cutoff effects on the latter (cf. fig. 2.19). Since cosmic ray decreases of a few percent or more occur much more frequently than proton flare events (Kane, 1977), these may play the more important but as yet undefined role in thunderstorm triggering or in the weak electrification of rainclouds without lightning through alteration of the low-altitude electrical field strength. The increased field at low heights is in substantial agreement with the magnitude of enhancements observed by Reiter (1969) atop Zugspitze (3 km height) in the Bavarian Alps about 2 days after the occurrence of major solar flares.

Even though the foregoing analysis is replete with simplifying assumptions and coarse estimates of atmospheric electrical quantities, the results suggest a definite solar disturbance effect on the atmospheric electrical field that is substantiated by measurements. The assumption of an unchanged conduction current density during a disturbance is not quite correct, however, because both Cobb (1967) and Reiter (1969, 1972) noted increases of 12–50% in the air-Earth current density following solar flares, more or less concurrent with

30–60% increases in electrical field strength at 3 km altitude. A reason for the reported increase in current density might be developed using equations (3.2) and (3.3). Noting that the ionospheric potential increases by the order of 50% following solar flares (cf. fig. 4.6), it is evident from equation (3.2) that J would increase proportionately if the columnar resistance remained constant. However, integration of the quiet and disturbed conductivity profiles (fig. 6.11) in accordance with equation (3.3) indicates that R_H would decrease by only 1 or 2% in an event of the magnitude of that of August 1972. This decrease, although small, would add to the increase in J, as is clear from equation (3.2). The major enhancement of J would be due to the increase in ionospheric potential. Combined with the calculated decrease in conductivity associated with the Forbush decrease in cosmic ray ion-pair production, the enhancement in air-Earth current density would increase the electrical field strength below 15 km even more than that indicated in figure 6.12.

The details of particular events may well differ from each other and from the typical sequence sketched above because of differences in solar proton acceleration mechanisms, solar magnetic shielding effects on cosmic rays near the Earth, and anisotropies in incoming cosmic rays (cf. Dutt et al., 1973), all of which would affect the temporal and spatial distribution of the atmospheric effects. On the whole, however, it appears that the sequence of atmospheric electrical variations parallel those of the associated solar proton and cosmic ray phenomena. The manner in which the changes in atmospheric electrical parameters may initiate thunderstorm development is examined in the next section (6.6.2).

6.6.2 Thunderstorm Initiation: Proposed Mechanism

The foregoing analysis concerns conductivity and electrical field changes in the "fair-weather" atmospheric picture. To explain correlations between solar-related disturbances and thunderstorm activity, it is necessary to link solar-induced changes in the atmospheric electrical parameters to thunderstorm development. Noting that the thunderstorm ". . . represents an intense form of shower or an advanced stage in the development of convection in moist air" (Byers, 1951), it is tempting to believe that the establishment of this link will also shed light on a way in which weak electrification in clouds might produce precipitable water drops resulting in rain showers unaccompanied by lightning discharge phenomena.

Although thunderstorm electrification is not completely understood, it is possible to describe a thundercloud model with attributes common to most current theories. It is generally agreed (cf. Chalmers, 1967, p. 309) that an excess of positive charge exists at the top of the thundercloud, and an excess of negative charge is found near the base of the cloud. Sometimes there is a smaller region of positive charge below the main region of negative charge, because of point discharge (corona) at the ground. In this classic model of charge distribution, between the two main charge centers the polarity is mixed, as depicted in figure 6.13. The negatively charged screening layer identified by Vonnegut et al. (1966), using aircraft measurements above the cloud top, represents, in our view, an addition to the classic model. It can be regarded as a space charge required by the change in conductivity between the inside and outside of the cloud.

There has been considerable debate regarding the charging mechanisms that might provide the classic distribution sketched in figure 6.13 and subsequently build up the intense electrical fields required for lightning discharge (cf. Mason, 1972, 1976a; Gunn, 1954; Sartor, 1961, 1967; Levin and Ziv, 1974; Ziv and Levin, 1974; Kamra, 1970, 1975, 1976; Moore, 1976a,b; Griffiths et al., 1974; Griffiths and Latham, 1975; Griffiths, 1976; Paluch and Sartor, 1973a,b; and the review by Stow, 1969). The basic processes addressed appear to have been the generation of charges and subsequent separation of those charges, to build up and maintain the distribution depicted in figure 6.13. It is beyond the scope of this book to consider the many theories; the interested reader is referred to chapter 16 of Chalmers (1967) and the excellent treatment by Stow (1969). Implicit in all the theories is the necessary assumption that the whole process somehow gets started, but there have been few explicit attempts to explain the triggering or initiation mechanisms.

The present objective is to suggest possible initiation mechanisms related to atmospheric electrical variations introduced by cosmic ray decreases and solar proton enhancements. From the analysis in the previous section, the enhanced electrical field, induced by cosmic ray decreases and energetic proton showers, alters the electrical characteristics of the lower atmosphere. In addition, the extra charges generated by protons at and above 20 km altitude may somehow make their way down to heights commensurate with thunderclouds (i.e., the order of 10 km and below). Implicit is the concept that the actual conditions for thunderstorm generation have already been established

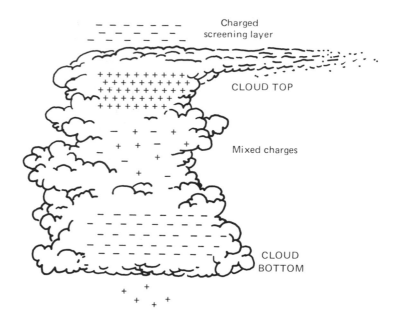

Figure 6.13. Classic model of charge distribution in a thundercloud (from Chalmers, 1967). The negatively charged screening layer is added on the basis of aircraft measurements by Vonnegut et al. (1966).

by suitable meteorological conditions, and that these events enhance the probability of formation. In this context, we must recognize that, although proton showers may occur with more intensity and induce a stronger local effect, cosmic ray decreases occur more frequently. This fact, coupled with their direct effect in the lower atmosphere and over a much larger geographic area to lower latitudes, makes them the more probable candidate source for the mechanism to be discussed.

Since the electrical field in a thunderstorm is of the order of 10^5 V m^{-1} (cf. Mason, 1972), it is obvious that the rather small field changes induced by the protons and cosmic rays in the low atmosphere can only serve as a trigger. However, when meteorological conditions along a weather front are receptive to thunderstorm development (strong updrafts with moist air present), the increase in electrical field strength may be sufficient to begin or assist the development.

For example, the enhanced field can promote the coalescence of extremely small water droplets by increasing their collision efficiencies (see Latham, 1969, p. 89), if above the freezing level ice crystals would be formed with radii of perhaps 50 μm (Stow, 1969). Now, if meteorological processes along the front generate hail pellets of average radius 2 mm, the hail will fall faster than the ice crystals. Large charges will be accumulated by the pellets as they fall through the ice crystals, and the resultant separation of charges will increase the electrical field, as shown below. If the hail falls through the ice crystals (of density 10^5 m^{-3}) with a relative velocity of 7.75 m s^{-1}, the hail density is 0.5 g cm^{-3}, and the precipitation rate is 5 mm/hr, the electric field buildup will be (Stow, 1969):

$$\ln(E/E_o) = 6.8(10^{-3})t - 0.88(1 - \exp(-t/100)) \qquad (6.2)$$

When $t = 0$, $E = E_o$, and it can be seen that if E_o is increased by external solar-related influences, the time (t) required for E to build up to thunderstorm proportions will decrease.

Note that the falling hail model used here is not suggested as *the* correct explanation for charge separation and field buildup; there are a number of possible candidates, as discussed in the Chalmers and Stow references cited above as well as in more recent theories under development. Also, there is no general agreement on how large E_o must be before a lightning flash is triggered. It was selected only to illustrate the possible effects of an electrical field enhancement due to solar-related processes. The results do suggest that a thunderstorm could develop if a weather front with its attendant receptive meteorological conditions existed or developed at the time of solar proton enhancements and associated cosmic ray decreases.

An additional contributing agent may be that the ions produced by incoming energetic particles make their way to lower heights. The downward migration might take the form of preferential transport of the ions with an electrical field driver or by bulk transport wherein the ions are swept down along with neutral air.

Under the action of the downward-directed fair weather atmospheric electrical field, the positive ions would be forced downward. A crude estimate of the distance to which the positive ions would be driven below the bottom of the deposition layer can be calculated. The lifetime of the ions, that is the half-life required for the density of initially produced ions (N_o) to decay to the background density (N), is given by $t(\text{sec}) = 1/\alpha N$, if $N_o \gg N$. At 20 km, $N \approx 10^3$ cm^{-3}, and α

(from fig. 6.10) is $6(10^{-7})$ cm^3 s^{-1}. The time for decay to $N_o/2$ is thus approximately $1.7(10^3)$ sec. Shortly after being produced, the ions will be small, and their subsequent lifetimes and disappearance rates will be governed by α and N. However, a fraction of them will attach to aerosols and other heavy agglomerates to produce large ions with much slower loss rates and thereby extend the effective lifetimes. The large ion loss rates may be as much as a factor of 5 less than those for the small ions; therefore the average half-life of heavy ions could be on the order of 8500 sec. The heavy ions would thus control the ion lifetimes.

During their lifetime, the positive ions are forced downward at an average velocity given by $E_o\mu$, where E_o is the fair weather field strength and μ is, as before, the mobility. A generally accepted value for μ_+ is $1.7(10^{-4})$ m s^{-1} per V m^{-1} at STP (Hale et al., 1972), which in a standard atmosphere at 20 km height would be about $25(10^{-4})$ m s^{-1} per V m^{-1} (assuming $P_o = 1000$ mb; $P = 50$ mb; $T_o = 300$ K; and $T = 220$ K). The quiet time electrical field at 20 km is on the order of 1 V m^{-1} (Hake et al., 1973), but could be reduced during solar events. The average downward velocity of the positive ions due to the electrical field would thus approach values of 10^{-2} m s^{-1}, and they would move about 85 m before being lost. With a sufficiently long lifetime the ions would eventually migrate down to thunderstorm heights where they could be accelerated by the relatively stronger electrical field, although this seems unlikely based on the present arguments.

A possible way for the energetic protons to influence the vertical electrical field at the Earth's surface has been considered by Herman and Goldberg (1978) and Herman et al. (1977). Briefly, it is postulated that poleward of the proton cutoff latitude (cf. fig. 2.19), the incoming protons will enhance the conductivity in the manner shown in figure 6.11 ("disturbed" curve) and thereby lower the effective height of the electrosphere. Equatorward of this cutoff the conductivity remains unchanged or even decreases ("quiet" curve in fig. 6.11). This action introduces a strong horizontal gradient across the cutoff latitude in the conductivity distribution, with a consequent perturbation in the equipotential surfaces (fig. 6.14). Based on preliminary calculations, it appears that the alteration in conductivity distribution will enhance the vertical potential gradient at the surface poleward of the cutoff latitude (as evidenced by the closer spacing of field lines in fig. 6.14). Near the cutoff, it appears that horizontal electrical fields may be generated.

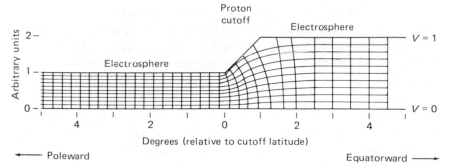

Figure 6.14. Model of proton effects on the electrosphere and potential gradient (electrical field) in the vicinity of the proton cutoff latitude. Horizontal lines with perturbations are equipotential surfaces, and vertical lines are electrical field lines between the electrosphere at a relative total potential of $V = 1$ and the ground with a relative potential of $V = 0$. From Herman et al. (1977).

Finally, since nontropical thunderstorms have a tendency to be associated with weather fronts, the possibility of stratospheric ions being swept downward along with neutral air (bulk transport) must also be considered. Cold fronts and their associated storm systems are frequently found in the neighborhood of the polar jet stream. The jet stream, in turn, has an associated tropopause gap wherein stratospheric air can penetrate into the troposphere, as depicted in figure 6.15, i.e., between the warm air mass and the cold air mass. Ionized

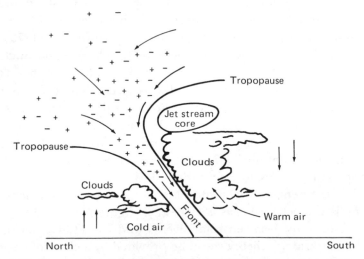

Figure 6.15. Penetration of stratospheric air and ions to tropospheric heights near a jet stream. From Reiter (1967, p. 158).

particles produced at the 20–30-km level by a solar proton event, as indicated by the charge signs in figure 6.15, will be transported downward along with the neutral air by the sinking motion along the front. Wind speeds across the jet stream gap coupled with strong downdrafts within the troposphere could bring the ions to thunderstorm heights within the ion lifetimes. In the thunderstorm itself, the vertical speeds can be as high as 10–15 m s^{-1} (Byers, 1951). Whether these speeds can be expected at heights near 20 km is speculatory, but if 1 m s^{-1} were possible, the ions would be swept downward 8.5 km for the half-life of 8500 sec estimated above, and one-half would still exist at this level.

6.6.3 Additional Considerations

Two additional factors associated with the proton flux may serve to enhance the initial triggering process proposed here. A question that does not seem to have been asked before is, what happens to the solar protons after they have become thermalized in the lower atmosphere? They are, after all, hydrogen ions, and when a proton captures an electron it becomes a neutral hydrogen atom. Thus those existing as thermalized hydrogen ions may become hydrated and add to Mohnen's (1971) population of $H^+ \cdot (H_2O)_n$ and, under the action of the atmospheric electrical field, also add to the positive space charge center at the cloud top level.

The second additional factor is that those thermalized protons which capture an electron and become free hydrogen atoms may ultimately enter a scheme recently proposed by Dickinson (1975). According to Dickinson, cloud droplets are unlikely to be nucleated directly by ionization, and he suggests that instead stratospheric aerosols produced by the ionization could serve as condensation nuclei. In his view, the major stratospheric aerosol is a sulfuric acid-water mixture. The sulfuric acid aerosol greatly lowers the saturation vapor pressure of water over its pure value, and, according to Dickinson, it may be the dominant nucleating agent of clouds just above and below the tropopause in middle and high latitudes. The aerosol, once formed, could persist in the atmosphere long enough to participate in the proposed mechanism, as is evident in figure 6.16.

The association between solar events and the H_2SO_4 aerosol required in Dickinson's theory could be provided by a chain of chemical reactions involving the hydrogen atoms yielded by the thermalized protons.

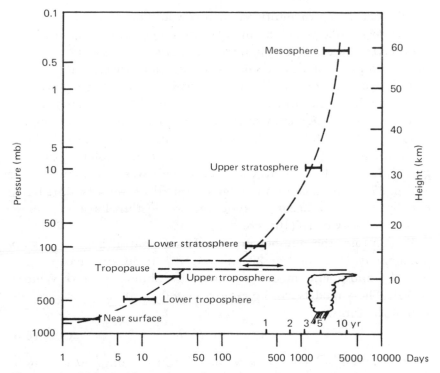

Figure 6.16. Mean residence times of aerosols as a function of height. The double-headed arrow between the two tropopause height limits (horizontal dashed lines) indicates uncertainty in lifetimes in this height regime. From Bach (1976).

Two important reactions would be (Shimazaki and Whitten, 1976):

$$H + NO_2 \longrightarrow HO + NO \qquad (k = 2.97(10^{-11}) \, cm^3 \, s^{-1}) \qquad (6.3)$$

$$H + O_3 \longrightarrow HO + O_2 \qquad (k = 2.60(10^{-11}) \, cm^3 \, s^{-1}) \qquad (6.4)$$

The formation of sulfuric acid would then proceed principally by (Davis, 1974):

$$2HO + SO_2 \longrightarrow H_2SO_4 \qquad (6.5)$$

In reaction (6.5) the HO molecules are supplied by reactions (6.3) and (6.4), and the SO_2 presumably comes up from the ground. A number of other reactions are available for depleting H (Shimazaki and Whitten, 1976), but their reaction rates (k) are all much slower than those for (6.3) and (6.4). Some of the HO molecules from these two reactions might combine with ozone to yield $HO_2 + O_2$ with a rate of $1.7(10^{-14}) \, cm^3 \, s^{-1}$, but the HO_2 would also oxidize sulfur dioxide to produce H_2SO_4 (Davis, 1974).

Whether these two additional factors would be significant depends on the magnitude of the thermalized proton contribution to the total hydrogen population. To obtain a rough guess, let us assume that all protons stopping at altitudes below the atmospheric electrical equalization layer (approximately 50 km) will be subject to downward migration due to the atmospheric electric field as long as they remain hydrogen ions. The energy of the protons meeting this stopping criterion is $E \geq 30$ MeV (Reid, 1974). For the solar disturbed period from August 4, 1972, 0700 UT, to August 7, 1972, 1500 UT, the integrated flux of solar protons with $E \geq 30$ MeV was $8(10^9)$ cm^{-2} (table 2.3, p. 57). After a certain passage of time they could be distributed equally from 0 to 50 km altitude and would thus have an average number density of $1.6(10^3)$ cm^{-3}.

By contrast, the number density [H] of neutral hydrogen is approximately 10^{-1} cm^{-3} at 20 km and 10^6 at 50 km, according to several atmospheric models reviewed by Shimazaki and Whitten (1976). These models can be approximated by an analytical expression of the form:

$$[H] = K \exp(h/h_o) \qquad (6.6)$$

where K and h_o are constants evaluated from the data, which can be used to determine an average number density of $3.2(10^2)$ in the height range 20–50 km. Thus it is conceivable that the thermalized protons, having been transformed to hydrogen atoms by electron capture, could increase the hydrogen density by a factor of 5 and ultimately increase the population of H_2SO_4.

Although not strictly germane to the present argument, it is of interest to digress a moment to consider the old question of whether increased thunderstorm activity is the cause or the result of an increase in atmospheric electrical field (potential gradient). Consideration of the morphology of apparent atmospheric responses to solar activity may shed some light on this question. In a typical sequence beginning with a major solar flare eruption, the conductivity would begin to increase (and the potential gradient to decrease) at altitudes at and above about 20 km approximately 1–3 hr later because of the arrival of high-energy solar protons, and would continue to be enhanced (electrical field depressed) for 1–5 days, or as long as the solar proton bombardment persisted. There would, of course, be variations in magnitude marked by a maximum some 3–12 hr after flare beginning and a gradual recovery to preflare conditions as the proton flux decayed. About 1 day after the flare eruption, the conductivity below about 15 km height would start to decrease, with an attendant increase in potential gradient due to the Forbush decrease in cosmic ray intensity as measured at the ground (McCracken, 1963). Minimum conductivity (and maximum potential gradient) would be reached approximately 8 hr after the start of the Forbush decrease, with a gradual return to preflare conditions over the next 2–4 days. Thus the action of the Forbush decrease would tend to maximize the potential gradient (at heights below 15 km) 1–2 days after solar flare occurrence. A superposed epoch analysis of Zugspitze data for March 1966–July 1968 (Reiter, 1971) showed that the potential gradient began increasing about 1 day after the occurrence of proton and Hα flares and maximized 2–3 days after the flare, in keeping with the suggested Forbush-decrease effect.

In contrast, enhanced worldwide thunderstorm activity (Bossolasco et al., 1972) and European thunderstorm occurrence (Reiter, 1969) maximize about 4 days after the flare occurrence, or about 2 days after the maximum in potential gradient. From these statistics it appears that the potential gradient increases first, followed by increased thunderstorm activity; thus the activity is the result rather than the cause of the increased potential gradient.

6.7 Gravity Wave Feedback

A rather "ingenious" (Kellogg, 1975) mechanism to explain meteorological responses to solar activity has been formulated by Hines (Hines, 1974; Hines and Halevy, 1975, 1977). The basic premise is that energy generated in the troposphere by meteorological phenomena propagates upward via gravity waves (sec. 5.1.1), and, under certain assumed conditions, the upper atmosphere will reflect those waves back down to interfere constructively or destructively with the original source. If constructive, an amplification of the meteorological phenomenon would take place, so that the upper atmosphere can be considered to have modulated the tropospheric event. It has been known for many years that the upper atmosphere responds to solar activity, and if that response is such that the gravity-wave reflection properties of the upper atmosphere are altered, there could be an indirect influence of solar activity on tropospheric events.

To explain observed correlations between geomagnetic activity and the weather, Hines (1973) suggested that the origin of the energy might be in the tropospheric phenomenon, so that it propagates upward to the ionosphere to produce changes leading to magnetic fluctuations. This argument was abandoned as being untenable because of the reasons given in section 5.1.2, and Hines (1974) searched for a new mechanism that would explain the sector boundary crossing correlations of Wilcox et al. (1973a,b) without straying too far from his original premise. He suggested that the tropospheric energy contained in storms propagates upward via gravity waves and is reflected back toward the Earth by a boundary in the upper atmosphere to either reinforce or damp at the origin. The reflection properties of the upper atmosphere would be altered by sector boundary passage and other solar activity parameters.

Hines and Halevy (1975; 1977) now propose that the solar influence would be a modulation of the meteorological noise that would have occurred in any event, rather than the generation of a meteorological signal (a storm?) that is superimposed on the noise. Rises and declines of the vorticity area index, they believe, may be shifted in time through a phase modulation introduced by solar activity. This influence can selectively advance or retard the timing of the natural amplitude variations of the vorticity area index so that ultimately minimum values of the index tend to be found at about the times solar sector boundaries move past the Earth, rather than at times that are random with respect to boundary passage. No physical explanation of how this phase shifting comes about has been attempted, but Hines and Halevy say that they have been able to simulate the Wilcox results by "phase shifting" vorticity data obtained from randomly selected days. Without a physical explanation it is difficult to imagine how the phase shifting can be accomplished except by purely arbitrary means. Alternately, the results of King et al. (1977) and the theoretical arguments of Volland (1977a,b), as discussed in section 6.1.1, suggest that the increased oscillations of planetary standing waves would strengthen the upward propagating waves. This process would be appropriately reflected in the vorticity area index.

6.8 Convective Rain from Cosmic Ray Showers?

In section 6.6 an argument for thunderstorm triggering by decreases in cosmic ray intensity was postulated. Here, a speculation is offered to explain the initiation of convective rain by cosmic ray extensive air showers (EAS).

A point that seems to be generally overlooked in the cosmic ray literature is that the radiation reaching ground level is not a homogeneous flux that varies only slowly with time and magnetic rigidity (or geomagnetic latitude). Rather, there must be significant horizontal gradients or step increases over distances of a few kilometers that are not detected because of the extreme paucity of measuring stations. There is, however, some evidence for this spatially uneven precipitation of cosmic ray secondaries in the form of EAS.

Extensive air showers are produced by energetic primary cosmic ray particles, and the number of EAS particles reaching sea level is nearly proportional to the energy of the primary, with roughly 10^9–10^{10} primary eV per secondary electron (Delvaille, 1974). Thus a single cosmic ray particle of energy 10^{19} eV will produce approximately 10^{10} secondary electrons at sea level. The electrons so produced are spread out over an area with a radius of approximately 70–1000 m, which would result in a significantly ionized column extending up toward the tropopause.

Associated with this column would be horizontal thermal gradients that would set up density gradients leading to atmospheric instability. That is, the heated air would rise, producing decreased pressure and upward convection, the latter of which would release moisture (Byers, 1954). The resultant precipitation is referred to by meteorologists as "convective rain showers." It appears that the upward convection would only be triggered by a cosmic ray EAS, since the heated column due to a single particle would be 1 km or less in radius. Once initiated, however, the process would affect a larger area, because the horizontal pressure gradient would produce wind to transport surrounding air into the local low-pressure column. The precipitation in turn would release latent heat, which would further reduce the pressure.

Unfortunately, this simple sequence of events would occur only rarely, since, according to present-day observations, few cosmic rays of energy on the order of 10^{19} eV are encountered. However, as seen in section 2.4.2, a reasonable flux of 10^9 eV (1 GeV) primary cosmic ray particles can be expected, and, through the cascading process of secondary particles, these deposit their energy mainly in the atmosphere well below 20 km altitude, as noted in section 2.4.4. To test this suggestion, it would be of interest to attempt the detection of radio emissions theoretically predicted by Thompkins (1974) to be produced through a Cerenkov process involving the EAS electrons. Such emission from weakly electrified clouds without lightning has apparently been detected by Zonge and Evans (1966), although at that time no attempt was made to associate it with cosmic ray secondary electrons. Future experiments would require coordinated meteorological observations along with simultaneous radio emission and cosmic ray electron measurements. The low-energy cosmic-ray counting technique described by Shaw (1967) might be applicable for the latter measurement, if possible effects due to acceleration processes by strong electrical fields within thunderclouds can be accounted for.

7 Recapitulation of Sun-Weather Relationships

Since a rather substantial number of topics have been addressed in the foregoing chapters, it is useful to summarize the principal findings before going on to the experimental planning and suggestions for future investigations in chapter 8. Thus, in section 7.1 a narrative summary of Sun-weather relationships is given, and in section 7.2 an extensive table of previously reported correlations between solar activity and weather and climate is compiled.

7.1 Highlights of the Review

Although some investigators (e.g., Hammond, 1973) reject all possibility of solar activity influence on weather, and others exclude it as a trigger mechanism for decadel or millenial climate changes (Bryson, 1974), the evidence presented in this book is strongly suggestive of a genuine link between transient energy-generating processes on the Sun and meteorological responses. The strongest meteorological effects are observed in northern hemisphere winter, when solar insolation is least effective, at middle to high latitudes.

On a long-term basis, a number of statistically significant correlations that may be regarded as circumstantial evidence have been found between sunspot number and meteorological parameters. Although it is recognized that sunspot number variations offer only the most general indications of solar activity, the fact that correlations are found at all is an encouragement to have a closer look. Sunspots are either a barometer for changes in solar constant or reflect direct processes related to solar activity which interact with the Earth's atmosphere to affect weather and climate.

The amount of annual rainfall, for example, exhibits a dependence on the 11-yr sunspot cycle in many land areas of the world. There is a pronounced trend for greater than average rainfall during solar maximum years in equatorial latitudes ($\pm 20°$), and less than average in middle latitude regions from about 20° to 40°. However, there are a number of locations in the world where orographic and other meteorological factors override any solar cycle influence.

Major grain-producing regions that are prone to periodic droughts seem to lie near the latitude parallels separating areas of greater than normal from less than normal rainfall in solar maximum years. The midwestern states of the United States (Kansas, Nebraska), for example, lie near 40°N latitude, and the wheat-growing region between Rostov and Omsk, Russia, is at roughly 45°N. On the equatorward side of the 20°–40° belt lies the Sahel region just south of the Sahara Desert, which is prone to devastating droughts. There may be long-term north-south shifts in the latitudinal region of sunspot-associated low rainfall. Some evidence for this is given by cyclone tracks in Australia and storm tracks in the northern hemisphere.

Eight successive droughts in Nebraska recurred at 20–22 yr intervals between 1820 and 1955, each falling near a sunspot minimum period following a negative maximum in the Hale 22-yr sunspot cycle. None occurred at the minimum after a positive maximum. The ninth drought occurred on schedule in this region in the period 1974–1976. Recent analysis has shown that the area of the region affected by drought in the western half of the United States follows this same pattern. Whether other drought regions of the world show a similar relationship with solar cycle remains to be investigated.

Long-term variations in surface temperature show some relationship with sunspot cycle. On a global basis, the mean annual temperatures for the years 1804–1910 were lower at sunspot maximum than at minimum. Analysis of a recent study by the National Academy of Sciences shows that the semiglobal (northern hemisphere) annual mean temperature between 1880 and 1968 was also lowest at or near sunspot maximum and highest at sunspot minimum in almost every solar cycle covered. The exceptions occur in the most recent years and may be related to a longer-term (80-yr) trend in solar activity. The magnitude of temperature variation between maximum and minimum sunspot years is on the order of 0.3°C, sufficient to cause profound changes in the general circulation and climatic patterns. Regional, as opposed to global, analyses indicate that more than half the studied locations exhibit the same negative correlation between surface temperature and sunspot number.

It is satisfying, meteorologically speaking, to find that in solar maximum years, when more rain falls, the surface temperature tends to be lower. Such a relationship would follow if it is considered that more rain means more clouds, which are better reflectors of the Sun's radiant energy than is the ground, and there would be more evaporation; thus lower temperatures would result.

The atmospheric pressure at the Earth's surface (1000-mb level) also exhibits a response to long-term variations in solar activity as measured by annual sunspot number. Early studies of global pressure distributions show a general tendency for the annual mean pressure to be lower than normal near sunspot maximum years in equatorial regions and higher than normal in temperate regions. Poleward of about 45° latitude in both hemispheres, the mean wintertime surface pressure is lower than normal in sunspot maximum years.

The global distribution of pressure changes at the surface and 500 mb height with respect to the 11-yr cycle and the 27-day solar rotation period have been explained recently in terms of standing planetary wave oscillations induced by solar activity. One type of wave pattern explains the latitudinal effect averaged over all longitudes wherein the pressure is above normal poleward of about 45° latitude and below normal in equatorial and subtropical latitudes. It also explains why there is no marked difference between the average pressure in sunspot maximum and minimum years near 45° latitude. Another type of standing wave shows that the pressure variation with the solar 11-yr cycle and 27-day rotation is markedly longitude dependent. The pressure variation is least near longitudes of 0°, 170°, and 270°E.

The semipermanent low-pressure centers north of 40°N near southern Greenland and Iceland in the Atlantic Ocean, and just south of the Aleutians and stretching into the Gulf of Alaska on the Pacific side, seem to be closer to the pole in years of low sunspot activity and move toward the equator in high sunspot years. Storm tracks likewise seem to migrate equatorward as annual sunspot activity increases; this may be due to alterations of the latitudinal temperature gradient and planetary wave pressure structure.

A particular type of weather, the thunderstorm, and its closely associated atmospheric electrical parameter, the potential gradient, are positively correlated with the sunspot cycle in some areas, especially in high latitudes. There appears to be no correlation, however, in locations in which orographic and other local meteorological influences on thunderstorm activity are strong. The most pronounced relationship is found in Siberia, where the correlation coefficient between the regional total annual occurrence of thunderstorms and sunspot number is a rather remarkable +.88.

Analyses of short-term correlations between meteorological parameters and solar activity expressed in terms of solar flare occurrence, solar corpuscular emission, geomagnetic disturbances, and solar magnetic sector structure have revealed a number of interesting relationships and have led to several speculations on physical processes and cause-effect mechanisms.

The response of thunderstorm activity to apparent solar influence can be plausibly explained, albeit in a somewhat surprising way. Global thunderstorm activity increases by 50–70% about 4 days after a major flare eruption and so does the potential gradient and ionospheric potential, measured at mountain locations above the atmospheric mixing layer. Also, an increase in thunderstorm occurrence in the United States accompanies the passage of the Earth through a solar magnetic sector boundary where the interplanetary magnetic field reverses direction from away from the Sun to toward the Sun. Variations in galactic cosmic ray intensity in relation to solar activity, such as the pronounced minimum at sunspot maximum and the Forbush decrease following solar flares, coupled with high-energy solar protons injected into the atmosphere, may provide a physical mechanism to explain the observed correlations between thunderstorms and solar activity. In brief, the lack of cosmic rays reduces air conductivity in the 10–20 km height area, thus increasing the potential gradient, while the solar protons provide additional atmospheric ionization at and above about 20 km altitude.

Atmospheric pressure both at the surface and in the upper levels to about 200 mb responds to major solar flare eruptions and geomagnetic disturbances. Independent investigations have shown that the pressure decreases in some places and increases in others, that surface and 500-mb responses are similar, and that the response time increases with decreasing altitude. At 300 mb it is less than 1 day; at the surface it is 2–4 days. Global distributions of pressure changes in solar active periods during winter months are characteristically cellular; in Eastern USSR the pressure increases as it does in Western Canada, but in the Aleutians it falls. The distributions are understandable in terms of planetary standing waves, which oscillate in magnitude but do not propagate. In the semipermanent low-pressure areas south of Iceland and south of the Aleutians, the pressure decreases even more in winter following flares and geomagnetic disturbances. Measured in terms of the vorticity area index, low-pressure troughs forming in or moving eastward through the North Pacific area south of the Aleutians about 3 days after a geomagnetic storm begins, tend to deepen more than troughs moving through at other times. The vorticity area index for the entire northern hemisphere north of 20° latitude reaches a minimum about 1 day after a magnetic sector boundary passage; by the 4th day it recovers to or exceeds the precrossing level.

Physical mechanisms postulated to explain observed solar-weather correlations may be grouped into "direct" and "indirect" processes of injection of solar energy into the atmospheric system. Both types of processes, however, rely on an intermediate step for final coupling into weather changes. This intermediate step, in summary, either (1) alters the amount of insolation reaching the Earth's surface by introducing cirrus clouds, variations in atmospheric ozone content, or aerosols, and the resultant surface cooling fosters changes in atmospheric circulation; or (2) changes the vertical distribution of atmospheric constituents to disturb the heat balance near the tropopause, thereby inducing vertical and horizontal wind motions which would eventually result in pressure changes and a consequent alteration of the atmospheric circulation.

Direct processes of energy injection include solar corpuscular radiation and UV and X-ray bursts associated with solar flares or coronal holes, which may penetrate down to the lower stratosphere and upper troposphere. Galactic cosmic rays associated with the thunderstorm production mechanism are included here. Solar protons with insufficient energy to penetrate that low may interact with the atmosphere at higher altitudes to produce secondary radiation in the form of infrared heat which would then propagate downward the rest of the way.

Indirect processes depend on the solar wind for the primary contribution of energy from the Sun. This kinetic energy, delivered by low-energy solar particles, is first stored in the Earth's magnetotail and, at intermittent intervals, later goes into the acceleration of magnetospheric electrons which precipitate down magnetic field lines into the upper atmosphere. The energy of the electrons ($E \gtrless 150$ keV) is too low to permit direct access to the stratosphere/troposphere region and must be converted to bremsstrahlung X-rays to gain entry to the atmospheric system. The energy finally deposited in the stratosphere would produce ionized molecules to act as condensation nuclei, or alter the atmospheric chemistry. In particular, REP events would produce bremsstrahlung with sufficient energy to enter the troposphere.

Some consideration has been given to the relative amounts of energy involved in these various processes, and in some cases it is questionable whether the amount is sufficient to cause an appreciable change in atmospheric circulation. Additional work is required on this aspect (Willis, 1976), as well as on many other aspects of the problem, before an unqualified answer can be given to the question, "Are there any climatological or meteorological responses to solar and geomagnetic activity?" At present, the answer can be only a qualified "yes."

Investigation of possible lunar influences on geomagnetic disturbance occurrence indicates that lunar modulation of the neutral sheet in the magnetotail may initiate precipitation of accelerated particles into the upper atmosphere, thereby perturbing the magnetic field.

It is interesting that many, if not most, of the specified meteorological phenomena are controlled by the position of the jet stream. Perhaps solar activity influences this parameter through alterations of meridional temperature and pressure gradients, as suggested by the vorticity index correlations.

In summary, the correlations between solar activity and meteorological responses are highly suggestive and require further investigation. To take an agnostic point of view, these relationships have not been proven or disproven and therefore require further attention. The only appropriate way to place these relationships on firm ground is via the study of the causal mechanisms. This approach requires postulation and identification of specific physical and chemical processes. These should be followed by a dedicated experimental program designed to evaluate the proposed (probable?) processes. The subtle nature of such mechanisms requires simultaneous investigation of numerous parameters across several disciplines.

7.2 Summary of Solar Activity/Meteorological Correlations

In this section, a short summary of the salient features of reported Sun-weather correlations is given. The correlations are grouped according to variations in solar cycle (sunspot number), solar flare occurrence, geomagnetic storm occurrence, and solar magnetic sector boundary passage. The responses to these solar activity indicators are subdivided by the observed meteorological parameter, and an indication of whether the parameter is global, regional, or seasonal is given. A plus sign on the right side indicates that the meteorological variation is in phase with the sunspot cycle. Finally, the section number wherein the correlation is discussed is given in parentheses. Cases in which correlations have reversed or failed in long spans of data are summarized in a previous chapter (table 3.6).

Solar Cycle Correlations

Rainfall (sec. 3.1.1, 3.1.2)	Annual	Equatorial regions (±20° latitude)	+
		Middle latitudes (20°-40°)	−
		Subauroral latitudes (>40°)	+
	Seasonal	Interior continental latitudes	
		Winter	−
		Summer	+
		Coastal middle latitudes	
		Winter	+
		Summer	−
Temperature, surface (sec. 3.1.3)	Global annual average		−
	Northern hemisphere annual average	Years 1804-1960	−
		Years near 1964	+
	Regional annual average	Equatorial latitudes	−
		Temperate latitudes	−
		Arid (subtropical) regions	+
		London, England only	+
	Seasonal temperature at middle latitudes	Winter	−
		Summer	+
		Spring	+
Atmospheric pressure, surface (sec. 3.1.5)	Regional annual mean	Continental middle latitudes	+
		Equatorial region	−
		High latitudes	+

Seasonal average pressure	Winter	
	Equatorial latitudes	−
	Middle latitudes	+
	Subauroral (near 55°) latitudes	−
	Auroral region	+
	Summer	
	Equatorial latitudes	−
	Middle latitudes	
	Southern hemisphere	−
	Northern hemisphere	+
	Auroral region	+ or −
Upper-level pressures and winds (sec. 3.1.6)	Etesian winds across Greece	+
	Westerlies across England	−
Storm tracks (sec. 3.1.7)	Northern and southern hemisphere cyclones	Displaced equatorward during sunspot maximum years
Atmospheric electrical parameters	Potential gradient (diurnal and annual range) (sec. 3.4.2)	+
	Air conductivity (sec. 3.4.3)	−
	Air ionization rate (from cosmic rays) (sec. 3.4.4)	−
	Thunderstorm occurrence frequency (sec. 3.4.4)	
	Middle to high latitudes	+
	Equatorial latitudes	− or none
Ozone (sec. 3.5.3)	Globally integrated total (results conflict)	+ or −
	High latitudes, altitudes > 30 km	+

Hale 22-Yr Solar Cycle

Rainfall (sec. 3.2.1)	Fortaleza, Brazil (1865–1925) annual average	+
	Fortaleza, Brazil (1925–1960) annual average	–
	South Africa (1910–1965) annual average	+
	Adelaide, Australia (1844–1944) time for ¼ annual rainfall	–
Droughts (sec. 3.2.2)	Midwestern United States (1800–1976)	Occur in sunspot minimum years following a negative sunspot maximum
Temperature (sec. 3.2.3)	Boston, Massachusetts (winter)	–
	Omaha, Nebraska (summer)	–
	Maryland, Virginia, and Delaware (winter)	–
Atmospheric pressure (sec. 3.2.4, 3.3.3)	High latitudes (annual average)	+

Solar Flare Occurrence

Atmospheric pressure: 500-mb level (sec. 4.1.1)	70° latitude	Pressure falls after flare
	Equatorial latitudes	No apparent response
	30°–70° latitude band	Fall or rise depending on location (rises where pressure is normally low; e.g., Greenland); pronounced cellular structure

Atmospheric pressure: vertical distribution	Subauroral (50°–60°) latitude, western hemisphere	Maximum response at 300-mb level, fall or rise depending on longitude; time delay of response greatest at surface
Atmospheric electrical parameters (sec. 4.1.2)	Potential gradient	Increases, peaks 1–3 days after flare
	Air-Earth current	Increases, peaks 1–3 days after flare
	Thunderstorms, global	Increase 2–4 days after flare
Total ozone (sec. 4.1.3)	Low to high latitudes	Significant reduction, persisting for several months in seasonal averages

Geomagnetic Storms (Solar Corpuscular Radiation)

Atmospheric pressure, sea level (sec. 4.2.1)	Greenland-Iceland area	Rise 2–3 days after geomagnetic storm begins
	Middle latitudes (40°–60°)	Rise in some areas, decrease in others, 2–3 days after geomagnetic storm commencement
Upper-level pressure and circulation (sec. 4.2.2)		Increased geostrophic wind flow at 700 mb 4 days after geomagnetic storm begins
Atmospheric pressure, 300-mb level (sec. 4.2.3)	Gulf of Alaska	Low-pressure trough develops after Kp rise; vorticity area index increases
Total ozone (sec. 4.2.4)		Results inconclusive, but some evidence for decreased ozone with Kp rise at high latitudes, increased ozone with Kp rise at low latitudes

Solar Magnetic Sector Boundary Passage

Atmospheric pressure (sec. 4.3.1)	High latitudes	Pressure-level height increases 2-4 days after MSB crossing
	Middle latitudes	Pressure-level heights decrease 2-4 days after crossing
	Equatorial latitudes	No reported response
Upper-level pressure and circulation (sec. 4.3.2)		Pressure-height differences between middle and high latitude zones decrease following MSB passage
Vorticity area index (200-850-mb levels) (sec. 4.3.3)	Middle to high latitudes	Maximum increase at 300 mb 2-4 days after MSB crossing; minimum index about 1 day after crossing; no response above 100-mb level
Thunderstorm occurrence frequency (sec. 4.3.4)	Northern United States	Increase within 1 day of MSB dividing positive to negative sector; no apparent change going from negative to positive sector
	Mediterranean area	Approximate 15% decrease in lightning frequency with Earth near a positive to negative sector boundary; no change going from negative to positive sector
Polar cap atmospheric electrical field (sec. 4.3.5)	Vostok, Antarctica	Approximate 15% decrease in vertical field 1-3 days after sector boundary crossing, followed by 30% increase from 3rd to 4th day; same effect for positive to negative and negative to positive crossings

8 Guidelines for Experiments

Because of the complexity of possible relationships between the variable Sun and meteorological phenomena, it is clear that a multidisciplinary approach is required in future investigations if progress in understanding is to be achieved. That is, contributions from and the cooperation of scientists and engineers will be needed in the fields of meteorology, climatology, aeronomy, geomagnetism, ionospheric, magnetospheric and solar physics, atmospheric electricity, chemistry, and physics, in short, almost every discipline of geophysics. Further, regional, national, and international cooperative efforts are needed.

It is perhaps small wonder that so little apparent progress has been made, and so much controversy has existed during the past century or more (Meadows, 1975). Because of the enormity of the task, it might well be asked whether it is worthwhile to continue, much less intensify, efforts to achieve a greater understanding of Sun-weather relationships. In the authors' opinion, the task is not only worthwhile, but should be assigned a high priority by the policymakers in national and international scientific bodies. Some of the obvious reasons for this opinion are discussed in section 8.1. The ultimate objective of the task, as intimated elsewhere in this book, should be to improve the predictability of weather and climate.

The results of past analyses covered in the preceding chapters, although interesting, are hardly an adequate basis for formulating improved prediction techniques. A possible exception to this is the 22-yr periodicity in United States midwestern droughts as related to the Hale cycle. This inadequacy is due largely to the fact that few physical mechanisms have been identified to couple the variable solar energy into the atmospheric system responsible for weather and climate, and none has been proved (cf. ch. 6). In turn, identification of mechanisms has been difficult because the past statistical and case-study analyses have had to rely on insufficient information either because it was not available or because it was not recognized as being necessary. This has introduced a certain degree of ambiguity in the results. As a consequence, either several explanations could be invoked with equal plausibility, or no explanation could be made at all.

From this point, further progress is dependent on the identification and quantification of realistic physical mechanisms. Theoretical studies and coordinated analyses of the vast meteorological and solar activity data bank spanning more than a century of observations will be helpful in this regard, but the main thrust should be in the direction of carefully planned and executed experiments. The experiments must be designed to provide quantitative, simultaneous measurements of all the meteorological and solar parameters of pertinence to the particular physical mechanisms under investigation. Desirable measurement parameters are summarized in section 8.2, and some guidelines for experimental programs are suggested in section 8.3. These are not meant to be complete or conclusive; they are rather regarded as a starting point for future research and are included here to stimulate ideas from the readers. Additional suggestions for NASA participation in a proposed climate research program are given in a recent report by Goddard Space Flight Center (1977).

8.1 Relevant Weather and Climate Factors

In this section some of the more important weather and climate phenomena are summarized. The list is incomplete, but it is meant to highlight those phenomena having the greatest impact on man and his activities. Primary factors directly affecting mankind are given in section 8.1.1, including some that have not been considered to be influenced by solar variability. Secondary meteorological phenomena that have been reported to respond to solar activity and modify the primary phenomena affecting mankind are summarized briefly in section 8.1.2. Arguments for a continuation and intensification of Sun-weather studies follow in section 8.1.3.

8.1.1 Primary Weather and Climate

Meteorological parameters directly affecting man and his activities include:

Surface temperature: The air temperature near the ground affects man's comfort, amount of energy consumption, and activities in agriculture, construction, and transportation. Excessively hot and cold temperatures lead to energy consumption through air conditioning and heating, respectively.

Rainfall amount: Both too much and too little rainfall adversely affect agriculture. Its extremes of drought on one hand and flooding on the other both lead to food shortages, and the latter causes extensive damage to dwellings, businesses, and farms. Wintertime precipitation, usually in the form of snowfall, creates problems for transportation, snow removal, and, in extreme storms, poses hazards for life, livestock, and property.

Thunderstorms: This parameter causes lightning, hail, and wind damage to crops, structures, power distribution systems, and people. It also has a strong bearing on aviation activities.

Winds: Adverse effects of this parameter include structural damage and wind chill factors. On the beneficial side, they are a source of energy in regions in which they blow moderately and consistently (e.g., Hawaii).

Cloud cover: The amount of cloud cover affects solar energy utilization for man by direct shielding of the Sun's rays from collectors on the ground. It also influences the air temperature near the Earth's surface both by reducing the solar radiation intensity reaching the Earth and trapping the outgoing infrared radiation from the Earth's surface.

Severe storms: Included here are monsoons, tidal waves, hurricanes or typhoons, and tornadoes. The destructive effects of such storms are well known.

8.1.2 Secondary Weather and Climatic Factors

Meteorological parameters and processes that affect the primary factors include:

Atmospheric pressure: Global and regional pressure variations lead to circulation changes that affect air temperature, precipitation amount (rainfall, snowfall), and wind velocities in particular locales.

Storm tracks: In the northern hemisphere, the latitudinal variation in storm tracks affects the amount of rainfall, snowfall, wind velocity, and temperature in different locales in different ways. A northward shift of storm tracks in the United States brings up warm moist air from the south, creating warm temperatures along the east coast and a greater incidence of winter rainfall. In the Midwest, low-pressure centers bring up hot, dry air into the midcontinent, causing droughts in the grain-producing states.

With a southward shift of storm tracks, the circulation around the low centers produces colder temperatures in the northeast and heavier snowfall along the eastern seaboard, resulting in greater energy consumption, snow removal costs, and the slowdown of transportation.

Excess cloudiness associated with these storms degrades the efficiency of solar energy collector installations, forcing greater utilization of oil and gas for energy needs.

Ozone layer: As a direct impact on man, reduction of the ozone density leads to a greater influx of UV radiation reaching the Earth's surface and a consequent increase in the incidence of skin cancer. Indirectly, it has been suggested that the ozone layer may modulate the amount of solar energy reaching the lower stratosphere and troposphere, with an accompanying effect on meteorological processes. Modulation of the intensity of the UV portion of the spectrum may also affect crop growth. A shift of a few angstroms in the UV cutoff frequency may introduce selectivity in the kinds of plants that can and cannot be grown.

8.1.3 Discussion

It is starkly evident from the above that man and his activities are profoundly affected by the weather and climate. In the major areas of energy consumption, the possible utilization of solar energy for human needs and world food production, adverse weather behavior can be disastrous.

Discounting the possibility of large-scale (even global) control of the weather and climate by man's intervention, the alternative is to improve the predictability of weather and climate to avert future disasters. For example, if droughts and their regions of occurrence can be predicted in advance, a greater production in the growing regions not expected to be affected can be encouraged, and a better balance of world food production can be achieved on a year-to-year basis. The political ramifications of food as a negotiating weapon should not be overlooked.

To anticipate energy demands by geographic region, temperature extremes must be predicted well in advance, as must the amount, duration, and areal extent of cloudiness. The latter factor not only affects the amount of energy required by man for lighting, heating, and so on, but also the amount of solar energy reaching ground-based solar collectors to supply those requirements.

Another climate factor worthy of mention is that of water control as it applies to flooding, drinking water supplies, irrigation, and hydroelectric power. Under drought conditions when rainfall is short, irrigation can be used to maintain crop growth, but as the water supplies diminish with drought severity, the possibility of irrigation is lessened. Man can live without watering his lawn or washing his car, but when his drinking water is shut off for 18 hours a day as in England in the drought of 1976, or rationed as in California in 1977, the prolonged lack of rain is vividly evident. Long-term climatic shifts in rainfall occurrence with respect to both time periods and regions affected must be anticipated to alleviate the worst effects. It is not suggested that intensified study of solar activity effects on climate will be the panacea, but positive results would greatly improve predictability.

As emphasized throughout this book, the present status of Sun-weather correlations is marked by many inconsistencies, reversals, or breakdowns in correlation and lack a unified analysis of all factors over common time periods. There is, nevertheless, considerable evidence suggesting that weather and climate do respond to changes in solar activity on both long- and short-term bases. Moreover, there is generally a lag in time between the solar event and the later-occurring meteorological change.

This time lag offers the tantalizing possibility that measurement and observation of changes in solar activity can be used for predicting subsequent changes in weather on a short-term basis (time scales on the order of a few days to a few months) and changes in climate on a long-term basis (a few years to several decades). Before this possibility can be realized, however, a much better understanding of Sun-weather relationships than is now available must be gained.

To resolve the past inconsistencies and identify physical mechanisms that would explain how the variable solar energy is coupled into the atmospheric system to cause weather and climate changes, carefully coordinated experiments must be conducted. These experiments and analyses should be planned and carried out in such a manner that the results can be utilized for improving the prediction techniques for weather and climate.

8.2 Experimental Parameters

On the basis of earlier correlative studies and the suggested linking mechanisms discussed in chapter 6, it is evident that a number of parameters must be measured to place the study of Sun-weather relationships on a quantitative, integrated footing. Here, those parameters are identified and separated as to solar activity indicators, energy inputs to the atmospheric system, and meteorological responses.

The discussion is meant to be suggestive rather than conclusive. Because of the many competing meteorological processes and feedback mechanisms, it is necessary to examine program outlines in greater detail than is possible here. For example, the relative magnitudes of the various energy input mechanisms and subsequent alteration of the atmosphere must be assessed carefully before a particular experimental program is committed. Many of the observing platforms, fixed and mobile on the Earth's surface, and rocket, aircraft, balloon, and satellite platforms for upper-altitude measurements already exist and are in use. Those germane to Sun-weather studies must be specifically identified, and coordination of operations for data collection and subsequent analysis must be planned. Repetitive measurements at different phases of the sunspot cycle will be required to study climatic variations.

The types of instrumentation and measurement procedures for collecting relevant data must be identified, and a more definitive assessment of the unique capabilities that the space laboratory might afford for some of these measurements must be made.

8.2.1 Solar Activity Precursors and Indicators

For experiments and observational programs that can be activated on short notice and are designed to measure short-term responses of the atmosphere to solar activity, the eruption of a major solar flare may be used to initiate the measurements.

The global network of solar observatories that report solar flare eruptions on a real-time basis to a central point can supply 24-hr monitoring of the Sun. With appropriate communications links, the central control point can alert all experiment sites prepared for specific, coordinated observations.

Along with the primary sighting of a solar flare, monitoring of concurrent enhancements of solar X-rays, UV radiation, and solar radio emissions is desirable. Following the flare eruption, continuous monitoring of the flux and energy spectra of solar protons by geostationary and orbiting satellites will be an important adjunct.

Other primary indicators of unusual activity on the Sun that should be observed include discontinuities in solar wind speed, passage of solar magnetic sector boundaries across the Sun's central meridian, and active and growing sunspot groups. When a lead time longer than that provided by flare eruptions is required, the probability of being in operation during a significant period can be improved if observations can be commenced within 7 days of the appearance of an unusually active sunspot group at the Sun's east limb. For a 27-day lead time, recourse can be made to the recent history of active M-regions or persistent coronal holes.

Secondary indicators of solar activity that can be routinely monitored to provide supporting data for subsequent analyses include cosmic rays, geomagnetic activity, ionospheric characteristics, magnetospheric precipitating particles, and visual aurora. The signatures of importance in these secondary indicators are Forbush decreases and ground-level enhancements (GLE) of cosmic rays; gradual and sudden storm commencements of substorms in the Earth's magnetic field; intensification and motion of the main ionospheric trough, polar cap absorption (PCA) events, and auroral absorption as observable in ionospheric measurements; occurrence and/or intensification of the flux of precipitating electrons and hardening of the energy spectrum in magnetospheric particle measurements; the occurrence and type (active or quiescent) of visual aurora.

8.2.2 Energy Inputs to the Atmospheric System

The penetration depth into the atmosphere of solar-related energy inputs is a function of the form and spectral characteristics of that energy. The primary forms that are recognized as possibly important in altering the atmosphere to produce meteorological responses to solar activity are electromagnetic radiation (visible light, UV, X-rays) and solar particles (principally protons). Secondary forms that are triggered or modulated by solar activity are principally galactic cosmic rays, precipitating magnetospheric electrons, and bremsstrahlung or gamma radiation produced by the precipitating electrons and solar protons, respectively.

It is still unclear to what depth the variable solar energy must be injected to produce a meteorological (weather) response; thus all the above energy forms must be considered to be potentially important. Approximate altitudes to which the various forms of energy may penetrate are listed in table 8.1; the heights vary with changing atmospheric density and composition. From table 8.1 it is clear that

Table 8.1.—*Approximate Altitudes for Major Energy Deposition in a Standard Atmosphere at Vertical Incidence*

Quantity	Radiation Wavelength (nm)	Particle Energy (MeV)	Minimum Altitude (km)	Reference
Solar X-rays	0.1		45	Friedman, 1960
	0.25		65	Friedman, 1960
	0.50		75	Friedman, 1960
	1.0		90	Friedman, 1960
	2.0		100	Friedman, 1960
Solar UV radiation	20		120	Friedman, 1960
	70		160	Friedman, 1960
	110		80	Friedman, 1960
	150		110	Friedman, 1960
	220–280		35	Friedman, 1960
Solar protons		1	90	Reid, 1974
		10	65	Reid, 1974
		100	30	Reid, 1974
		1000	8	Reid, 1974
Alpha particles		1	95	Reid, 1974
		10	80	Reid, 1974
		100	55	Reid, 1974
		1000	25	Reid, 1974
Electrons		0.02	90	Berger et al., 1974
		0.1	80	Berger et al., 1974
		0.2	70	Berger et al., 1974
		100	10	Kellogg, 1975
Bremsstrahlung		0.005	75	Berger and Seltzer, 1972, and Berger et al., 1974
		0.05	35	Berger and Seltzer, 1972, and Berger et al., 1974
		0.20	30	Berger and Seltzer, 1972, and Berger et al., 1974

energy reaching the stratosphere and troposphere is in the form of near-UV radiation, bremsstrahlung, and high-energy protons and electrons. Not listed in the table but also important are visible radiation and near infrared; these rays penetrate all the way to the surface. Infrared radiation is absorbed largely in the atmosphere by CO_2 and water vapor, depending on wavelength, and, since about half the solar constant is carried by infrared radiation at wavelengths $\gtrsim 700$ nm (Thekaekara, 1975), this part of the solar spectrum may be exceedingly important.

8.2.3 Meteorological Response Indicators

To obtain maximum data for investigating mechanisms linking solar activity with meteorological phenomena, coordinated measurements of weather and climate parameters must be carried out along with the suggested solar observations. Depending on the type of weather or atmospheric parameter, the measurements may be conducted by ground-based meteorological observatories and fixed-site routine or special mobile-site launches of rockets and balloons, instrumented aircraft, or satellites. The Spacelab, scheduled for launch on the space shuttle beginning in the late 1970s, may be particularly well suited for some of the experiments.

The parameters of importance are discussed in section 8.1. These are summarized in table 8.2, not necessarily in order of importance, but with an indication of how they are being (or could be) measured. For cloud cover, the areal extent, location, and type of cloud should be recorded. Atmospheric pressure is measured routinely at many surface observatories, and a network of aerological observatories carry out pressure-height profiles. Vorticity area indices are derived from pressure measurements. Temperature profiles as well as regional and global surface measurements are collected on a routine basis.

Table 8.2.—Meteorological Parameters That May Be Related to Solar Activity Parameters

Meteorological Parameter	Observing Platform
Cloud cover (especially cirrus, nacreous, and noctilucent)	Ground, satellite, rocket
Precipitation	Ground
Atmospheric pressure	Ground, balloon, rocket
Temperature	Ground, balloon, satellite
Freezing line location	Satellite
Snow cover, ice cover	Ground, satellite
Winds	Ground, balloon, rocket

8.2.4 Parameters Observable from Spacelab and Free Flyers

With appropriate planning, instrumentation selection, and experiment coordination, a number of parameters useful for Sun-weather experimental studies can be measured using the Spacelab as an observing platform. In principle, both input parameters from the Sun as well as possibly responsive meteorological phenomena could be monitored from Spacelab for short-term effects such as those following solar flares. Repetitive experiments over a solar cycle would be appropriate for climatic effects, but continuous observations by meteorological and other solar terrestrial satellites would be better suited for the study of phenomena which are difficult to predict and/or which occur for periods exceeding single Spacelab flights.

The energy inputs amenable to Spacelab detection and measurement include high-energy solar protons and electrons, lower-energy precipitating particles, solar UV and X-ray bursts, bremsstrahlung X-ray radiation (Goldberg et al., 1975, 1978), and possibly galactic cosmic rays.

Other parameters of interest that should be considered include magnetic activity, ozone (profiles and total), neutral density, ionospheric electron and ion density, downward and/or upward propagating infrared radiation, and electrical fields. Meteorological observables include cloud cover, surface temperature, and lightning from thunderstorm activity.

8.3 Experiment Guidelines

To investigate the physical mechanisms discussed in chapter 6, experimental programs must be devised to obtain correlative data on the solar energy input and meteorological response parameters identified in section 8.2. In this section an attempt is made to group the parameters according to each appropriate physical mechanism and identify where and when the measurements should be conducted.

8.3.1 Thunderstorms, Cosmic Rays, and Solar Protons
WHAT:
   The parameters to be measured are:
   1. Cosmic ray intensity (as function of altitude, latitude, longitude, time)
   2. Solar proton energy spectra (at the top of the atmosphere and at balloon heights, as function of latitude and time)
   3. Lightning signatures (visible light or radio) and cloud cover for thunderstorm detection

4. Atmospheric electrical parameters (air conductivity, electrical field intensity, air-Earth current, ionospheric potential)
5. Other atmospheric parameters (ion density as function of position and time; height of thunderstorm cloud tops; composition, especially concentrations of NO_x, O_3, H_2SO_4, H_2O)
6. Supporting data (solar flare occurrence, magnetic sector boundary crossing)

WHEN:

For case studies, the time of measurement should be from the beginning of a major solar flare to $t_o + 7$ days, or from a solar magnetic sector boundary crossing to at least 7 days. Note that the foot of a boundary on the surface of the Sun crosses the central meridian about 4 days before the boundary at 1 AU sweeps past the Earth. Continuous routine measurements over long periods using meteorological satellites and other free flyers are required for statistical studies.

WHERE:

The best locations for measurement are those areas in which thunderstorm occurrence has been observed to correlate with solar activity parameters, i.e., northeastern United States; Siberia in the geographic region bounded by 43°–71°N latitude, 59°–150°E longitude; Great Britain; West Indies; tropical Pacific region.

8.3.2 Atmospheric Ozone Shielding

WHAT:

The primary parameters for measurement are:
1. Atmospheric ozone concentration, both total and height profiles
2. Solar UV radiation at top of atmosphere down to the Earth's surface
3. Atmospheric temperature at the surface and temperature profiles
4. Solar proton flux
5. Bremsstrahlung X-rays
6. Cosmic ray intensity
7. Concentration of oxides of nitrogen and other minor constituents entering ozone chemistry

WHEN:

Initial measurements of solar UV radiation must be made on the day side of the Earth. Remaining parameters should be measured on both day and night sides.

WHERE:

Latitudinal profiles of the parameters should be taken, with particular attention being paid to areas poleward of about 40° latitude. From ionospheric studies it is known that the most pronounced electromagnetic deposition in the D-region from solar flares is at the subsolar point; thus longitudinal as well as latitudinal profiles should be taken.

8.3.3 Cloud Formation by Condensation Nuclei

WHAT:

The parameters to be measured are:
1. Cloud cover and type (especially cirrus, nacreous, and noctilucent)
2. Solar proton flux
3. Bremsstrahlung X-rays
4. Atmospheric ion profiles
5. Atmospheric pressure profiles
6. Atmospheric temperature profiles
7. Water vapor, ice crystal, and hydrated ion profiles

WHEN:

Times of measurement should be immediately following solar proton flare eruptions or magnetic sector boundary passages and during and after visual auroral displays and geomagnetic storms. Nacreous and noctilucent clouds must be studied during local winter and summer, respectively.

WHERE:

This mechanism is expected to be manifest at subauroral to auroral latitudes. Measurements should be made at latitudes poleward of about 50°, with special attention being paid to the regions of the Gulf of Alaska, the North American continent, and Iceland. Local winter and summer conditions in both northern and southern hemispheres should be studied.

8.3.4 Storm Tracks and Circulation Changes

WHAT:

The parameters for measurement are:
1. Solar proton flux
2. Magnetospheric precipitating particle flux
3. Bremsstrahlung radiation
4. Magnetic activity
5. Position and depth of main ionospheric trough
6. Atmospheric pressure profiles
7. Atmospheric temperature profiles
8. Vorticity area index
9. Position of jet stream
10. Position of low-pressure storm tracks

WHEN:

Measurements should be conducted for at least 10 days immediately following major solar flares, magnetic sector boundary passage, or the beginning of geomagnetic storms.

WHERE:

The mechanism underlying this program is expected to first become apparent in auroral latitudes equal to and poleward of about 45° geomagnetic latitude. Pressure or vorticity changes in the vicinity of the Aleutian Low and subsequently in the Gulf of Alaska will be especially important, and intensified lows should be tracked across the North American continent. Similar processes may be initiated near the Icelandic Low, depending on the time of day that conditions conducive to initiating the mechanism first appear. (It may be that the intensified low-pressure troughs observed over the Gulf of Alaska by Roberts and Olson are an eastward progression of a heightened disturbance in the region of the Aleutians.)

8.3.5 The Solar Constant

WHAT:

The parameters to be measured are:
1. Solar irradiance at top of atmosphere (both total and spectral)
2. Irradiance as function of atmospheric depth down to the surface
3. Atmospheric temperature and density as function of height

4. Cloud cover
5. Concentration of minor constituents

WHEN:

Measurements should be continuous, or at least several times daily. Particular attention should be paid to possible irradiance variations as a function of the amount of solar activity as measured by sunspots, calcium plage areas, solar flare eruptions, and so on. Both summer and winter observations would be desirable, and the question of spectral resolution must be addressed.

WHERE:

Any changes in total irradiance would be manifest in temperature variations on a global basis, but particular attention should be paid to equatorial and low-latitude regions.

8.3.6 Concluding Remarks

The foregoing suggestions barely scratch the surface of the many experiments and observations that might be carried out to achieve an improved understanding of Sun-weather relationships. Scrutiny of these few, however, illustrates the necessity for a multidisciplinary approach. Parameters from almost every area of geophysics must be measured on a closely coordinated basis, using instrumentations fixed on the ground and carried aloft by balloons, aircraft, rockets, and spacecraft. The diverse measurement results must then be assembled, analyzed, assimilated, and applied to prediction techniques for them to be useful.

Is the world scientific community equipped to meet the challenge of such a vast, complex undertaking? Each geophysical discipline certainly has the scientific and engineering personnel, equipment, and experimental techniques required to carry out measurements and observations of the parameters within its sphere of interest and to analyze and interpret the results. International large-scale cooperative efforts have been successfully undertaken in the past, as witnessed by the International Polar Years of 1932–1933, the International Geophysical Year (IGY) of 1957–1958, and the International Quiet Sun Year (IQSY) of 1964. Each of these efforts was successively better organized and coordinated, and the organization experience was applied to the Global Atmospheric Research Project (GARP) of the late 1960s. Tighter organization, coordination, and cooperation is planned for the International Magnetospheric Study (IMS) scheduled for 1976–1979 (Roederer, 1976; Manka, 1976).

New concepts in active, real-time international scientific cooperation developed for IMS would be specifically applicable to a similar attack on Sun-weather relationships. For example, a "Satellite Situation Center" has been established by NASA "to provide short-term information on predicted positions and operational modes of IMS-related satellites, to act as a switching center to direct ground-based, balloon, and rocket experimenters to the appropriate satellite investigators and vice versa, and to keep a regularly updated computerized file on all IMS programs" (Roederer, 1976). More than 20 countries are participating, and over a thousand individual research programs are registered in detail. The IMS may in fact contribute technical results useful for Sun-weather investigations, but its largest contribution would be in the area of broad organizational concepts.

For implementation near the end of IMS, plans have been proposed to concentrate on a major 5-yr study of the middle atmosphere (~ 15–100 km). These plans, presently known as the "Middle Atmosphere Program (MAP)," were formulated at the Urbana Planning Conference held in July 1976 (Bowhill, 1977). The technical results from MAP can be expected to be very beneficial to Sun-weather and other solar-terrestrial problems.

It appears that the world scientific community is indeed capable of undertaking a concerted effort to unravel the mysteries of solar activity effects on meteorological phenomena. The success of such an effort ultimately depends on the wisdom of those assigned to assimilate the diverse results into prediction schemes for weather and climate. The ultimate beneficiary is mankind.

Appendix A
Physical Properties of the
Atmosphere and Conversion
Factors

The physical characteristics of the Earth's atmosphere of interest here are the temperature, pressure, and density. The basic relationship between these three quantities is given by the equation of state:

$$\varrho = \frac{pM}{RT} \qquad (A.1)$$

where

ϱ = air density
p = atmospheric pressure
T = temperature (K)
M = molecular weight of air
R = universal gas constant = $8.314(10^7)$ ergs/mole-degree

The change in pressure, Δp, with height, Δh, is given by the hydrostatic equation:

$$\Delta p = -G\varrho\Delta h \qquad (A.2)$$

where G = gravitational constant = 980.655 cm s^{-2}.

From these two equations, it is evident that

$$\frac{\Delta p}{p} = -\frac{MG}{RT}\Delta h \qquad (A.3)$$

From this fundamental equation (A.3), the pressure can be calculated if the temperature and molecular weight are known, and the temperature can be derived from measurements of pressure and molecular weight.

Several model atmospheres have been developed from these equations and in situ measurements. For convenience, models for temperature and pressure up to 50 km (Valley, 1965) are given in table A.1. Vertical profiles of atmospheric number density, from the same source, are given in table A.2.

Table A-1. — Model Atmospheres, Showing Latitudinal and Seasonal Variability of Pressure and Temperature

Height (km)	Tropical Pressure (mb)	Tropical Temperature (K)	Middle Latitude Winter Pressure (mb)	Middle Latitude Winter Temperature (K)	Middle Latitude Summer Pressure (mb)	Middle Latitude Summer Temperature (K)	Subarctic Winter Pressure (mb)	Subarctic Winter Temperature (K)	Subarctic Summer Pressure (mb)	Subarctic Summer Temperature (K)
0	$1.013(10^3)$	300.0	$1.018(10^3)$	272.2	$1.013(10^3)$	294.0	$1.013(10^3)$	257.1	$1.010(10^3)$	287.0
1	$9.040(10^2)$	294.0	$8.973(10^2)$	268.7	$9.020(10^2)$	290.0	$8.878(10^2)$	259.1	$8.960(10^2)$	282.0
2	$8.050(10^2)$	288.0	$7.897(10^2)$	265.2	$8.020(10^2)$	285.0	$7.775(10^2)$	255.9	$7.929(10^2)$	276.0
3	$7.150(10^2)$	284.0	$6.938(10^2)$	261.7	$7.100(10^2)$	279.0	$6.798(10^2)$	252.7	$7.000(10^2)$	271.0
4	$6.330(10^2)$	277.0	$6.081(10^2)$	255.7	$6.280(10^2)$	273.0	$5.932(10^2)$	247.7	$6.160(10^2)$	266.0
5	$5.590(10^2)$	270.0	$5.313(10^2)$	249.7	$5.540(10^2)$	267.0	$5.158(10^2)$	240.9	$5.410(10^2)$	260.0
6	$4.920(10^2)$	264.0	$4.627(10^2)$	243.7	$4.870(10^2)$	261.0	$4.467(10^2)$	234.1	$4.730(10^2)$	253.0
7	$4.320(10^2)$	257.0	$4.016(10^2)$	237.7	$4.260(10^2)$	255.0	$3.853(10^2)$	227.3	$4.130(10^2)$	246.0
8	$3.780(10^2)$	250.0	$3.473(10^2)$	231.7	$3.720(10^2)$	248.0	$3.308(10^2)$	220.6	$3.590(10^2)$	239.0
9	$3.290(10^2)$	244.0	$2.992(10^2)$	225.7	$3.240(10^2)$	242.0	$2.829(10^2)$	217.2	$3.107(10^2)$	232.0
10	$2.860(10^2)$	237.0	$2.568(10^2)$	219.7	$2.810(10^2)$	235.0	$2.418(10^2)$	217.2	$2.677(10^2)$	225.0
11	$2.470(10^2)$	230.0	$2.199(10^2)$	219.2	$2.430(10^2)$	229.0	$2.067(10^2)$	217.2	$2.300(10^2)$	225.0
12	$2.130(10^2)$	224.0	$1.882(10^2)$	218.7	$2.090(10^2)$	222.0	$1.766(10^2)$	217.2	$1.977(10^2)$	225.0
13	$1.820(10^2)$	217.0	$1.610(10^2)$	218.2	$1.790(10^2)$	216.0	$1.510(10^2)$	217.2	$1.700(10^2)$	225.0
14	$1.560(10^2)$	210.0	$1.378(10^2)$	217.7	$1.530(10^2)$	216.0	$1.291(10^2)$	217.2	$1.460(10^2)$	225.0
15	$1.320(10^2)$	204.0	$1.178(10^2)$	217.2	$1.300(10^2)$	216.0	$1.103(10^2)$	217.2	$1.250(10^2)$	225.0
16	$1.110(10^2)$	197.0	$1.007(10^2)$	216.7	$1.110(10^2)$	216.0	$9.431(10^1)$	216.6	$1.080(10^2)$	225.0
17	$9.370(10^1)$	195.0	$8.610(10^1)$	216.2	$9.500(10^1)$	216.0	$8.058(10^1)$	216.0	$9.280(10^1)$	225.0
18	$7.890(10^1)$	199.0	$7.350(10^1)$	215.7	$8.120(10^1)$	216.0	$6.882(10^1)$	215.4	$7.980(10^1)$	225.0
19	$6.660(10^1)$	203.0	$6.280(10^1)$	215.2	$6.950(10^1)$	217.0	$5.875(10^1)$	214.8	$6.860(10^1)$	225.0
20	$5.650(10^1)$	207.0	$5.370(10^1)$	215.2	$5.950(10^1)$	218.0	$5.014(10^1)$	214.1	$5.890(10^1)$	225.0
21	$4.800(10^1)$	211.0	$4.580(10^1)$	215.2	$5.100(10^1)$	219.0	$4.277(10^1)$	213.6	$5.070(10^1)$	225.0
22	$4.090(10^1)$	215.0	$3.910(10^1)$	215.2	$4.370(10^1)$	220.0	$3.647(10^1)$	213.0	$4.360(10^1)$	225.0
23	$3.500(10^1)$	217.0	$3.340(10^1)$	215.2	$3.760(10^1)$	222.0	$3.109(10^1)$	212.4	$3.750(10^1)$	225.0
24	$3.000(10^1)$	219.0	$2.860(10^1)$	215.2	$3.220(10^1)$	223.0	$2.649(10^1)$	211.8	$3.227(10^1)$	226.0
25	$2.570(10^1)$	221.0	$2.430(10^1)$	215.2	$2.770(10^1)$	224.0	$2.256(10^1)$	211.2	$2.780(10^1)$	228.0
30	$1.220(10^1)$	232.0	$1.110(10^1)$	217.4	$1.320(10^1)$	234.0	$1.020(10^1)$	216.0	$1.340(10^1)$	235.0
35	$6.000(10^0)$	243.0	$5.180(10^0)$	227.8	$6.520(10^0)$	245.0	$4.701(10^0)$	222.2	$6.610(10^0)$	247.0
40	$3.050(10^0)$	254.0	$2.530(10^0)$	243.2	$3.330(10^0)$	258.0	$2.243(10^0)$	234.7	$3.400(10^0)$	262.0
45	$1.590(10^0)$	265.0	$1.290(10^0)$	258.5	$1.760(10^0)$	270.0	$1.113(10^0)$	247.0	$1.810(10^0)$	274.0
50	$8.540(10^{-1})$	270.0	$6.820(10^{-1})$	265.7	$9.510(10^{-1})$	276.0	$5.719(10^{-1})$	259.3	$9.870(10^{-1})$	277.0

Source: Valley (1965).

Table A-2. — Vertical Profiles of Atmospheric Density (Molecules/cm³)

Altitude (km)	Tropical		Middle latitude		Subarctic	
	Summer	Winter	Summer	Winter	Summer	Winter
0	$2.44(10^{19})$	$2.44(10^{19})$	$2.49(10^{19})$	$2.72(10^{19})$	$2.55(10^{19})$	$2.87(10^{19})$
1	$2.22(10^{19})$	$2.22(10^{19})$	$2.26(10^{19})$	$2.43(10^{19})$	$2.32(10^{19})$	$2.49(10^{19})$
2	$2.02(10^{19})$	$2.02(10^{19})$	$2.04(10^{19})$	$2.17(10^{19})$	$2.08(10^{19})$	$2.21(10^{19})$
3	$1.83(10^{19})$	$1.83(10^{19})$	$1.85(10^{19})$	$1.93(10^{19})$	$1.88(10^{19})$	$1.96(10^{19})$
4	$1.66(10^{19})$	$1.66(10^{19})$	$1.67(10^{19})$	$1.73(10^{19})$	$1.69(10^{19})$	$1.74(10^{19})$
5	$1.50(10^{19})$	$1.50(10^{19})$	$1.51(10^{19})$	$1.55(10^{19})$	$1.51(10^{19})$	$1.56(10^{19})$
6	$1.36(10^{19})$	$1.36(10^{19})$	$1.35(10^{19})$	$1.38(10^{19})$	$1.36(10^{19})$	$1.39(10^{19})$
7	$1.22(10^{19})$	$1.22(10^{19})$	$1.22(10^{19})$	$1.23(10^{19})$	$1.22(10^{19})$	$1.23(10^{19})$
8	$1.10(10^{19})$	$1.10(10^{19})$	$1.09(10^{19})$	$1.09(10^{19})$	$1.09(10^{19})$	$1.09(10^{19})$
9	$9.84(10^{18})$	$9.84(10^{18})$	$9.76(10^{18})$	$9.65(10^{18})$	$9.74(10^{18})$	$9.49(10^{18})$
10	$8.78(10^{18})$	$8.78(10^{18})$	$8.69(10^{18})$	$8.51(10^{18})$	$8.66(10^{18})$	$8.11(10^{18})$
11	$7.82(10^{18})$	$7.82(10^{18})$	$7.72(10^{18})$	$7.31(10^{18})$	$7.44(10^{18})$	$6.93(10^{18})$
12	$6.93(10^{18})$	$6.93(10^{18})$	$6.83(10^{18})$	$6.27(10^{18})$	$6.39(10^{18})$	$5.93(10^{18})$
13	$6.12(10^{18})$	$6.12(10^{18})$	$6.02(10^{18})$	$5.37(10^{18})$	$5.50(10^{18})$	$5.07(10^{18})$
14	$5.39(10^{18})$	$5.39(10^{18})$	$5.15(10^{18})$	$4.61(10^{18})$	$4.72(10^{18})$	$4.33(10^{18})$
15	$4.72(10^{18})$	$4.72(10^{18})$	$4.40(10^{18})$	$3.95(10^{18})$	$4.06(10^{18})$	$3.70(10^{18})$
16	$4.12(10^{18})$	$4.12(10^{18})$	$3.75(10^{18})$	$3.38(10^{18})$	$3.49(10^{18})$	$3.17(10^{18})$
17	$3.50(10^{18})$	$3.50(10^{18})$	$3.21(10^{18})$	$2.90(10^{18})$	$3.00(10^{18})$	$2.72(10^{18})$
18	$2.89(10^{18})$	$2.89(10^{18})$	$2.73(10^{18})$	$2.48(10^{18})$	$2.58(10^{18})$	$2.33(10^{18})$
19	$2.39(10^{18})$	$2.39(10^{18})$	$2.32(10^{18})$	$2.12(10^{18})$	$2.22(10^{18})$	$1.99(10^{18})$
20	$1.99(10^{18})$	$1.99(10^{18})$	$1.97(10^{18})$	$1.82(10^{18})$	$1.91(10^{18})$	$1.70(10^{18})$
21	$1.66(10^{18})$	$1.66(10^{18})$	$1.68(10^{18})$	$1.55(10^{18})$	$1.64(10^{18})$	$1.46(10^{18})$
22	$1.39(10^{18})$	$1.39(10^{18})$	$1.44(10^{18})$	$1.32(10^{18})$	$1.41(10^{18})$	$1.25(10^{18})$
23	$1.17(10^{18})$	$1.17(10^{18})$	$1.23(10^{18})$	$1.13(10^{18})$	$1.21(10^{18})$	$1.07(10^{18})$
24	$9.95(10^{17})$	$9.95(10^{17})$	$1.05(10^{18})$	$9.66(10^{17})$	$1.04(10^{18})$	$9.12(10^{17})$
25	$8.45(10^{17})$	$8.45(10^{17})$	$8.96(10^{17})$	$8.25(10^{17})$	$8.88(10^{17})$	$7.78(10^{17})$
30	$3.83(10^{17})$	$3.83(10^{17})$	$2.76(10^{17})$	$3.73(10^{17})$	$2.80(10^{17})$	$3.44(10^{17})$
35	$1.80(10^{17})$	$1.80(10^{17})$	$1.36(10^{17})$	$1.66(10^{17})$	$1.38(10^{17})$	$1.54(10^{17})$
40	$8.74(10^{16})$	$8.74(10^{16})$	$6.96(10^{16})$	$7.58(10^{16})$	$7.11(10^{16})$	$6.96(10^{16})$
45	$4.38(10^{16})$	$4.38(10^{16})$	$3.67(10^{16})$	$3.64(10^{16})$	$3.80(10^{16})$	$3.28(10^{16})$
50	$2.30(10^{16})$	$2.30(10^{16})$	$1.99(10^{16})$	$1.87(10^{16})$	$2.06(10^{16})$	$1.61(10^{16})$

In table A.1, only the annual mean temperature and pressure is given for tropical latitudes (specifically for 15°N), since the monthly variability in these latitudes appears to be smaller than in higher latitudes. Winter (January) and summer (July) values are listed for middle (45°N) and subarctic (60°N) latitudes.

Atmospheric pressure is commonly expressed in millibars (mb or mbar) in meteorological work, as it is in table A.1, but a number of other systems based on measurement are often encountered in the literature. The millibar is defined 1 mb = 1000 dynes cm^{-2}.

One "standard atmosphere" (of pressure), abbreviated atm, is defined as the mean or "normal" pressure at sea level at a standard temperature of 273 K.

$$1 \text{ atm} = 1013.25 \text{ millibars } (1.01325(10^3) \text{ mb})$$
$$= 101\,325 \text{ newtons per square meter } (1.01325(10^5)\text{N m}^{-2})$$
$$= 1.01325(10^6) \text{ dynes per square centimeter (dynes cm}^{-2})$$
$$= 29.921 \text{ inches of mercury (in. Hg)}$$
$$= 760.00 \text{ millimeters of mercury (mm Hg)}$$
$$= 14.696 \text{ pounds per square inch (lb in}^{-2})$$
$$= 1033 \text{ grams per square centimeter (g cm}^{-2})$$

Note that the pressure in $g \text{ cm}^{-2}$ is numerically nearly equal to the value in millibars. The ratio is $1000/980.655$.

Useful conversion factors are

$$1 \text{ lb in}^{-2} = 70.30 \text{ g cm}^{-2}$$
$$1 \text{ mb} = 1.02 \text{ g cm}^{-2} = 0.750062 \text{ mm Hg}$$
$$1 \text{ mm Hg} = 1.333 \text{ mb} = 0.03937 \text{ in. Hg} = 1 \text{ torr} = 133.322 \text{ N m}^{-2}$$

Appendix B
Abbreviations, Indices, Symbols, and Units of Measure

Abbreviations

ATS	Application Technology Satellite
AU	Astronomical unit (Sun to Earth distance)
B.P.	Before present
BUV	Backscattered Ultraviolet Experiment (Nimbus 4 Satellite)
CM	Central meridian (Sun)
CSG	Guiana Space Center
CW	Continuous wave
EAS	Extensive air shower
ERB	Earth Radiation Budget
ESROS	European Space Research Organization Satellite
EUV	Extreme ultraviolet
FD	Forbush decrease (cosmic ray decrease)
FFT	Fast Fourier transform
GARP	Global Atmosphere Research Project
geomag.	Geomagnetic
GLE	Ground level enhancement
IAU	International Astronomical Union
IGY	International Geophysical Year
IMF	Interplanetary magnetic field
IMP	Interplanetary Magnetospheric Probe
IMS	International Magnetospheric Study
INL	Invariant latitude
IRIS	Infrared Interferometer Experiment (Nimbus 4 Satellite)
IQSY	International Quiet Sun Year
lat.	Latitude
long.	Longitude
LT	Local time
Lyα	Lyman α radiation
M-region	Maunder region
mag. lat.	Magnetic latitude
MAP	Middle Atmosphere Program
max	Maximum
min	Minimum
MLT	Magnetic local time
MSB	Magnetic sector boundary (solar)
MUSE	Monitor of Ultraviolet Solar Energy
NASA	National Aeronautics and Space Administration
NH	Northern hemisphere

NLC	Noctilucent clouds
NRL	Naval Research Laboratory
OGO	Orbiting Geophysical Observatory
OSO	Orbiting Solar Observatory
PCA	Polar cap absorption
REP	Relativistic electron precipitation
rf	Radiofrequency
r.m.s.	Root mean square
SC	Gradual commencement, geomagnetic storm
SEMIS	Solar Energy Monitor in Space
SH	Southern hemisphere
SMM	Solar maximum mission
SSC	Geomagnetic storm sudden commencement
ssmax	Sunspot maximum
ssmin	Sunspot minimum
STP	Standard temperature and pressure
UT	Universal time
UV	Ultraviolet
VAI	Vorticity area index

Indices

aa	Global index of magnetic activity
AE	Index of auroral zone magnetic activity
Ap	Planetary index of magnetic activity
B	Brilliant (solar flare)
C	Local magnetic index
Ci	Global index of magnetic activity
Cp	Planetary index of magnetic activity
Dst	Index of equatorial geomagnetic activity
F	Faint (solar flare)
$F_{10.7}$	Solar radio flux (2800 MHz or 10.7 cm)
K	Local magnetic index
Kp	Planetary index of magnetic activity
N	Normal (solar flare)
Q	Index of auroral zone magnetic activity
R	Wolf sunspot number
R_z	Zurich relative sunspot number
SB	Bright subflare

Chemical Symbols

Be^7	Beryllium 7 isotope
C^{14}	Carbon 14 isotope
CO_2	Carbon dioxide
Fe	Iron
H	Hydrogen
[H]	H concentration

$H^+ \cdot (H_2O)n$	Hydronium water cluster ions
H_2O	Water
H_2SO_4	Sulfuric acid
He	Helium
Hg	Mercury
HNO_3	Nitric acid
HO	Hydroxyl
HO_2	Hydroperoxyl
HO_x	Odd hydrogen
Mg	Magnesium
NO	Nitric oxide
NO_2	Nitric dioxide
NO_3^-	Nitrate ion (negative charge)
NO_x	Odd nitrogen
O	Oxygen
O_2	Molecular oxygen
O_3	Ozone
O_x	Odd oxygen
O^{16}	Oxygen 16 isotope
O^{18}	Oxygen 18 isotope
OH	Hydroxyl
P^{32}	Phosphorous 32 isotope
SO_2	Sulfur dioxide

Symbols

A_μ	Microseismic amplitude
B	Magnetic field strength, eq. (2.5)
c	Velocity of light, eq. (2.6)
E	Atmospheric potential gradient, eq. (3.1)
E	Energy
E_o	Folding energy
E_p	Proton energy
e	Charge on an electron, eq. (2.6)
F	Solar energy flux
f	Total number of sunspots regardless of size, eq. (2.1)
f_n	Frequency
f_oF2	Critical frequency, F2 layer of ionosphere
g	Number of sunspot groups, eq. (2.1)
H	Horizontal component of Earth's magnetic field
H	Height
h	Stopping altitude; height
J	Current density

J	Integral flux, eq. (2.10)
J_c	Air-Earth current density, eq. (3.1)
J_o	Initial condition, integral flux, eqs. (2.12, 2.13)
k	Reaction rate
L	Magnetic coordinate defining magnetic shell in the B, L coordinate system.
m	Mass
m^+	Average positive ion mass
m_j	Mass of jth specie
m_o	Rest mass of particle, eq. (2.7)
N	Number density
$N(TS)$	Number of thunderstorm days
P	Pressure
p	Momentum, eq. (2.6)
Q	Ion-pair production rate
Q_s	Specific ionization rate
R	Magnetic rigidity, eq. (2.6)
R	Resistance of atmosphere
R	Wolf sunspot number
R_E	Earth radius
R_H	Atmospheric columnar resistance from Earth to height H, eq. (3.3)
R_o	Folding rate for rigidity, eq. (2.12)
R_z	Zurich relative sunspot number
r_m	Radius of magnetosphere, eq. (2.5)
T	Temperature
T_n	Period of time
t	Time
t_m	Geomagnetic storm key day
U_{EM}	Minimum amount of solar radiation available globally in winter
U_s	Total solar wind energy incident on top of magnetosphere per unit time, eq. (2.5)
V	Potential
V_i	Ionospheric potential, eq. (3.2)
V_s	Solar wind velocity, eq. (2.5)
v	Velocity
Z	Atomic number, eq. (2.6)
α	Effective ion-ion recombination coefficient
α_j	Effective recombination coefficient of jth specie
λ	Wavelength
μ	Mobility
μ_+	Positive ion mobility
μ_j	Mobility of jth charge carrier
μ_o	Permeability of free space

ν	Ion-neutral collision frequency
ν_{ij}	Collision frequency of jth specie with other species i
ϱ	Mass density of solar wind, eq. (2.5)
σ	Air electrical conductivity, eq. (3.1)

Units of Measure

A	Ampere
amu	Atomic mass unit
atm	Atmosphere
BeV	Billion electron volts
BV	Billion volts
°C	Degrees centigrade
cm	Centimeter
dm	Decameter
eV	Electron volt
g	Gram
g cm^{-2}	Atmospheric pressure, grammage, or radiation penetration
GeV	Gigaelectron volt
GHz	Gigahertz
gpdm	Geopotential decameter
GV	Gigavolts
hr	Hour
Hz	Hertz (cycles per second)
J	Joule
K	Kelvins
keV	Kiloelectron volt
kg	Kilogram
km	Kilometer
kV	Kilovolt
m	Meter
mol	Molecule
m-atm-cm	Dobson unit
mb	Millibar
MeV	Megaelectron volt
MHz	Megahertz
MV	Megavolt
mm	Millimeter
mm Hg	Pressure in millimeters of mercury
nm	Nanometer
ppb	Parts per billion
ppm	Parts per million
s, sec	Second
sr	Steradian
V	Volt
yr	Year
W	Watt
μW	Microwatt

References

Abbott, C. G. (1922) Application of solar radiation measurements, Annals of the Astrophysical Laboratory of the Smithsonian Institution, IV. Smithsonian Inst., Washington, D.C. Chap. 6.

Abbott, C. G. (1958) On Sterne and Dieter's paper, "The constancy of the solar constant." Smithsonian Contrib. Astrophys. *3*, 13.

Adderley, E. E. (1963) The influence of the moon on atmospheric ozone. J. Geophys. Res. *68*, 1405.

Ahmed, S. J. and A. Halim (1961) Total atmospheric ozone and geomagnetic activity. J. Geophys. Res. *66*, 3213.

Albrecht, R., H. M. Maitzen, and K. D. Rakos (1969) The sun as a variable star. Astronom. Astrophys. *3*, 236.

Anderson, R. Y. and L. H. Koopmans (1963) Harmonic analysis of varve time series. J. Geophys. Res. *68*, 877.

Angell, J. L. and J. Korshover (1973) Quasi-biennial and long-term fluctuations in total ozone. Monthly Weather Rev. *101*, 426.

Angell, J. L. and J. Korshover (1974) Quasi-biennial and long-term fluctuations in the centers of action. Monthly Weather Rev. *102*, 669.

Angell, J. L. and J. Korshover (1975) Global analysis of recent total-ozone fluctuations. NOAA Air Resources Laboratories (Rockville, Maryland), unpublished report (reviewed in EOS *56*, 584, 1975).

Arendt, P. R. and E. M. Frisby (1968) Possible relation of a specific ionospheric event to simultaneous meteorological data. Nature *219*, 475.

Asakura, T. and A. Katayama (1958) On the relationship between solar activity and general circulation of the atmosphere. Pap. Meteorol. Geophys. *9*, 15.

Bach, W. (1976) Global air pollution and climatic change. Rev. Geophys. Space Phys. *14*, 429.

Bailey, D. K. (1959) Abnormal ionization in the lower ionosphere associated with solar cosmic ray enhancements. Proc. IRE *47*, 255.

Baker, D. M. and K. Davies (1969) F2-region acoustic waves from severe weather. J. Atmos. Terr. Phys. *31*, 1345.

Bandeen, W. R. and S. P. Maran (eds.) (1975) *Possible Relationships Between Solar Activity and Meteorological Phenomena*. NASA SP-366, National Aeronautics and Space Administration, Washington, D.C.

Barcus, J. R. (1969a) Diurnal variation in low-energy cosmic ray cutoffs. Planet. Space Sci. *17*, 1173

Barcus, J. R. (1969b) Increase in cosmic-ray cutoffs at high latitudes during magnetospheric substorms. J. Geophys. Res. *74*, 4694.

Bargman, D. J., F. E. Lumb, and H. T. Mörth (1965) Lake levels in East Africa. Proc. Army Conf. Tropical Meteorology, University of Miami, Miami, Fla., p. 2.

Bartels, J. (1963) Behaupte Enflüsse des Mondes auf die erdmagnetishe Unruhe und ihr statistische Hintergrund, Naturwissenshaften *50*, 592.

Bartels, J. (1964) Statistiche hintergrunde fur geophysikalische synchronisierungs-versuche und kritic an behaupteten mond-einflussen auf die erdmagnetische aktivitat. Nachr. Akad. Wis. Goettingen, 2, Math. Physik. Kl. *1963*, 333-356.

Battan, L. J. (1974) *Weather*. Prentice-Hall, Englewood Cliffs, N.J.

Bauer, E. and F. R. Gilmore (1975) Effect of atmospheric nuclear explosions on total ozone. Rev. Geophys. Space Phys. *13*, 451-458.

Bauer, L. A. (1926) Sunspots and annual variations of atmospheric electricity with special reference to the Carnegie-observations 1915-1921. Res. Dep. Terr. Magn. Carnegie Inst. Wash., Publ. 175, Vol. 5, pp. 359-384. See also Terr. Magn. Atmos. Elec. *29*, 23 and 161, 1925; *30*, 17, 1925.

Bauer, S. J. (1957) A possible troposphere-ionosphere relationship. J. Geophys. Res. *62*, 425-430.

Bauer, S. J. (1958a) An apparent ionospheric response to the passage of hurricanes. J. Geophys. Res. *63*, 265-269.

Bauer, S. J. (1958b) Correlations between tropospheric and ionospheric parameters. Geofis. Pura Appl. *40*, 235.

Bazilevskaya, G. A., Yu. I. Stozhkov, A. N. Charakhchyan, and T. N. Charakhchyan (1973) Solar cosmic ray flares of August 4 to 9, 1972 as measured in the stratosphere. Collected Data Reports on August 1972 Solar-Terrestrial Events, Rpt. UAG-28, Part II (Helen C. Coffey, ed.). World Data Center, Boulder, Colorado, p. 460.

Bell, B. and R. J. Defouw (1964) Concerning a lunar modulation of geomagnetic activity. J. Geophys. Res. *69*, 3169-3174.

Bell, B. and R. J. Defouw (1966a) Dependence of the lunar modulation of geomagnetic activity on the celestial latitude. J. Geophys. Res. *71*, 951.

Bell, B. and R. J. Defouw (1966b) On the lunar modulation of geomagnetic activity, 1884-1931 and 1932-1959. J. Geophys. Res. *71*, 4599.

Berger, M. J. and S. M. Seltzer (1972) Bremsstrahlung in the atmosphere. J. Atmos. Terr. Phys. *34*, 85.

Berger, M. J., S. M. Seltzer, and K. Maeda (1974) Some new results on electron transport in the atmosphere. J. Atmos. Terr. Phys. *36*, 591.

Berko, F. W. and R. A. Hoffman (1974) Dependence of field-aligned electron precipitation occurrence on season and altitude. J. Geophys. Res. *79*(25), 3749-3754.

Besprozvannaya, A. S. (1962) Abnormal polar-cap absorption associated with strong chromospheric flares on the sun for the period 1938 to 1959. J. Geophys. Soc. Jap. Suppl. A-1 *17*, 146-150.

Bigelow, F. H. (1915) *A Meteorological Treatise on the Circulation and Radiation in the Atmospheres of the Earth and of the Sun*. Wiley, New York.

Bigg, E. K. (1963a) The influence of the moon on geomagnetic disturbances. J. Geophys. Res. *68*, 1409.

Bigg, E. K. (1963b) Lunar and planetary influences on geomagnetic disturbances. J. Geophys. Res. *68*, 4099.

Blackman, R. B. and J. W. Tukey (1958) *The Measurement of Power Spectra.* Dover, New York.

Borchert, J. R. (1971) The dust bowl in the 1970's. Ann. Assoc. Amer. Geog. *61*, 1.

Bossolasco, M. (ed.) (1973) Proceedings of the Symposium on Atmospheric Ozone, Arosa. Pure Appl. Geophys. *106–108*, special issue.

Bossolasco, M., I. Dagnino, A. Elena, and G. Flocchini (1972) Solar flare control of thunderstorm activity, in Studi in onore di G. Aliverti, Instituto Universitario Navale Di Napoli, p. 213.

Bossolasco, M., I. Dagnino, A. Elena, and G. Flocchini (1973a) The thunderstorm activity over the Mediterranean area. Rivista Italiana di Geofisica (cont. of *Geofisice E Meteorologia*) *12*, 293.

Bossolasco, M., I. Dagnino, A. Elena, and G. Flocchini (1973b) Thunderstorm activity and interplanetary magnetic field. Revista Italiana di Geofisica (cont. of *Geofisice E Meteoroligia*) *12*, 293.

Bowen, E. G. (1975) Kidson's relation between sunspot number and the movement of high pressure systems in Australia. Goddard Space Flight Center Special Report, NASA SP-366 (W. R. Bandeen and S. P. Maran, eds.) p. 43.

Bowhill, S. A. (chairman) (1977) *Middle Atmosphere Program Planning Document.* Prepared at MAP Planning Conference, Urbana, July 1976, available from Aeronomy Laboratory, Department of Electrical Engineering, University of Illinois, Urbana, Ill. 61801.

Bradley, R. S. (1973) Recent freezing level changes and climatic deterioration in the Canadian Arctic Archipelago. Nature *243*, 398.

Brasseur, G. and S. Cieslik (1973) On the behavior of nitrogen oxides in the stratosphere. Pure Appl. Geophys. *106–108*, 1431.

Bray, J. R. (1966) Prediction of the intensity of the present sunspot cycle. Nature *210*, 929.

Brewer, A. W. and A. W. Wilson (1968) The regions of formation of atmospheric ozone. Quart. J. R. Meteorol. Soc. *94*, 249.

Brier, G. W. (1961) Some statistical aspects of long-term fluctuations in solar and atmospheric phenomena. Ann. N.Y. Acad. Sci. *95*, 173.

Broecker, W. S. and J. Van Donk (1970) Insolation changes, ice volumes, and the O^{18} record in deep-sea cores. Rev. Geophys. Space Phys. *8*, 169.

Brooks, C. E. P. (1926) The relations of solar and meteorological phenomena—A summary of the literature from 1914 to 1924. First Report of the Commission for the Study of Solar and Terrestrial Relationships, ICSU, Paris, France, pp. 66–100.

Brooks, C. E. P. (1934) The variation of the annual frequency of thunderstorms in relation to sunspots. Quart. J. R. Meteorol. Soc. *60*, 153.

Brooks, C. E. P. (1936) The relations of solar and meteorological phenomena—A summary of the results from 1925 to 1934 inclusive. Fourth Report of the Commission for the Study of Solar and Terrestrial Relationships, ICSU, Florence, Italy, p. 147.

Brooks, C. E. P. (1939) The relations of solar and meteorological phenomena — A brief summary of the results from 1936 to 1938. Fifth Report of the Commission for the Study of Solar and Terrestrial Relationships, ICSU, Florence, Italy, p. 196.

Brooks, C. E. P. (1951) Geological and historical aspects of climatic change, in *Compendium of Meteorology*. American Meteorological Society, Boston, Mass. p. 1004.

Brooks, C. E. P. and N. Carruthers (1953) *Handbook of Statistical Methods in Meteorology*. Meteorological Office, Rpt. M.O. 538, H.M.S.O., London.

Brown, G. M. and J. I. John (1977) Solar cycle influences in tropospheric circulation. Eos *58,* 695.

Brunt, D. (1952) *Physical and Dynamical Meteorology*. The University Press, Cambridge, England.

Bryant, D. A., T. L. Cline, U. D. Desai, and F. B. McDonald (1962) Explorer 12 observations of solar cosmic rays and energetic storm particles after the solar flare of September 28, 1961. J. Geophys. Res. *67,* 4983.

Bryson, R. A. (1974) A perspective on climate change. Science *184,* 753.

Budyko, M. I. (1969) The effect of solar radiation variations on the climate of the earth. Tellus *21,* 611.

Budyko, M. I. (1972) The future climate. Eos *53,* 868.

Burch, J. L. (1974) Observations of interactions between interplanetary and geomagnetic fields. Rev. Geophys. Space Phys. *12,* 363.

Byers, H. R. (1951) Thunderstorms, in *Compendium of Meteorology* (T. F. Malone, ed.). American Meteorological Society, Boston, Mass. p. 681.

Byers, H. R. (1954) The atmosphere up to 30 kilometers, in *The Earth as a Planet* (G. P. Kuiper, ed.). University of Chicago Press, Chicago, Chap. 7, p. 299.

Calder, N. (1975) *The Weather Machine*. Viking Press, New York.

Callendar, G. S. (1961) Temperature fluctuations and trends over the Earth. Quart. J. R. Meteorol. Soc. *87,* 1.

Carapiperis, L. N. (1962) The Etesian winds. III. Secular changes and periodicity of the Etesian winds. Upomnemata Tou Ethnikon Asteroskopeion Athenon, Ser. II. (Meteorology), No. 11.

Castelli, J. P., J. Aarons, and G. A. Michael (1967) Flux density measurements of radio bursts of proton producing and nonproton flares. J. Geophys. Res. *72,* 5491.

Castelli, J. and W. R. Barron (1977) A catalog of solar radio bursts 1966–1976 having spectral characteristics predictive of proton activity. J. Geophys. Res. *82,* 1275.

Castelli, J. P. and D. W. Richards (1971) Observations of solar bursts at microwave and extreme ultraviolet wavelengths. J. Geophys. Res. *76,* 8409.

Chalmers, J. A. (1967) *Atmospheric Electricity,* 2nd Edition. Pergamon Press, Oxford.

Chamberlain, J. W. (1977) A mechanism for inducing climatic variations through the stratosphere: screening of cosmic rays by solar and terrestrial magnetic fields. J. Atmos. Sci. *34,* 737.

Chapman, R. D. and W. M. Neupert (1974) Slowly varying component of extreme ultraviolet solar radiation and its relation to solar radio radiation. J. Geophys. Res. *79*, 4138.

Chapman, S. (1930) A theory of upper-atmosphere ozone. Mem. R. Meteorol. Soc. *3*, 102.

Chapman, S. and J. Bartels (1940) *Geomagnetism.* Oxford Press, London.

Chernosky, E. J. (1966) Double sunspot-cycle variation in terrestrial magnetic activity, 1884-1963. J. Geophys. Res. *71*, 965.

Christie, A. D. (1973) Secular or cyclic change in ozone. Pure Appl. Geophys. *106-108*, 1000.

Clayton, H. H. (1923) *World Weather.* MacMillan, New York.

Cobb, W. E. (1967) Evidence of a solar influence on the atmospheric electric elements at Mauna Loa Observatory. Monthly Weather Rev. *95*, 12.

Coffey, H. C. (ed.) (1973) Collected Data Reports on August 1972 Solar-Terrestrial Events. Report UAG-28, Pt. II, World Data Center A, Boulder, Colorado.

Cohen, T. J. and P. R. Lintz (1974) Long term periodicities in the sunspot cycle. Nature *250*, 398.

Cole, R. K. and E. T. Pierce (1965) Electrification in the earth's atmosphere for altitudes between 0 and 100 km. J. Geophys. Res. *70*, 2735.

Cormier, R. J. (1973) Thule Riometer Observations of Polar Cap Absorption Events (1962-1972). Air Force Cambridge Research Laboratories, Rpt. No. AFCRL-TR-73-0060.

Cornish, E. A. (1936) On the secular variation of the rainfall at Adelaide, South Australia. Quart. J. R. Meteorol. Soc. *62*, 481.

Cornish, E. A. (1954) On the secular variation of rainfall at Adelaide, Australia. J. Phys. *7*, 334.

Courtillot, V., J. L. LeMouël, and P. N. Mayaud (1977) Maximum entropy spectral analysis of the geomagnetic activity index aa over a 107-year interval. J. Geophys. Res. *82*, 2641.

Craig, R. A. (1951) Radiative temperature changes in the ozone layer. *Compendium of Meteorology*, American Meteorological Society, Boston, Mass., p. 292.

Craig, R. A. and H. C. Willett (1951) Solar energy variations as a possible cause of anomalous weather changes. *Compendium of Meteorology*, American Meteorological Society, Boston, Mass., p. 379.

Crutzen, P. J. (1970) The influence of nitrogen oxides on the atmospheric ozone content. Quart. J. R. Meteorol. Soc. *96*, 320.

Crutzen, P. J. (1974a) Estimates of possible variations in total ozone due to natural causes and human activities. Ambio *3*, 201.

Crutzen, P. J. (1974b) Photochemical reactions initiated by and influencing ozone in unpolluted tropospheric air. Tellus *26*, 47.

Crutzen, P. J., I. S. A. Isaksen, and G. C. Reid (1975) Solar proton events: stratospheric source of nitric oxide. Science *189*, 457.

Currie, R. G. (1974) Solar cycle signal in surface air temperature. J. Geophys. Res. *79*, 5657.

Damon, P. E., A. Long, and D. C. Grey (1966) Fluctuation of atmospheric C^{14} during the last six millenia. J. Geophys. Res. *71*, 1055.

D'Angelo, N. and E. Ungstrup (1976) On the occurrence of widely observed noctilucent clouds. J. Geophys. Res. *81*, 1777.

Datlowe, D. W. and L. E. Peterson (1973) OSO-7 observations of solar X-ray bursts from 28 July to 9 August 1972. Collected Data Reports on August 1972 Solar-Terrestrial Events (Helen Coffey, ed.). World Data Center Rpt. UAG-28, Pt. II, p. 291.

Davidson, T. W. and D. F. Martyn (1964) A supposed dependence of geomagnetic storminess on lunar phase. J. Geophys. Res. *69*, 3973.

Davies, K. (1965) *Ionospheric Radio Propagation*. U.S. Govt. Printing Office, Washington, D.C.

Davies, K. and J. E. Jones (1971) Evidence for winds and waves in the ionospheric F region. Cospar paper no. C-7-9.

Davis, D. (1974) A kinetics review of atmospheric reactions involving H_xO_y compounds. Canad. J. Chem. *52*, 1405.

Davis, T. N. and M. Sugiura (1966) Auroral electrojet activity index AE and its universal time variations. J. Geophys. Res. *71*, 785.

Dehsara, M. and K. Cehak (1970) A global survey on periodicities in annual mean temperatures and precipitation totals. Arch. Met. Geoph. Biokl. Ser. B. *18*, 253.

Delvaille, J. P. (1974) Cosmic rays, in *The Encyclopedia of Physics, 2nd Edition* (R. M. Besançon, ed.). Van Nostrand Reinhold, New York, p. 175.

Dere, K. P., D. M. Horan, and R. W. Kreplin (1973) Solar X-ray emission measured by SOL-RADs 9 and 10 during the period July 26–August 14, 1972. Collected Data Reports on August 1972 Solar-Terrestrial Events (Helen Coffey, ed.). World Data Center Rpt. UAG-28, Pt. II, p. 298.

Dessler, A. J. (1975) Some problems in coupling solar activity to meteorological phenomena. Goddard Space Flight Center Special Report, NASA SP-366 (W. R. Bandeen and S. P. Maran, eds.), p. 187.

DeVries, H. (1958) Variation in concentration of radiocarbon with time and location on earth. Koninkl. Ned. Akad. Wetenschap. Proc., Ser. B *61*, 94.

Dickinson, R. E. (1975) Solar variability and the lower atmosphere. Bull. Amer. Meteorol. Soc. *56*, 1240.

Dittmer, P. H. (1975) The relationship between solar flares and solar sector boundaries. Solar Phys. *41*, 227.

Dobson, G. M. B. (1966) Annual variation of ozone in Antarctica. Quart. J. R. Meteorol. Soc. *92*, 549.

Dobson, G. M. B., D. N. Harrison, and J. Lawrence (1927) Observations of the amount of ozone in the earth's atmosphere and its relation to other geophysical conditions. Proc. R. Soc. London *A114*, 521.

Dobson, G. M. B., D. N. Harrison, and J. Lawrence (1929) Ozone and geomagnetic activity. Proc. R. Soc. London *A122*.

Dodson, H. W. and E. R. Hedeman (1964) An unexpected effect in solar cosmic ray data related to 29.5 days. J. Geophys. Res. *69*, 3965.

Dodson, H. W., E. R. Hedeman, and O. C. Mohler (1974) Comparison of activity in solar cycles 18, 19, and 20. Rev. Geophys. Space Phys. *12*, 329.

Domingo, V., D. Köhn, D. E. Page, B. G. Taylor, and K. P. Wenzel (1973) MeV electrons, protons and alpha particles, August 2–13, 1972. Collected Data Reports on August 1972 Solar-Terrestrial Events (Helen Coffey, ed.). World Data Center Rpt. UAG-28, p. 342.

Donahue, T. M., B. Guenther, and J. E. Blamont (1972) Noctilucent clouds in daytime: circumpolar particulate layers near the summer mesopause. J. Atmos. Sci. 29, 1205.

Donn, W. L. (1965) Meteorology, 3rd edition. McGraw-Hill, New York.

Douglass, A. E. (1919, 1928, 1936) Climatic Cycles and Tree Growth. Carnegie Inst. of Washington, Publ. 289; Part I, Part II, Part III.

Dubs, C., R. Filz, L. Smart, A. Weinberg, and K. Yates (1965) Corpuscular radiation, in Handbook of Geophysics. McGraw-Hill, New York, p. 17.

Duell, B. and G. Duell (1948) The behavior of atmospheric pressure during and after solar particle invasions and solar ultraviolet invasions. Smithsonian Misc. Collection 110, No. 8.

Duggal, S. P. and M. A. Pomerantz (1977) The origin of transient cosmic ray intensity variations. J. Geophys. Res. 82, 2170.

Dutt, J. C., J. E. Humble, and T. Thambyahpillai (1973) The unprecedented cosmic ray disturbances of early August 1972. Collected Data Reports on August 1972 Solar-Terrestrial Events (Helen Coffey, ed.). World Data Center Rpt. UAG-28, Pt. II, p. 423.

Ebel, A. and W. Bätz (1977) Response of stratospheric circulation at 10 mb to solar activity oscillations resulting from the sun's rotation. Tellus 29, 41.

Eddy, J. A. (1976) The Maunder minimum. Science 192, 1189.

Eddy, J. A. (1977) The case of the missing sunspots. Sci. Amer. 236, No. 5, p. 80.

Emiliani, C. (1955) Pleistocene temperatures. J. Geol. 63, 538.

Engelmann, J., R. J. Hynds, G. Morfill, F. Axisa, A. Bewick. A. C. Durney, and L. Koch (1971) Penetration of solar protons over the polar cap during the February 25, 1969 event. J. Geophys. Res. 76, 4245.

Fischer, H. J. and R. Mühleisen (1972) Variationen des Ionosphärenpotentials und der Weltgewittertätigkeit im elf-jährigen solaren Zyklus. Meteorologische Rundschau, 25, 6.

Fleming, J. A. (1939) The earth's magnetism and magnetic surveys, in Terrestrial Magnetism and Electricity (J. A. Fleming, ed.). McGraw-Hill, New York, Chap. 1, p. 1.

Flohn, H. (1950) Solare Korpuskularausbrüche und Gewitter-frequenz (Solar corpuscular eruptions and thunderstorm frequency), in Das Gewitter (H. Israel, ed.). Akad. Verlag Gesel., Leipzig, p. 143.

Fogle, B. and B. Haurwitz (1966) Noctilucent clouds. Space Sci. Rev. 6, 278.

Forbush, S. E. (1954) World-wide cosmic ray variations, 1937–1952. J. Geophys. Res. 59, 525.

Forbush, S. E. (1956) The 27-day variations in cosmic ray intensity and in geomagnetic activity, in Electromagnetic Phenomena in Cosmical Physics (Lehnert, ed.). University Press, Cambridge, England, p. 332.

Forbush, S. E. (1957) Solar influences on cosmic rays. Proc. Natl. Acad. Sci. USA 43, 28.

Forbush, S. E. (1973) Cosmic ray diurnal anisotropy 1937–1972. J. Geophys. Res. *78*, 7933.

Foukal, P. V., P. E. Mack, and J. F. Vernazza (1977) The effect of sunspots and faculae on the solar constant. Astrophys. J. *215*, 952.

Fowle, F. E. (1928) Ozone in the northern and southern hemispheres. Terr. Magnet. Atmos. Elec. *33*, 151.

Fowle, F. E. (1929) Atmospheric ozone; its relation to some solar and terrestrial phenomena. Smithsonian Inst. Misc. Collections *81*, 27.

Fowle, F. E. (1934) Further ozone measurements and the possible connection of ozone with the sunspot cycle. Trans. Amer. Geophys. Union *15*, 160.

Frank, L. A. (1971) Plasma in the earth's polar magnetosphere. J. Geophys. Res. *76*, 5202.

Freier, P. S. and W. R. Webber (1963) Exponential rigidity spectrum for solar-flare cosmic rays. J. Geophys. Res. *68*, 1605.

Friedman, H. (1960) The sun's ionizing radiations, in *Physics of the Upper Atmosphere* (J. A. Ratcliffe, ed.). Academic Press, New York, Chap. 4, p. 133.

Fritz, S. (1951) Ozone measurements during sudden ionospheric disturbances. Arch. Meteorol. Geophys. und Bioklimat. (A) *4*, 343.

Fröhlich, C. (1977) Contemporary measures of the solar constant, in *The Solar Output and Its Variations* (O. R. White, ed.). Colorado Associated University Press, Boulder, Colorado.

Fulks, G. J. (1975) Solar modulation of galactic cosmic ray electrons, protons, and alphas. J. Geophys. Res. *80*, 1701.

George, M. J. (1970) New data on the absolute cosmic ray ionization in the lower atmosphere. J. Geophys. Res. *75*, 3693.

Georges, T. M. (1968) HF doppler studies of travelling ionospheric disturbances. J. Atmos. Terr. Phys. *30*, 735.

Gerety, E. J., J. M. Wallace, and C. S. Zerefos (1977) Sunspots, geomagnetic indices and the weather: a cross-spectral analysis between sunspots, geomagnetic activity and global weather data. J. Atmos. Sci. *34*, 673.

Gherzi, E. (1950) Ionosphere and weather. Nature *165*, 38.

Gish, O. H. (1939) Atmospheric electricity, in *Terrestrial Magnetism and Electricity* (J. A. Fleming, ed.). McGraw-Hill, New York, Chap. 4, p. 149.

Gish, O. H. (1951) Universal aspects of atmospheric electricity, in *Compendium of Meteorology*. American Meteorological Society, Boston, Mass., p. 101.

Gleissberg, W. (1944) A table of secular variations of the solar cycle. Terr. Magnet. Atmos. Elec. *49*, 243.

Gloyne, R. W. (1973) The "growing season" at Eskdalemuir observatory, Dumfriesshire. Met. Mag. *102*, 174.

Goldberg, L. (1954) The absorption spectrum of the atmosphere, in *The Earth as a Planet* (G. P. Kuiper, ed.). University of Chicago Press, Chap. 9, p. 434.

Goldberg, R. A., K. L. Hallam, and J. G. Emming (1975) Space shuttle missions of the 80's. Paper no. AAS 75-261, in Proc. 21st Annual Meeting of American Astronautical Society, Denver, Colorado.

Goldberg, R. A., K. L. Hallam, and J. G. Emming (1978) Imaging of X-ray aurorae from Spacelab. Opt. Eng. *17*, 63.

Goldberg, R. A. and G. Witt (1977) Ion composition in a noctilucent cloud region. J. Geophys. Res. *82*, 2619.

Gossard, E. and W. Hooke (1975) *Waves in the Atmosphere*. Elsevier, Amsterdam.

Götz, F. W. P. (1951) Ozone in the atmosphere, in *Compendium of Meteorology*. American Meteorological Society, Boston, Mass., p. 275.

Grasnick, K. H. and G. Entzian (1973) Variations of the total amount of ozone and the behavior of some ionospheric parameters in the wintertime upper atmosphere. Pure Appl. Geophys. *106–108*, 1312.

Greenhill, J. G., K. B. Fenton, A. G. Fenton, and K. S. White (1972) 12.5 minute periodicity in solar proton fluxes at balloon altitude and in magnetic micropulsations. J. Geophys. Res. *77*, 6656.

Gribben, J. (1976) *Forecasts, Famines, and Freezes*. Walker and Company, New York.

Griffiths, R. F. (1976) Comments on "the role of electrical forces in charge separation by falling precipitation in thunderclouds." J. Atmos. Sci. *33*, 724.

Griffiths, R. F. and J. Latham (1975) Field generation and dissipation currents in thunderclouds as a result of the movement of charged hydrometeors. J. Atmos. Sci. *32*, 958.

Griffiths, R. F., J. Latham, and V. Myers (1974) The ionic conductivity of electrified clouds. Quart. J. R. Meteorol. Soc. *100*, 181.

Gunn, Ross (1954) Electric-field regeneration in thunderstorms. J. Meteorol. *11*, 130.

Hake, R. D., Jr., E. T. Pierce, and W. Viezee (1973) *Stratospheric Electricity*. Final Report on Contract N00014-72-C-0259, SRI Project 1724, Stanford Research Institute, Menlo Park, Calif.

Hakura, Y. (1965) Tables and maps of geomagnetic coordinates corrected by the higher order spherical harmonic terms. Rpt. Ionos. Space Res. Jap. *19*, 121.

Hakura, Y. and T. Goh (1959) Pre-sc polar cap ionospheric blackout and type IV solar radio outburst. J. Radio Res. Lab. Jap. *6*, 635.

Hale, G. E. (1908) On the probable existence of magnetic fields in sunspots. Astrophys. J. *28*, 315-343.

Hale, G. E. and S. B. Nicholson (1925) The law of sun-spot polarity. Astrophys. J. *62*, 270.

Hale, L. C. (1974) Positive ions in the mesosphere, in *Methods of Measurements and Results of Lower Ionosphere Structure* (K. Rawer, ed.). Akademie-Verlag, Berlin, p. 219.

Hale, L. C., J. R. Mentzer, and L. C. Nickell (1972) Blunt probe measurements during a PCA event, in Proceedings of Cospar Symposium on Solar

Particle Event of November 1969 (J. C. Ulwick, ed.). AFCRL-72-0474, Special Reports No. 144, Air Force Cambridge Research Laboratories, Bedford, Mass., p. 333.

Hall, L. A., J. E. Higgens, C. W. Chagnon, and H. E. Hinteregger (1969) Solar-cycle variation of extreme ultraviolet radiation. J. Geophys. Res. *74*, 4181–4183.

Hall, L. A. and H. E. Hinteregger (1969) Solar EUV enhancements associated with flares, in *Solar Flares and Space Research* (C. Dejager and Z. Svestka, eds.). North Holland Press, Amsterdam, pp. 81–86.

Hall, L. A. and H. E. Hinteregger (1970) Solar radiation in the extreme ultraviolet and its variation with solar rotation. J. Geophys. Res..*75*, 6959–6965.

Hammond, A. L. (1973) Research progress on a broad front, earth and planetary science. Science *182*, 1329–1331.

Hanzlik, S. (1930) Der Luftdruckeffekt der Sonnenfleckenperiode. I. Mitteilung: Jahresmittal. Beitr. Geophys. *28*, 114–125.

Hanzlik, S. (1931) Der Luftdruckeffekt der Sonnenfleckenperiode für die Monate Dezember, Januar, Februar, und Juni, Juli, August. II. Mitteilung: I, Dezember, Januar, und Februar. Beitr. Geophys. *29*, 138–155.

Harang, L. (1951) *The Aurorae*. Chapman and Hall, London.

Hays, J. D., J. Imbrie, and N. J. Shackleton (1976) Variation in the Earth's orbit: pacemaker of the ice ages. Science *194*, 1121.

Healey, R. H. (1938) The effect of a thunderstorm on the upper atmosphere. A. W. A. Tech. Rev. *3*, 215–227.

Heath, D. F. (1973) Space observations of the variability of solar irradiance in the near and far ultraviolet. J. Geophys. Res. *78*, 2779–2792.

Heath, D. F. (1974) Recent advances in satellite observations of solar variability and global atmospheric ozone. NASA Preprint X 912 74 190, Goddard Space Flight Center.

Heath, D. F., E. Hilsenrath, A. J. Krueger, W. Nordberg, C. Prabhakara, and J. S. Theon (1974) Observations of the global structure of the stratosphere and mesosphere with sounding rockets and with remote sensing techniques from satellites, in *Structure and Dynamics of the Upper Atmosphere* (F. Verniani, ed.). Elsevier, Amsterdam, pp. 131–198.

Heath, D. F., A. J. Krueger, and P. J. Crutzen (1977) Solar proton event: influence on stratospheric ozone. Science *197*, 886.

Heath, D. F. and M. P. Thekaekara (1977) Measures of the solar spectral irradiance between 1200 and 3000 A, in *The Solar Output and Its Variation* (O. R. White, ed.). Colorado Associated University Press, Boulder, Colorado.

Heath, D. F. and J. M. Wilcox (1975) A possible correlation between maxima of the far ultraviolet and solar irradiance and central meridian passages of solar magnetic sector boundaries. Goddard Space Flight Center Special Report, NASA SP-366 (W. R. Bandeen and S. P. Maran, eds.), p. 79.

Heath, D. F., J. M. Wilcox, L. Svalgaard, and T. L. Duvall (1975) Relation of the observed far ultraviolet solar irradiance to the solar magnetic sector structure. Solar Phys. *45*, 79.

Heikkila, W. J. and J. D. Winningham (1971) Penetration of magneto-sheath plasma to low altitudes through the dayside magnetospheric cusps. J. Geophys. Res. *76*, 883.

Helland-Hansen, B. and F. Nansen (1920) Temperature variations in the North Atlantic Ocean and in the atmosphere. Smithsonian Misc. Collection *70*, No. 4.

Helliwell, R. A. (1965) *Whistlers and Related Ionospheric Phenomena*. Stanford University Press, Stanford, Calif.

Herman, J. R. (1966a) Spread F and ionospheric F-region irregularities. Rev. Geophys. *4*(2), 255-299.

Herman, J. R. (1966b) A charged particle production mechanism for spread F irregularities, in *Ionospheric F Region Irregularities*, Agardograph 95 (P. Newman, ed.). Vistavision Publishing Co., Maidenhead, England, pp. 567-578.

Herman, J. R. (1970) RF heating of the ionosphere by lightning discharges. Unpublished manuscript.

Herman, J. R. and R. A. Goldberg (1976) Solar activity and thunderstorm occurrence. Eos *57*, 971.

Herman, J. R. and R. A. Goldberg (1978) Initiation of non-tropical thunderstorms by solar activity. J. Atmos. Terr. Phys. *40*, 121.

Herman, J. R., R. A. Goldberg, and J. R. Herman (1977) Thunderstorm triggering by solar activity. Eos *58*, 1220.

Hill, G. E. (1963) Synoptic charts of fmin, in *Research Concerning Forecasting Anomalous Propagation at High Latitudes* (S. C. Coroniti et al., eds.). Rpt. No. AFCRL-63-54, Avco Corp., Wilmington, Mass., p. 33.

Hill, T. W. and M. E. Rassbach (1975) Interplanetary magnetic field direction and the configuration of the day side magnetosphere. J. Geophys. Res. *80*(1), 1.

Hilsenrath, E. (1971) Ozone measurements in the mesosphere and stratosphere during two significant geophysical events. J. Atmos. Sci. *28*, 295.

Hines, C. O. (1965) Wind-induced magnetic fluctuations. J. Geophys. Res. *70*, 1758-1761.

Hines, C. O. (1973) Comments on a test of an apparent response of the lower atmosphere to solar corpuscular radiation. J. Atmos. Sci. *30*, 739-744.

Hines, C. O. (1974) A possible mechanism for the production of sun-weather correlations. J. Atmos. Sci. *31*(2), 589.

Hines, C. O. and I. Halevy (1975) Reality and nature of a sun-weather correlation. Nature *258*, 313.

Hines, C. O. and I. Halevy (1977) On the reality and nature of a certain sun-weather correlation. J. Atmos. Sci. *34*, 382.

Hinteregger, H. (1977) EUV flux variation during end of solar cycle 20 and beginning cycle 21, observed from AE-C satellite. Geophys. Res. Lett. *4*, 231.

Hirshberg, J. and D. S. Colburn (1973) Geomagnetic activity at sector boundaries. J. Geophys. Res. *78*, 3952.

Hoffman, G. W. and V. D. Hopper (1969) Electric field and conductivity measurements in the stratosphere, in *Planetary Electrodynamics*, Vol. 2

(S. C. Coroniti and J. Hughes, eds.). Gordon and Breach, New York, p. 475.

Holton, J. R. (1972) *An Introduction to Dynamic Meteorology*. Academic Press, New York.

Holton, J. R. (1975) *The Dynamic Meteorology of the Stratosphere and Mesosphere*. American Meteorological Society, Boston, Mass., Meteorological Monographs, Vol. 15, No. 37.

Holzer, E. E. (1973) Electricity, atmospheric. Encyclopedia Britannica *8*, 185.

Holzworth, R. H. and F. S. Mozer (1977) Direct evidence of solar flare effects on weather related electric fields at balloon altitudes. Eos *58*, 402.

Hoppel, W. A. (1969) Application of three-body recombination and attachment coefficients to tropospheric ions. Pure Appl. Geophys. *75*, 158.

Hummel, J. R. and J. J. Olivero (1976) Satellite observation of the mesospheric scattering layer and implied climatic consequences. J. Geophys. Res. *81*, 3177.

Hung, R. J., G. L. Rao, R. E. Smith, G. S. West, and B. B. Henson (1975) Ionospheric disturbances during severe weather activities (paper 3-9, Preprint). Proc. Symp. Effects of the Ionosphere on Space Systems and Communications, Naval Research Laboratory, January 20-22.

Imhof, W. L., J. B. Reagan, and E. E. Gaines (1971) Solar particle cutoffs as observed at low altitudes. J. Geophys. Res. *76*(19), 4276.

Israel, H. (1970) *Atmospheric Electricity, Vol. I, Fundamentals, Conductivity, Ions*. Israel Program for Scientific Translations, Jerusalem, NTIS Doc. TT-67-51394/1.

Israel, H. (1973) *Atmospheric Electricity, Vol. II, Fields, Charges, Currents*. Israel Program for Scientific Translations, Jerusalem, NTIS Doc. TT-67-51394/2.

Israel, H., H. W. Kasemir, and K. Wienert (1951) Luftelektrische Tagesgänge und Massenaustausch im Hochgebirge der Alpen I., Die luftelectrischen Verhältnisse am Jungfraujoch (3472 m). Arch. Met. Geophys. Bioklim. (A) *3*, 357.

Johnson, R. G. and W. L. Imhof (1975) Direct satellite observations on bremsstrahlung radiation as a technique to investigate its role in meteorological processes. Goddard Space Flight Center Special Report, NASA SP-366 (W. R. Bandeen and S. P. Maran, eds.), p. 89.

Johnston, H. S. (1968) *Kinetics of Neutral Oxygen Species*, Vol. 20. National Bureau of Standards, National Standard Reference Data System.

Johnston, H. S. (1974) Supersonic aircraft and the ozone layer. Environ. Change *2*, 339.

Johnston, H. S. and E. Quitevis (1974) The oxides of nitrogen with respect to smog, supersonic transports, and global methane. Paper given at 5th International Conference on Radiation Research, Seattle, Wash., July 14-20.

Johnston, H. S. and G. Whitten (1973) Instantaneous photochemical rates in the global stratosphere. Pure Appl. Geophys. *106–108*, 1468.

Jokipii, J. R. (1971) Propagation of cosmic rays in the solar wind. Rev. Geophys. Space Phys. *9*, 27.

Jones, H. S. (1955) *Sunspot and Geomagnetic Storm Data 1874–1954*. Royal Greenwich Observatory, H. M. Stationery Office, London.

Jose, P. D. (1965) Sun's motion and sunspots. Astronom. J. *70*, 193.

Kähler, K. (1925) Das Luftelektrische Potentialgefälle in Potsdam 1904–1923. Meteoral. Z. *42*, 69.

Kamra, A. K. (1970) Effect of electric field on charge separation by the falling precipitation mechanism in thunderclouds. J. Atmos. Sci. *27*, 1182.

Kamra, A. K. (1975) The role of electrical forces in charge separation by falling precipitation in thunderclouds. J. Atmos. Sci. *32*, 143.

Kamra, A. K. (1976) Reply. J. Atmos. Sci. *33*, 726.

Kane, R. P. (1977) A comparative study of geomagnetic, interplanetary, and cosmic ray storms. J. Geophys. Res. *82*, 561.

Kasimirovskii, E. S. and V. F. Loginov (1973) Effects of solar activity on zonal winds in the stratosphere and lower mesosphere. Soviet Astronomy-AJ *16*, 700.

Kellogg, W. W. (1975) Correlations and linkages between the sun and the earth's atmosphere: needed measurements and observations. Goddard Space Flight Center Special Report, SP-366 (W. R. Bandeen and S. P. Maran, eds.), p. 227.

Kellogg, W. W. and S. H. Schneider (1974) Climate stabilization: for better or for worse? Science *186*, 1163.

Kent, D. W. and M. A. Pomerantz (1971) Cosmic ray intensity variations in the lower atmosphere. J. Geophys. Res. *76*, 1652.

Kidson, E. (1925) Some periods in Australian weather. Bull. No. 17, Bureau of Meteorology, Melbourne, Australia.

King, J. W. (1973) Solar radiation changes and the weather. Nature *245*, 443.

King, J. W. (1974) Weather and the earth's magnetic field. Nature *247*, 131.

King, J. W. (1975) Sun-weather relationships. Astronaut. Aeronaut. p. 10, April.

King, J. W., E. Hurst, A. J. Slater, P. A. Smith, and B. Tamkin (1974) Agriculture and sunspots. Nature *252*, 2.

King, J. W., A. J. Slater, A. D. Stevens, P. A. Smith, and D. M. Willis (1977) Large-amplitude stationary planetary waves induced in the troposphere by the sun. J. Atmos. Terr. Phys. *39*, 1357.

Kohl, J. W., C. O. Bostrom, and D. J. Williams (1973) Particle observations of the 1972 solar events by Explorers 41 and 43. Collected Data Reports on August 1972 Solar Terrestrial Events. World Data Center Report UAG-28, Pt. II, p. 330.

Komhyr, W. D., R. D. Grass, and G. Slocum (1973) Total ozone increase over North America during the 1960's. Pure Appl. Geophys. *106–108*, 981.

Köppen, W. (1873) Über Mehrjährige Perioden der Witterung, insbesondere über die 11-jährige Periode der Temperatur. Z. öst. Ges. Meteorol. *8*, 241.

Köppen, W. (1914) Luftemperaturen, Sonnenflecken und Vulkanausbrüche. Meteorol. Zeitschrift. *31*, 305.

Krueger, A. J. and R. A. Minzner (1974) *A Mid-Latitude Ozone Model for the U.S. Standard Atmosphere 1975 (Summary)*. Goddard Space Flight Center, Rpt. X-912-74-291.

Kubyshkin, V. V. (1966a) Solar activity and pressure variations in the troposphere. Sov. Astron.-AJ (English trans.) *9*, 606.

Kubyshkin, V. V. (1966b) The distribution of solar-tropospheric disturbances over the Earth's surface. Sov. Astron.-AJ (English trans.) *10*, 295.

Kuliyeva, R. N. (1975a) Relation between the sector structure of the interplanetary magnetic field and zonal circulation indexes. Geomag. Aeron. *15*, 278.

Kuliyeva, R. N. (1975b) Effect of the sector structure of the interplanetary magnetic field on atmospheric circulation. Geomag. Aeron. *15*, 438.

Kullmer, C. J. (1917) Second Pan American Scientific Congress Proceedings, Vol. II. Washington, D.C., p. 338.

Kullmer, C. J. (1933) The latitude shift of the storm track in the 11-yr solar period. Smithsonian Misc. Collection *89*, No. 2.

Kullmer, C. J. (1943) A remarkable reversal in the distribution of storm frequency in the U.S. in the double Hale solar cycles. Smithsonian Misc. Collection *103*, 20.

Lamb, H. H. (1963) On the nature of certain climatic epochs which differed from the modern (1900–1939) normal, in *Changes of Climate*. UNESCO Arid Zone Research, No. 20, Paris, p. 125.

Lamb, H. H. (1965) Frequency of weather types. Weather *20*, 9.

Lamb, H. H. (1972) *Climate: Past, Present and Future*. Methuen Press, London.

Landsberg, H. E. and R. E. Kaylor (1976) Spectral analysis of long meteorological series. J. Interdiscipl. Cycle Res. *7*, 237.

Landsberg, H. E. and R. E. Kaylor (1977) Statistical analysis of Tokyo winter temperature approximations, 1443–1970. Geophys. Res. Lett. *4*, 105.

Landsberg, H. E., J. M. Mitchell, Jr., and H. L. Crutcher (1959) Power spectrum analysis of climatological data for Woodstock College, Maryland. Monthly Weather Rev. *87*, 283.

Lanzerotti, C. J. and C. G. Maclennan (1973) Low energy interplanetary particles during the August 1972 events. Collected Data Reports on August 1972 Solar-Terrestrial Events, World Data Center A Rpt. UAG-28, Pt. II (Helen E. Coffey, ed.), WDC-A, Boulder, Colorado, pp. 338–341.

Larsen, T. R., J. B. Reagan, W. L. Imhof, L. E. Montbriand, and J. S. Belrose (1976) A coordinated study of energetic electron precipitation and D region electron concentrations over Ottawa during disturbed conditions. J. Geophys. Res. *81*, 2200.

Latham, J. (1969) Cloud physics. Rpts. Prog. Phys. *32*, Part 1, 69.

Laur, T. M. (1976) The world food problem and the role of climate. EOS *57*(4), 189.

Levin, Z. and A. Ziv (1974) The electrification of thunderclouds and the rain gush. J. Geophys. Res. *79*, 2699.

Lezniak, J. A. and W. R. Webber (1971) Solar modulation of cosmic ray protons, helium nuclei, and electrons. J. Geophys. Res. 76(7), 1605.

Lingenfelter, R. E. (1963) Production of carbon 14 by cosmic-ray neutrons. Rev. Geophys. 1, 35.

Lockwood, G. W. (1975) Planetary brightness changes: evidence for solar variability. Science 190, 560.

Lockwood, J. A., L. Hsieh, and J. J. Quenby (1975) Some unusual features of the cosmic ray storm in August 1972. J. Geophys. Res. 80(13), 1725.

Loewenstein, M. and H. Savage (1975) Latitudinal measurements of NO and O_3 in the lower stratosphere from 5° to 82° north. Geophys. Res. Lett. 2, 448-450.

London, J. and M. W. Haurwitz (1963) Ozone and Sunspots. J. Geophys. Res. 68, 795-801.

London, J. and S. Oltmans (1973) Further studies of ozone and sunspots. Pure Appl. Geophys. 106-108, 1302-1307.

Lutz, C. W. (1939) Die wichtigsten luftelektrischen Grössen für München (The most important atmospheric electric parameters for Munich). Gerl. Beitr. ys., Geophys. 54, 337-347.

Macdonald, B. C. and E. R. Reiter (1975) On possible interactions between upper and lower atmosphere. Goddard Space Flight Center Special Report SP-366 (W. R. Bandeen and S. P. Maran, eds.). p. 59.

Macdonald, N. J. and W. O. Roberts (1960) Further evidence of a solar corpuscular influence on large-scale circulation at 300 mb. J. Geophys. Res. 65, 529-534.

Macdonald, N. J. and W. O. Roberts (1961) The effect of solar corpuscular emission on the development of large troughs in the atmosphere. J. Meteorol. 18, 116-118.

Maksimov, I. V. and B. A. Slepcov-Sevlevic (1971) On the relationship between solar activity and pressure field of the northern hemisphere of the earth. Doklady Akad. Nauk. (Moscow) 201, 339.

Malurkar, S. L. (1954) Geomagnetic variations and diurnal range of atmospheric ozone. Ann. di Geofis. 7, 209.

Manka, R. H. (1976) U.S. Program for the IMS. Eos 57, 63.

Mansurov, S. M. (1969) New evidence of a relationship between magnetic fields in space and on Earth. Geomag. Aeron. 9, 622.

Mansurov, S. M., G. S. Mansurov, and L. G. Mansurov (1975) Certain regularities of geomagnetic and baric fields at high latitudes. Goddard Space Flight Center Special Report, SP-366 (W. R. Bandeen and S. P. Maran, eds.), p. 53.

Manzano, J. R. and J. R. Winckler (1965) Modulation of the primary spectrum during the recent solar cycle for rigidities between 4 and 12 billion volts. J. Geophys. Res. 70, 4097.

Marar, T. M. K., P. S. Freier, and C. J. Waddington (1971) Intensity and energy spectrum of energetic cosmic ray electrons. J. Geophys. Res. 76, 1625.

Märcz, F. (1976) Links between atmospheric electricity and ionospheric absorption due to extraterrestrial influences. J. Geophys. Res. 81, 4566.

Markson, R. (1971) Considerations regarding solar and lunar modulation of geophysical parameters, atmospheric electricity, and thunderstorms. Pure Appl. Geophys. *84*, 161.

Markson, R. (1975) Solar modulation of atmospheric electrification through variation of the conductivity over thunderstorms. Goddard Space Flight Center Special Report, SP-366 (W. R. Bandeen and S. P. Maran, eds.), p. 171.

Marshall, J. R. (1972) Precipitation patterns of the United States and sunspots. PhD. Thesis, University of Kansas, Lawrence, Kansas.

Mason, B. J. (1972) The physics of the thunderstorm. Proc. R. Soc. London *A327*, 443.

Mason, B. J. (1976a) In reply to a critique of precipitation theories of thunderstorm electrification by C. B. Moore. Quart. J. R. Meteorol. Soc. *102*, 219.

Mason, B. J. (1976b) Towards the understanding and prediction of climatic variations. Quart. J. R. Meteorol. Soc. *102*, 473.

Mather, J. R. (1974) *Climatology Fundamentals and Applications*. McGraw-Hill, New York.

Matsuno, T. (1970) Vertical propagation of stationary waves in the winter northern hemisphere. J. Atmos. Sci. *27*, 871.

Matsuno, T. (1971) A dynamical model of the stratospheric sudden warming. J. Atmos. Sci. *28*, 1479.

Matsuno, T. (1977) Weather of the stratosphere. Jap. Lett. (Sci.) *47*, 1.

Mayaud, P. N. (1972) The aa indices: A 100-year series characterizing the magnetic activity. J. Geophys. Res. *77*, 6870.

Mayaud, P. N. (1973) A 100-year series of geomagnetic data: Indices aa, storm sudden commencements. IAGA Bull. 33, Internatl. Union Geod. Geophys., Paris.

Mayaud, P. N. (1975) Analysis of storm sudden commencements for the years 1868-1967. J. Geophys. Res. *80*, 111.

Mayaud, P. N. (1977) On the reliability of the wolf number series for estimating long-term periodicities. J. Geophys. Res. *82*, 1271.

McCracken, K. G. (1963) Anisotropies in cosmic radiation of solar origin, in *Solar Proton Manual* (F. B. McDonald, ed.). Rpt. no. NASA TR R-169.

McDonald, F. B. and U. D. Desai (1971) Recurrent solar cosmic ray events and solar M regions. J. Geophys. Res. *76*, 808.

McElroy, M. B., S. Wofsey, J. Penner, and J. McConnell (1974) Atmospheric ozone: Possible impact of stratospheric aviation. J. Atmos. Sci. *31*, 287.

Meadows, A. J. (1975) A hundred years of controversy over sunspots and weather. Nature *256*, 95.

Meier, R. R. (1969) Temporal variations of solar lyman alpha. J. Geophys. Res. *74*, 6487.

Mendenhall, W. and R. L. Scheaffer (1973) *Mathematical Statistics with Applications*. Duxbury Press, North Scituate, Mass.

Michel, F. C., A. J. Dessler, and G. K. Walters (1964) A search for correlation between Kp and the lunar phase. J. Geophys. Res. *69*, 4177.

Milankovitch, M. (1930) Mathematische Klimalehre und astronomische

Theorie der Klimaschwankungen. *Handbuch der Klimatologie* (W. Köppen and R. Geiger, eds.), Vol. I, Part A. Gebr. Borntraeger, Berlin, pp. 1-76.

Milankovitch, M. (1938) Die chronologie des Pleistocans. Bull. Acad. Sci. Math. Nat. Belgrade *4*, 49.

Miles, M. K. (1974) The variation of annual mean surface pressure over the northern hemisphere during the double sunspot cycle. Meteorol. Mag. *103*, 93.

Mitchell, J. M., Jr. (1965) The solar inconstant, in Proceedings Seminar on Possible Responses of Weather Phenomena to Variable Extra-Terrestrial Influences, NCAR Tech Note TN-8, 155-174, Natl. Center for Atmospheric Research, Boulder, Colorado.

Mitchell, J. M. and H. E. Landsberg (1966) Comments on paper by D. Shaw, 1965, Sunspots and temperatures. J. Geophys. Res. *71*(22), 5487.

Mitchell, J. M., Jr., C. W. Stockton, and D. M. Meko (1977) Drought cycles in the United States and their relation to sunspot cycle since 1700 A.D. Eos *58*, 694.

Mohnen, V. A. (1971) Discussion of the formation of major positive and negative ions up to 50 km level. Pure Appl. Geophys. *84*, 141.

Monin, A. S. (1972) *Weather Forecasting as a Problem in Physics* (translated into English by Paul Superak). The MIT Press, Cambridge, Mass.

Mook, C. P. (1958) The apparent ionospheric response to the passage of hurricane Diane (1955) at Washington, D.C. J. Geophys. Res. *63*, 569-570.

Moore, C. B. (1976a) An assessment of thundercloud electrification mechanisms. *Electrical Processes in Atmospheres*, Proc. Int. Conf. on Atmospheric Electricity (H. Dolezalek and R. Reiter, eds.). Garmisch-Partenkirchen, p. 333.

Moore, C. B. (1976b) Reply to B. J. Mason criticism of a critique on thunderstorm electrification theories by Moore. Quart. J. R. Meteorol. Soc. *102*, 225.

Mühleisen, R. (1971) Neue Ergebnisse und Probleme in der Luftelektrizität. Zs. Geophysik *37*, 759.

Mühleisen, R. and R. Reiter (1973) Atmospheric electric data during August 4th-12th, 1972, Collected Data Reports on August 1972 Solar-Terrestrial Events. Rpt. UAG-28, Pt. II, World Data Center A, p. 809.

Muldrew, D. B. (1965) F-layer ionization troughs deduced from Alouette data. J. Geophys. Res., *70*, 2635.

Munro, R. H. and G. L. Withbroe (1972) Properties of a coronal 'hole' derived from E.U.V. observations. Astrophys. J., *176*, 511.

Murcray, D. G., D. B. Barker, J. N. Brooks, A. Goldman, and W. J. Williams (1975) Seasonal and latitudinal variation of the stratospheric concentration of HNO_3. Geophys. Res. Lett. *2*, 223.

Mustel, E. R. (1966) The influence of solar activity on the troposphere in the polar cap regions. Sov. Astron. AJ (English trans.) *10*, 188-194.

Mustel, E. R. (1970) On the circulation changes in the lower layers of the atmosphere after the penetration of a solar corpuscular stream into the earth's magnetosphere. Astron. Counc. Akad. Nauk USSR, Inter-Union Comm. on Solar Terr. Phys., Leningrad, pp. 36–66.

Mustel, E. R. (1972) On the reality of the influence of solar corpuscular streams upon the lower layer of the earth's atmosphere. Publ. No. 24, Astronomical Council, USSR Acad. of Sciences, Moscow.

Mustel, E. R., V. V. Kubyshkin, and I. V. Bonelis (1966) Corpuscular streams and cosmic rays of solar origin and their influence on the troposphere. Sov. Astron. AJ (English trans.) *9*, 957–970.

National Academy of Sciences (1975) *Environmental Impact of Stratospheric Flight*. Washington, D.C. p. 173.

National Academy of Sciences (1975) *Understanding Climatic Change*. Washington, D.C.

Neher, H. V. (1961) Cosmic-ray knee in 1958. J. Geophys. Res. *66*, 4007–4012.

Neher, H. V. (1967) Cosmic-ray particles that changed from 1954 to 1958 to 1965. J. Geophys. Res. *72*(5), 1527.

Neher, H. V. (1971) Cosmic-rays at high latitudes and altitudes covering four solar maxima. J. Geophys. Res. *76*(7), 1637.

Ness, N. F. (1965) The earth's magnetic tail. J. Geophys. Res. *70*, 2989.

Newman, E. (1965) Statistical investigation of anomalies in the winter temperature record of Boston, Massachusetts. J. Appl. Meteorol. *4*, 706.

Ney, E. P. (1959) Cosmic radiation and the weather. Nature *183*, 451.

Nicolet, M. (1953) The collisional frequency of electrons in the ionosphere. J. Atmos. Terr. Phys. *3*, 200.

Nicolet, M. (1970) Ozone and hydrogen reactions. Ann. Geophys. *26*, 531.

Nicolet, M. (1975) On the production of nitric oxide by cosmic rays in the mesosphere and stratosphere. Planet. Space Sci. *23*, 637.

Noto, H. (1932) Statistical investigations on thunderstorms in Japan. Jap. J. Astron. Geophys. *9*, 207.

Nuppen, W. and M. Kageorge (1958) *Bibliography on Solar-Weather Relationships*. American Meteorological Society, Washington, D.C., pp. 1-248.

Obridko, V. N., S. M. Mansurov, and L. G. Mansurov (1974) Solar proton flares and the sector structure of the interplanetary field. Geomag. Aeron. (English trans.) *14*, 1–4.

Okal, E. and E. L. Anderson (1975) On the planetary theory of sunspots. Nature *253*, 511.

Ölson, R. H., W. O. Roberts, and C. S. Zerefos (1975) Short term relationships between solar flares, geomagnetic storms, and tropospheric vorticity patterns. Nature *257*, 113.

Opik, E. J. (1964) Microvariability of the sun and stars. Irish Astronom. J. *6*, 174–182.

Paetzold, H. K. (1961) The photochemistry of the atmospheric ozone layer, in *Chemical Reactions in the Lower and Upper Atmosphere*. Interscience, Chichester, England, p. 181.

Paetzold, H. K. (1973) The influence of solar activity on the stratospheric ozone layer. Pure Appl. Geophys. *106–108*, 1308–1311.

Palmen, E. and C. W. Newton (1969) *Atmospheric Circulation Systems*. Academic Press, New York.

Paltridge, G. W. (1965) Experimental measurements of the small-ion density and electrical conductivity of the stratosphere. J. Geophys. Res. 70, 2751.

Paluch, I. R. and J. D. Sartor (1973a) Thunderstorm electrification by the inductive charging mechanism: I. Particle charges and electric fields. J. Atmos. Sci. 30, 1166.

Paluch, I. R. and J. D. Sartor (1973b) Thunderstorm electrification by the inductive charging mechanism. II. Possible effects of updraft on the charge separation process. J. Atmos. Sci. 30, 1174.

Park, C. G. (1976a) Downward mapping of high-latitude ionospheric electric fields to the ground. J. Geophys. Res. 81, 168.

Park, C. G. (1976b) Solar magnetic sector effects on the vertical atmospheric electric field at Vostok, Antarctica. Geophys. Res. Lett. 3(8), 475.

Paulikas, G. A. (1971) The patterns and sources of high-latitude particle precipitation. Rev. Geophys. Space Phys. 9, 659.

Pomerantz, M. A. and S. P. Duggal (1973) Remarkable cosmic ray storm and associated relativistic solar particle events of August 1972, Collected Data Reports on August 1972 Solar-Terrestrial Events. Rpt. UAG-28, Pt. II, World Data Center A, p. 430.

Pomerantz, M. A. and S. P. Duggal (1974) The sun and cosmic rays. Rev. Geophys. Space Phys. 12, 343.

Prag, A. B. and F. A. Morse (1970) Variations in the solar ultraviolet flux from July 13 to August 9, 1968. J. Geophys. Res. 75, 4613–4621.

Radoski, H. R., P. F. Fougere, and E. J. Zawalik (1975) A comparison of power spectral estimates and applications of the maximum entropy model. J. Geophys. Res. 80, 619.

Ramakrishna, S. and D. F. Heath (1977) Temperature changes associated with geomagnetic activity at Wallops Island. Eos 58, 696.

Ramakrishna, S. and R. Seshamani (1976) Day-night dependence of geomagnetic activity effects on mesospheric temperature. J. Geophys. Res. 81, 6173.

Rao-Vupputuri, R. K. (1975) Seasonal and latitudinal variations in N_2O and NO_x in the stratosphere. J. Geophys. Res. 80, 1125–1132.

Ratcliffe, J. A. and K. Weekes (1960) The ionosphere, in Physics of the Upper Atmosphere (J. A. Ratcliffe, ed.). Academic Press, New York, Chap. 9, p. 377–470.

Reagan, J. B. and T. M. Watt (1976) Simultaneous satellite and radar studies of the D region ionosphere during the intense solar particle events of August 1972. J. Geophys. Res. 81, 4579.

Reck, R. A. (1976a) Stratospheric ozone effects on temperature. Science 192, 557.

Reck, R. A. (1976b) Atmospheric temperatures calculated for ozone depletions. Nature 263, 116.

Reid, G. C. (1974) Polar-cap absorption-observations and theory, in Fundamentals of Cosmic Physics, Vol. 1. Gordon and Breach, London, p. 167.

Reid, G. C. and C. Collins (1959) Observations of abnormal VHF radiowave absorption at medium and high latitudes. J. Atmos. Terr. Phys. 14, 63–81.

Reid, G. C. and H. Leinbach (1959) Low-energy cosmic-ray events associated with solar flares. J. Geophys. Res. *64*, 1801–1805.

Reifsnyder, W. E. (1964) What is weather? in *Medical Climatology* (S. Licht, ed.). Elizabeth Licht, Publisher, New Haven, Conn., Chap. 1, pp. 1–41.

Reitan, C. H. (1974) Frequencies of cyclones and cyclogenesis for North America, 1951–1970. Monthly Weather Rev. *102*(12), 861.

Reiter, E. R. (1967) *Jet Streams*. Doubleday, Garden City, New York.

Reiter, R. (1969) Solar flares and their impact on potential gradient and air-earth current characteristics at high mountain stations. Pure Appl. Geophys. *72*, 259–267.

Reiter, R. (1971) Further evidence for impact of solar flares on potential gradient and air-earth current characteristics at high mountain stations. Pure Appl. Geophys. *86*, 142–158.

Reiter, R. (1972) Case study concerning the impact of solar activity upon potential gradient and air-earth current in the lower troposphere. Pure Appl. Geophys. *94*, 218–225.

Reiter, R. (1973) Increased influx of stratospheric air into the lower troposphere after solar H_α and X-ray flares. J. Geophys. Res. *78*, 6167.

Reiter, R. (1976) The electric potential of the ionosphere as controlled by the solar magnetic sector structure. Die Naturwissenschaften *63*, Part 4, 192.

Reiter, R. (1977) The electric potential of the ionosphere as controlled by the solar magnetic sector structure result of a study over the period of a solar cycle. J. Atmos. Terr. Phys. *39*, 95.

Rickett, B. J., D. G. Sime, N. R. Sheeley, Jr., W. R. Crockett, and R. Tousey (1976) High-latitude observations of solar wind streams and coronal holes. J. Geophys. Res. *81*, 3845.

Roberts, W. O. (1975) Relationship between solar activity and climate change. Goddard Space Flight Center, Special Report NASA SP-366 (W. R. Bandeen and S. P. Maran, eds.), p. 13.

Roberts, W. O. and R. H. Olson (1973a) New evidence for effects of variable solar corpuscular emission on the weather. Rev. Geophys. Space Phys. *11*(3), 731–740.

Roberts, W. O. and R. H. Olson (1973b) Geomagnetic storms and wintertime 300-mb trough development in the North Pacific-North America area. J. Atmos. Sci. *30*, 135.

Roederer, J. G. (1976) IMS 1976–1979: New concepts in international scientific cooperation. Eos *57*(1), 6.

Roosen, R. G. and R. J. Angione (1975) Possible relationships between solar activity and atmospheric constituents. Goddard Space Flight Center, Special Report NASA SP-366 (W. R. Bandeen and S. P. Maran, eds.), p. 149.

Rosenberg, R. L. and P. J. Coleman, Jr. (1969) Heliographic latitude dependence of the dominant polarity of the interplanetary magnetic field. J. Geophys. Res. *74*, 5611–5622.

Rostoker, G. (1972) Geomagnetic indices. Rev. Geophys. Space Phys. *10*, 935–950.

Rourke, G. R. (1965) K index of magnetic activity in the Antarctic. *Antarctic Research Series, Vol. 4, Geomagnetism and Aeronomy* (A. H. Waynick, ed.). American Geophysical Union, Washington, D.C. p. 123.

Ruderman, M. A. and J. W. Chamberlain (1975) Origin of the sunspot modulation of ozone: its implications for stratospheric NO injection. Planet. Space Sci. *23*, 247–268.

Sabine, E. (1852) On periodical laws discoverable in the mean effects of the larger magnetic disturbances. Phil. Trans. London 103–124.

Sao, K. (1967) Correlations between solar activity and the atmospheric potential gradient at the earth's surface in the polar regions. J. Atmos. Terr. Phys. *29*, 213–216.

Sartor, J. D. (1961) Calculations of cloud electrification based on a general charge-separation mechanism. J. Geophys. Res. *66*, 831.

Sartor, J. D. (1967) The role of particle interactions in the distribution of electricity in thunderstorms. J. Atmos. Sci. *24*, 601.

Sarukhanyan, E. I. and N. P. Smirnov (1970) Solar activity, earth's pressure field, and atmospheric circulation. Geomag. Aeron. *10*, 309–392.

Sawyer, C. (1974) Semiannual and solar-cycle variation of sector structure. Geophys. Res. Lett. *1*(7), 295.

Schödel, J. P., J. Klostermeyer, J. Röttger, and G. Stilke (1973) Evidence for tropospheric-ionospheric coupling by atmospheric gravity waves. Zeit. Geophys. *39*, 1063.

Schove, D. J. (1955) The sunspot cycle, 649 B.C. to A.D. 2000. J. Geophys. Res. *60*, 127.

Schultz, M. (1973) Interplanetary sector structure and the heliomagnetic equator. Astrophys. Space Sci. *24*, 371.

Schuurmans, C. J. E. (1965) Influence of solar flare particles on the general circulations of the atmosphere. Nature *205*, 167.

Schuurmans, C. J. E. (1969) The influence of solar flares on the tropospheric circulation. Report of Royal Netherland Meteorological Institute, DeBilt, the Netherlands.

Schuurmans, C. J. E. (1975) On climate changes related to the 22-year solar cycle. Goddard Space Flight Center Special Report SP-366 (W. R. Bandeen and S. P. Maran, eds.), p. 161.

Schuurmans, C. J. E. and A. H. Oort (1969) A statistical study of pressure changes in the troposphere and lower stratosphere after strong solar flares. Pure Appl. Geophys. *75*, 233–246.

Schwabe, A. N. (1844) Sounen-Beobachtungen in jahre 1843. Astron. Nachr. *21*, 233.

Septer, E. (1926) Sonnenflecken und Gewitter in Sibirien (Sunspots and thunderstorms in Siberia). Meteorol. Z. *43*, 229–231.

Shapiro, R. (1956) Further evidence of a solar-weather effect. J. Meteorol. *13*, 335–340.

Shapiro, R. (1959) A comparison of the response of the North American and European surface pressure distributions to large geomagnetic disturbances. J. Meteorol. *16*, 569–572.

Shapiro, R. (1972) A test of the apparent response of the lower atmosphere to solar corpuscular radiation. J. Atmos. Sci. *29*, 1213–1216.

Shapiro, R. (1974) Geomagnetic activity in the vicinity of sector boundaries. J. Geophys. Res. *79*(1), 289.

Shapiro, R. and F. Ward (1966) Three peaks near 27 days in a high-resolution spectrum of the international magnetic character figure, Ci, J. Geophys. Res. *71*, 2385.

Shapley, A. H. and H. W. Kroehl (1977) *Solar-Terrestrial Physics and Meteorology: Working Document—II*. Special Committee for Solar-Terrestrial Physics, National Academy of Sciences, Washington, D.C.

Shapley, A. H., H. W. Kroehl, and J. H. Allen (1975) *Solar-Terrestrial Physics and Meteorology: A Working Document*. Special Committee for Solar-Terrestrial Physics, National Academy of Sciences, Washington, D.C.

Shaw, D. (1965) Sunspots and temperatures. J. Geophys. Res. *70*(20), 4997.

Shaw, G. E. (1967) Background cosmic count increase associated with thunderstorms. J. Geophys. Res. *72*, 4623.

Shaw, Sir Napier (1928) *Manual of Meteorology, Vol. II., Comparative Meteorology*, The University Press, Cambridge, England.

Shea, M. A., D. F. Smart, and K. G. McCracken (1965) A study of vertical cutoff rigidities using sixth degree simulations of the geomagnetic field. J. Geophys. Res. *70*(17), 4117.

Shimazaki, T. and R. C. Whitten (1976) A comparison of one-dimensional theoretical models of stratospheric minor constituents. Rev. Geophys. Space Phys. *14*, 1.

Sidorenkov, N. S. (1974) Solar corpuscular streams and weather on the earth (English trans.) Rpt. No. JPRS 62197, Joint Publications Research Service (available from Natl. Tech. Info. Service, Springfield, Va.), p. 21.

Simpson, J. A. (1957) Solar origin of changes in the primary cosmic radiation. Proc. Natl. Acad. Sci. USA *43*, 42.

Sleeper, H. P., Jr. (1972) Planetary resonances, bi-stable oscillation modes, and solar activity cycles. NASA Contractor Rpt., NASA CR-2035, National Aeronautics and Space Admin., Washington, D.C.

Smart, D. F. and M. A. Shea (1972) Daily variation of electron and proton geomagnetic cutoffs calculated for Fort Churchill, Canada. J. Geophys. Res. *77*, 4595.

Smart, D. F., M. A. Shea, and R. Gall (1969) The daily variation of trajectory-derived high-latitude cutoff rigidities in a model magnetosphere. J. Geophys. Res. *74*, 4731.

Smith, E. V. P. and D. M. Gottlieb (1975) Solar flux and its variations, in *Possible Relationships Between Solar Activity and Meteorological Phenomena* (W. R. Bandeen and S. P. Maran, eds.), NASA SP-366, p. 97.

Smith, H. J. and E. V. P. Smith (1963) *Solar Flares*. Macmillan, New York.

Smythe, C. M. and J. A. Eddy (1977) Planetary tides during the Maunder sunspot minimum. Nature *266*, 434.

Stagg, J. M. (1927) On magnetic fluctuations and sunspot frequency. Geophys. Memorand. No. 36, Meteorological Office, London, p. 24.

Starr, V. P. and A. H. Oort (1973) Five-year climatic trend for the northern hemisphere. Nature *242*, 310.

Steblova, R. S. (1968) Solar flare effects in the ozonosphere. Geomag. Aeron. 8(2), 299–301.

Stolov, H. L. (1965) Further investigations of a variation of geomagnetic activity with lunar phase. J. Geophys. Res., 70, 4921.

Stolov, H. L. and A. G. W. Cameron (1964) Variations of geomagnetic activity with lunar phase. J. Geophys. Res. 69, 4975–4982.

Stolov, H. L. and R. Shapiro (1969) Further investigations of alleged tropospheric responses to chromospheric flares. J. Atmos. Sci. 26, 1355–1359.

Stolov, H. L. and R. Shapiro (1971) Report on an investigation of solar corpuscular influences on the general circulation. Paper presented at Symposium on Solar Corpuscular Effects in the Troposphere and Stratosphere, Int. Un. Geod. and Geophys., Moscow.

Stolov, H. L. and R. Shapiro (1974) Investigation of the responses of the general circulation at 700-mb to solar geomagnetic disturbance. J. Geophys. Res. 79(15), 2161.

Stolov, H. L. and J. Spar (1968) Search for tropospheric responses to chromospheric flares. J. Atmos. Sci. 25, 126–132.

Storey, L. R. O. (1962) Whistler theory, in Monograph on Radio Noise of Terrestrial Origin (F. Horner, ed.). Elsevier, New York, p. 134.

Störmer, C. (1955) The Polar Aurora. Clarendon Press, Oxford.

Stow, C. D. (1969) Atmospheric electricity. Rep. Prog. Phys. 32, Part 1, 1.

Stringfellow, M. F. (1974) Lightning incidence in Britain and the solar cycle. Nature 249, 332.

Stuiver, M. (1961) Variations in radiocarbon concentration and sunspot activity. J. Geophys. Res. 66, 273.

Sucksdorff, E. (1956) The influence of the moon and the inner planets on the geomagnetic activity. Geophys. Helsenki 5, 95.

Suess, H. E. (1965) Secular variations of the cosmic-ray-produced carbon 14 in the atmosphere and their interpretations. J. Geophys. Res. 70, 5937.

Sugiura, M. (1964) Hourly values of equatorial Dst for the IGY. Ann. Int. Geophys. Year 35, 9.

Svalgaard, L. (1968) Sector structure of the interplanetary magnetic field and daily variation of the geomagnetic field at high latitudes. Geophysics Paper R-6, Dan. Meteorol. Inst., Copenhagen, Denmark.

Svalgaard, L. (1972) Interplanetary magnetic sector structure 1926–1971. J. Geophys. Res. 77, 4027.

Svalgaard, L. (1973) Solar Activity and the Weather. SUIPR Rpt. No. 526, Institute for Plasma Research, Stanford University, Stanford, Calif.

Svalgaard, L. (1975a) An Atlas of Interplanetary Sector Structure 1957–1974. Rpt. SUIPR No. 629, Institute for Plasma Research, Stanford University, Stanford, Calif.

Svalgaard, L. (1975b) Geomagnetic responses to the solar wind and to solar activity. Goddard Space Flight Center, Special Report NASA SP-366 (W. R. Bandeen and S. P. Maran, eds.), p. 119.

Svalgaard, L. and J. M. Wilcox (1976) Structure of the extended solar magnetic field and the sunspot cycle variation in cosmic ray intensity. Nature 262, 766.

Svalgaard, L., J. M. Wilcox, and T. L. Duvall (1974) A model combining the polar and the sector structured solar magnetic field. Solar Phys. *37*, 157.

Svestka, Z. (1976) *Solar Flares*. D. Reidel, Dordrecht, Holland.

Svestka, Z. and P. Simon (eds.) (1975) *Catalog of Solar Particle Events 1955–1969*. D. Reidel, Dordrecht, Holland.

Swider, W. and T. Keneshea (1973) Decrease of ozone and atomic oxygen in the lower mesosphere during a PCA event. Planet. Space Sci. *21*, 1969.

Talbot, R. J., Jr., D. M. Butler, and M. J. Newman (1976) Climatic effects during passage of the solar system through interstellar clouds. Nature *262*, 561.

Thekaekara, M. P. (1974) Solar constant and solar spectrum, in *The Encyclopedia of Physics*, 2nd edition (R. M. Besançon, ed.), p. 853.

Thekaekara, M. P. (1975) The total and spectral solar irradiance and its possible variations. NASA Preprint, X-912-75-155, Goddard Space Flight Center.

Thompkins, D. R., Jr. (1974) Thundercloud radio emission from cosmic-ray-shower ionization electrons. Phys. Rev. D *10*, 136.

Thompson, L. M. (1973) Cyclical weather patterns in the middle latitudes. J. Soil Water Conserv. *28*, 87–89.

Thorne, R. M. (1977) Energetic radiation belt electron precipitation: a natural depletion mechanism for stratospheric ozone. Science *195*, 287.

Timothy, A. F., A. S. Krieger, and G. S. Vaiana (1975) The structure and evolution of coronal holes. Solar Phys. *42*, 135.

Timothy, A. F. and J. G. Timothy (1970) Long-term intensity variations in the solar helium II Lyman alpha line. J. Geophys. Res. *75*, 6950–6958.

Toman, K. (1967) On the possible existence of a 29-day period in the sunspot number series 1940–1964. J. Geophys. Res. *72*, 5570.

Troup, A. J. (1962) A secular change in the relation between the sunspot cycle and the temperature in the tropics. Geofis. Pure Appl. *51*, 184.

Twitchell, P. F. (1963) Geomagnetic storms and 500-mb trough behavior. Bull. Geophys. *13*, 69–84.

Utlaut, W. F. (1970a) Radio-wave modification of the ionosphere; an ionospheric modification experiment using very high power, high frequency transmission. J. Geophys. Res. *75*, 6402–6405.

Utlaut, W. F. (1970b) Radio-wave modification of the ionosphere; some ionosonde observations of ionospheric modification by very high power, high frequency ground-based transmission. J. Geophys. Res. 77 6429–6435.

Valley, S. L. (ed.) (1965) *Handbook of Geophysics and Space Environments*. Air Force Cambridge Research Laboratories, Bedford, Mass.

Van Allen, J. A., J. F. Fennell, and N. F. Ness (1971) Asymmetric access of energetic solar protons to the earth's north and south polar caps. J. Geophys. Res. *76*(19), 4262.

Verschell, H. J., R. B. Mendell, S. A. Korff, and E. C. Roelof (1975) Two classes of cosmic ray decrease. J. Geophys. Res. *80*(10), 1189.

Volland, H. (1977a) Can sunspots influence our weather? Nature *269*, 400.

Volland, H. (1977b) Periodic variations of the solar radiation—a possible source of solar activity-weather effects. J. Atmos. Terr. Phys. *39*, 69.

Vonnegut, B., C. B. Moore, R. P. Espinola, and J. J. Blau, Jr. (1966) Electric potential gradients above thunderstorms. J. Atmos. Sci. *23*, 764.

Wait, G. R. (1937) Change from year to year in the potential gradient and the electrical conductivity of the atmosphere at Ebro, Watheroo and Huancayo. UCGI (Assoc. Terr. Magnet. and Elec.) Bull. No. 10, Trans. Edinburgh Mett., 395–397.

Wait, G. R. and J. Mauchly (1937) World-wide changes in potential gradient. Trans. Amer. Geophys. Union *18*, 169–170.

Waldmeier, M. (1961) *The sunspot activity in the years 1610–1960*. Zurich Schulthess Co., Zurich, Switzerland.

Wales-Smith, B. G. (1973) An analysis of monthly rainfall totals representative of Kew, Surrey from 1697 to 1970. Meteorol. Mag. *102*(1211), 157–171.

Walker, G. T. (1915) Correlation in seasonal weather. V. Sunspots and Temperature. Mem. India Meteorol. Dept. *21*, 61–90.

Walker, G. T. and E. W. Bliss (1928) World Weather III, Mem. R. Meteorol. Soc. *2*, 97.

Wallis, J. R. (1977) Climate, climatic change, and water supply, Eos *58*, 1012.

Warneck, P. (1972) Cosmic radiation as a source of odd nitrogen in the stratosphere. J. Geophys. Res. *77*, 6589–6591.

Watson, R. A. (1928) Electric potential gradient measurements at Eskdalemuir 1913–1923. Geophys. Mem. London *4*, No. 38.

Webber, W. (1962) The production of free electrons in the ionospheric D layer by solar and galactic cosmic rays and the resultant absorption of radio waves. J. Geophys. Res. *67*, 5091.

Webber, W. R. and J. A. Lockwood (1962) Comparison of Forbush decrease measurements made at balloon altitude and ground elevation. J. Geophys. Res. *67*, 5347.

Weeks, L. H., R. S. Cuikay, and J. R. Corbin (1972) Ozone measurements in the mesosphere during the solar proton event of 2 November 1969. J. Atmos. Sci. *29*, 1138–1142.

Wende, C. D. (1969a) The correlation of solar microwave and soft X-ray radiation. 1. The solar cycle and slowly varying components. J. Geophys. Res. *74*, 4649–4660.

Wende, C. D. (1969b) Correlation of solar microwave and soft X-ray radiation. 2. The burst component. J. Geophys. Res. *74*, 6471–6481.

Wexler, H. (1950) Possible effects of ozone heating on sea-level pressure. J. Meteorol. *7*, 340.

White, W. C. and A. J. Krueger (1968) Shipboard observations of total ozone from 38°N to 60°S. J. Atmos. Terr. Phys. *30*, 1615–1622.

Wilcox, J. M. (1968) The interplanetary magnetic field. Solar origin and terrestrial effects. Space Sci. Rev. *8*, 258.

Wilcox, J. M. (1972) Inferring the interplanetary magnetic field by observing the polar geomagnetic field. Rev. Geophys. Space Phys. *10*(4), 1003.

Wilcox, J. M. (1975) Solar activity and the weather. J. Atmos. Terr. Phys. *37*, 237.

Wilcox, J. M. and D. S. Colburn (1969) Interplanetary sector structure in the rising portion of the sunspot cycle. J. Geophys. Res. *74*, 2388.

Wilcox, J. M. and D. S. Colburn (1970) Interplanetary sector structure near the maximum of the sunspot cycle. J. Geophys. Res. *75*, 6366.

Wilcox, J. M. and D. S. Colburn (1972) Interplanetary sector structure at solar maximum. J. Geophys. Res. *77*, 751–756.

Wilcox, J. M. and N. F. Ness (1965) Quasi-stationary corotation structure in the interplanetary medium. J. Geophys. Res. *70*, 5793.

Wilcox, J. M. and P. H. Scherrer (1972) Annual and solar-magnetic-cycle variations in the interplanetary magnetic field. SUIPR Rpt. No. 466, Institute for Plasma Research, Stanford University, Stanford, Calif.

Wilcox, J. M. and P. H. Scherrer, L. Svalgaard, W. O. Roberts, and R. H. Olson (1973a) Solar magnetic structure: Influence on stratospheric circulation. Science *180*, 185–186.

Wilcox, J. M., P. H. Scherrer, L. Svalgaard, W. O. Roberts, R. H. Olson, R. L. Jenne (1973b) Influence of solar magnetic sector structure on terrestrial atmospheric vorticity. Institute for Plasma Research, Stanford University, Stanford, Calif. SUIPR Rpt. No. 530.

Wilcox, J. M., P. H. Scherrer, L. Svalgaard, W. O. Roberts, R. H. Olson, and R. L. Jenne (1974) Influence of solar magnetic sector structure on terrestrial atmospheric vorticity. J. Atmos. Sci. *31*(2), 581.

Wilcox, J. M., L. Svalgaard, and P. H. Scherrer (1975) Seasonal variation and magnitude of the solar sector structure-atmospheric vorticity effect, Nature *255*, 539.

Willett, H. C. (1962) The relationship of total atmospheric ozone to the sunspot cycle. J. Geophys. Res. *67*(2), 661–670.

Willett, H. C. (1965) Solar-climatic relationships in light of standardized climatic data. J. Atmos. Sci. *22*, 120.

Willett, H. C. (1968) Remarks on the seasonal changes of temperature and of ozone in the Arctic and the Antarctic stratosphere. J. Atmos. Sci. *25*(3), 341–360.

Willett, H. C. (1974) Recent statistical evidence in support of the predictive significance of solar-climatic cycles. Monthly Weather Rev. *102*(10), 679.

Willett, H. C. and J. Prohaska (1965) Further evidence of sunspot-ozone relationships. J. Atmos. Sci. *22*(5), 493–497.

Willis, D. M. (1976) The energetics of sun-weather relationships: magnetospheric processes. J. Atmos. Terr. Phys. *38*, 685.

Winstanley, D. (1973) Recent rainfall trends in Africa, the Middle East, and India. Nature *243*, 464–465.

Wofsy, S. C., M. B. McElroy, and Y. L. Yung (1975) The chemistry of atmospheric bromine. Geophys. Res. Lett. *2*(6), 215.

Wood, R. M. and K. D. Wood (1965) Solar motion and sunspot comparison. Nature *208*, 129.

Wulf, O. R. (1971) Winter-summer difference in geomagnetic activity. J. Geophys. Res. *76*(7), 1837.

Wulf, O. R. and S. B. Nicholson (1948) Recurrent geomagnetic activity and lunar declination. Astron. Soc. Pacific Publ. *60*, 259.

Xanthakis, J. (1973) Solar activity and precipitation, in *Solar Activity and Related Interplanetary and Terrestrial Phenomena* (J. Xanthakis, ed.). Springer-Verlag, New York, p. 20.

Yates, G. K., L. Katz, B. Sellers, and F. A. Hanser (1973) Proton and alpha particle fluxes observed aboard OV5-6 in August 1972. Collected Data Reports on August 1972 Solar Terrestrial Events, Rpt. UAG-28, Pt. II, World Data Center A, Boulder, Colorado, p. 348.

Yeh, K. C. and C. H. Liu (1974) Acoustic-gravity waves in the upper atmosphere. Rev. Geophys. Space Phys. *12*, 193.

Yule, G. U. (1927) On a method of investigating periodicities in disturbed series, with special reference to Wolfer's sunspot numbers. Phil. Trans. R. Soc. London *A226*, 267.

Zatopek, A. and L. Krivsky (1974) On the correlation between meteorological microseisms and solar activity. Bull. Astron. Inst. Czech. *25*(4), 257.

Zerefos, C. S., R. H. Olson, and W. O. Roberts (1975) Atmospheric vorticity area index during different phases of the sunspot cycle (abstract), EOS *56*(6), 364.

Zirker, J. B. (1977) Coronal holes and high-speed wind streams. Rev. Geophys. Space Phys. *15*, 257.

Ziv, A. and Z. Levin (1974) Thundercloud electrification: Cloud growth and electrical development. J. Atmos. Sci. *31*, 1652.

Zmuda, A. J. and T. A. Potemra (1972) Bombardment of the polar-cap ionosphere by solar cosmic rays. Rev. Geophys. Space Phys. *10*, 981.

Zonge, K. L. and W. H. Evans (1966) Prestroke radiation for thunderclouds. J. Geophys. Res. *71*, 1519.

Author Index

Subject Index

☆ U.S. GOVERNMENT PRINTING OFFICE : 1978 O—277-294